D0007989

REACTION HEATS AND BOND STRENGTHS

ADIWES INTERNATIONAL SERIES
IN CHEMISTRY

This book is in the

ADDISON-WESLEY SERIES IN CHEMISTRY

Sidney Golden, Consulting Editor

REACTION HEATS and BOND STRENGTHS

BASED ON A SERIES OF LECTURES GIVEN TO POSTGRADUATE STUDENTS AT THE UNIVERSITY OF KEELE, 1960

C. T. MORTIMER

University of Keele

PERGAMON PRESS

NEW YORK · OXFORD · LONDON · PARIS

1962

ADDISON-WESLEY PUBLISHING COMPANY, INC.

READING, MASSACHUSETTS · PALO ALTO · LONDON

U.S.A. Edition distributed by
Addison-Wesley Publishing Company, Inc.
Reading, Massachusetts, U.S.A.

Library of Congress Card Number 61-17034

Made in England

ACKNOWLEDGEMENTS

The Author and Publishers wish to express their thanks to the following for permission to reproduce material from their published works:

BUTTERWORTHS SCIENTIFIC PUBLICATIONS
The Strengths of Chemical Bonds; Theoretical Organic Chemistry, Ch. 2 Figs. 13, 16, 17; Ch. 4, Fig. 3, 5, 9; Ch. 10, Fig. 5, 6.

INTERSCIENCE PUBLISHERS, INC.
Experimental Thermochemistry (Copyright 1956). Ch. 1, Fig. 7.

LEWIS & CO. LTD.
Theoretical Chemistry, Ch. 10, Fig. 4.

AMERICAN CHEMICAL SOCIETY
Journal of the American Chemical Society. Ch. 1, Fig. 3; Ch. 2, Fig. 6; Ch. 6, Fig. 1; Ch. 8, Table 4.

CHEMICAL SOCIETY
Journal of the Chemical Society. Ch. 4, Fig. 2; Ch. 5, Table 7; Fig. 1; Ch. 6, Table 2; Ch. 8, Fig. 2; Ch. 10, Fig. 7.
Quarterly Reviews of the Chemical Society. Ch. 5, Tables 2, 3.

FARADAY SOCIETY
Transactions of the Faraday Society. Ch. 1, Fig. 4, 5, 6, 8; Ch. 5, Tables 5, 6; Ch. 9, Fig. 2.

PERGAMON PRESS, LTD.
Journal of Inorganic & Nuclear Chemistry. Ch. 8, Fig. 5; Tables 8, 9.

GOVERNMENT PRINTING OFFICE, WASHINGTON
Journal of Research of the National Bureau of Standards. Ch. 1, Fig. 2.

MACMILLAN & CO., LTD.
Nature. Ch. 3, Tables 8, 9.

AMERICAN INSTITUTE OF PHYSICS
Journal of Chemical Physics, Ch. 6 Tables 4, 5.

ROYAL INSTITUTE OF CHEMISTRY
Royal Institute of Chemistry Monographs, Ch. 8, Table 6.

PREFACE

THE HEATS of a large number of chemical reactions have been measured with great accuracy in recent years. These data have been used to calculate the strengths of chemical bonds and also strain and stabilization energies in various molecules. Although a number of review papers have been published on these topics, it seemed that there was a need to gather together some of this information under one title.

In this book the variations in the heats of particular types of reaction are considered. These include, for example, hydrogenation and polymerization of olefinic compounds; the dissociation of organic and organo-metallic compounds and also of molecular-addition compounds. An attempt has been made to interpret these variations in simple terms and also to indicate the great wealth of information which can be gained about the strengths of chemical bonds from the measurement of heats of chemical reactions.

In presenting this book, I would like to thank the following: Dr. H. A. Skinner, who introduced me to thermochemistry, for reading and criticizing the text; my Wife for typing the script; Professor H. D. Springall for his help and encouragement; and the many thermochemical colleagues who have offered valuable advice and friendly hospitality.

C. T. M.

University of Keele
Keele, Staffordshire

CONTENTS

CHAPTER 1

THE THERMOCHEMICAL APPROACH

Introduction

Towards the end of the 19th Century many thermochemical measurements were made by outstanding chemists, such as M. Berthelot[1] and J. Thomsen[2]. Heats of reaction were determined, either directly or calculated indirectly from heats of combustion data, because it was thought at the time that the heat change, ΔH, was the sole driving force of a chemical reaction. Much interest in measuring heat changes was lost when it was shown that the free energy change, ΔG, is the driving force of a reaction, and that this is influenced not only by ΔH, but also by the entropy term, $T \Delta S$, according to the relationship $\Delta G = \Delta H - T \Delta S$. This loss of interest was mainly because the entropy changes, ΔS, were neither known nor easily measured, and without this additional knowledge free energy changes could not be derived from this relationship.

The revival of interest in thermochemical measurement some thirty years ago was due, in part, to the suggestion by Pauling[3] and others that the heat of formation of a compound, from its constituent atoms, could be taken as a measure of the strength of the bonds in a molecule. Very soon the ideas of bond energy and bond dissociation energy were given more precise definition and it became possible to give a quantitative measure to the strength of a chemical bond. But to show up small variations in bond strengths in isomers, or deviations from regular trends in homologous series of compounds, calorimetric techniques for measuring heats of reaction had to be refined. At the beginning of this period accurate thermochemical data for organic compounds were confined, almost entirely, to those containing only carbon, hydrogen and oxygen, but with the development of thermochemical techniques, especially over the last ten to fifteen years, it is now possible to obtain precise data for organic compounds containing metals, metalloids, such as silicon and phosphorus, and even those containing sulphur, or the halogens. There is now a large body of thermochemical information for covalent compounds containing a diversity of elements in addition to carbon, hydrogen and oxygen. From these data it is possible to examine such effects as strain and stabilization (due to electron delocalization) on the strengths of chemical bonds in a variety of molecules. We shall be concerned mainly with this type of problem; how the heats of chemical reactions can be interpreted in terms of bond strength, and why these bond strengths vary within series of similar compounds.

The vast improvement in calorimetric techniques enables one to measure very accurately small heats of reaction, such as those of ionization in dilute solution. Developments in other directions have provided means whereby the heats of comparatively slow reactions can be obtained. Typical examples of these are polymerization reactions. With the accumulated body of information about the entropy changes accompanying these types of reactions, it is possible to compare the influence of the ΔH and $T\Delta S$ terms on the free energy change, ΔG. We shall touch on this topic and some mention will be made of the effect of the ΔH term on the free energies of reactions, especially of polymerizations and of ionization processes in aqueous solution.

Energy Changes in Heats of Reaction

By far the largest body of thermochemical data applies to covalent compounds, and it is with this type of compound that we shall be concerned, except for one topic, the ionization of organic acids and bases, where the thermochemistry of ions in aqueous solution will be considered. This means that we shall be considering the heat changes which occur when large assemblages of discrete molecules react with one another. In the gaseous state, where intermolecular forces are usually very small indeed, these reaction heats can be thought of as corresponding to energy changes in the individual molecules taking part in the reaction.

We ought then to look at the ways in which energy may appear in a molecule, to see what is included in the overall heat of reaction which may be measured. This has been described by Cottrell[4] in the following terms: "At normal temperatures molecular energy in gases can be divided into three components which are effectively independent: translational, rotational, and vibrational. Energy is distributed among these components according to the laws of statistical mechanics. *Translational* energy is the average energy of motion through space of the molecule as a whole, in which there are three degrees of freedom. Because the quanta are very small indeed, this energy may be regarded as classically distributed; in which case the translational energy per molecule is $\frac{3}{2}RT$ per mole, where R is the gas constant. This is about 0·9 kcal per mole at room temperature. For linear molecules there are two degrees of *rotational* freedom possible (for non-linear molecules there are three) and the quanta involved are also small, so that at ordinary temperatures this energy is classically distributed and is RT per mole for linear molecules and $\frac{3}{2}RT$ per mole for non-linear molecules. Linear molecules have only two rotational degrees of freedom because they are axially symmetrical, and rotation about the axis of symmetry involves no distinguishable change of position; similarly, atoms which are spherically symmetrical have no rotational degrees of freedom. The number of *vibrational* degrees of freedom depends on the number of atoms, n, in the molecules, being $3n - 5$ for linear molecules and $3n - 6$ for non-linear molecules, because the total number of degrees of freedom is $3n$. For at least some of the vibrational degrees of freedom in most molecules, the vibrational quantum, $h\nu$ where h is Planck's constant and ν the vibration frequency, is large compared with kT, so that vibrational energy is not distributed classically."

These thermal energy quantities are statistical averages, characteristic properties of an assembly of molecules. In addition to this the molecule itself may be regarded as having a *potential* energy due to the forces between the atoms themselves; energy due to the bonding. Consequently the heat of a chemical reaction in the gas phase reflects changes in both the thermal energy of the molecule and also in the bonding energies of the atoms making up these molecules.

Generally we are concerned with observing the *difference* between the heats of two similar reactions, and since the differences due to bonding energies are very much greater than those due to thermal energies, these latter can usually be neglected.

Definitions of Bond Strength

1. Bond Energies

A common expression of the strength of a chemical bond is the *bond energy*. In order to derive these values, we arbitrarily take the elements in their normal states to have zero heat content, and define the standard heat of formation of a compound, ΔH_f^0, as the heat change when it is formed from the elements. In the case of a simple alkane, C_nH_m, this standard heat of formation can be measured from its heat of combustion to carbon dioxide and water. The heat of combustion, ΔH_c^0, is simply the difference between the heats of formation of the products (carbon dioxide and water) and the hydrocarbon, a relationship which is shown in an energy diagram in Fig. 1. In general terms the heat of any reaction can be

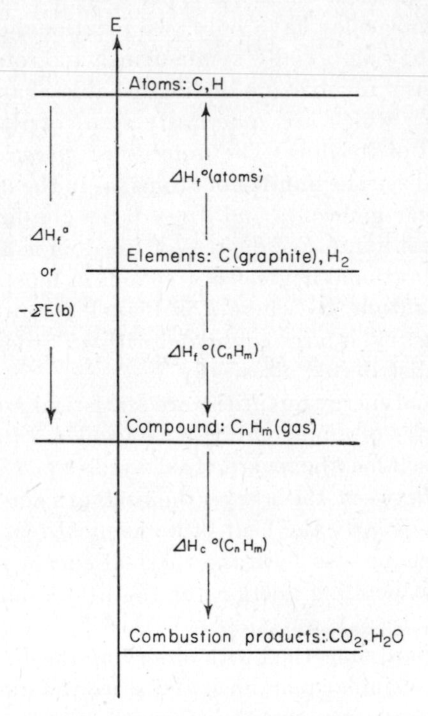

FIG. 1. Energy diagram relating heats of formation, combustion, atomization, and bond energies.

equated to the difference between the sum of the heats of formation of the products of the reaction and the sum of the heats of formation of the reactants, or

$$\Delta H_r = \Sigma \Delta H_f^0(\text{products}) - \Sigma \Delta H_f^0(\text{reactants}).$$

If the heat of reaction is measured, and all but one of the heats of formation are known, this unknown heat of formation is easily calculated.

From the standard heat of formation of the gaseous compound, in this particular example an alkane, it is possible to calculate the heat of formation *from the atoms*, ΔH_f^a, from the relationship $\Delta H_f^a = \Delta H_f^0 - \Sigma \Delta H_f^0(\text{atoms})$. Here $\Sigma \Delta H_f^0(\text{atoms})$ is the sum of the heats of formation of the ground-state atoms, in this case carbon and hydrogen. The reverse of this formation process corresponds to the dissociation of the compound into the separate constituent atoms, with the rupture of a number of carbon–carbon and carbon–hydrogen bonds. The heat change of this dissociation is put equal to the sum of the *bond energies* in the molecule, $\Sigma E\,(\text{b})$. Hence we may write

$$\Delta H_f^a = -\Sigma E\,(\text{b}).$$

This relationship is also shown in Fig. 1.

For a molecule of the type AB_n, containing only A–B bonds, it is reasonable to divide the heat of atomization of the compound amongst the n bonds A–B, so that the *bond energy* of the A–B bond, E(A–B), in the gaseous state is defined by the expression

$$E\,(\text{A–B}) = -1/n\; \Delta H_f^a\,(\text{AB}_n, \text{g}).$$

It should be remembered, however, that the idea of the energy of a molecule being 'localized' in a number of bonds between atoms is a highly artificial one, in that the total energy of the molecule is the resultant of the attractive and repulsive energies between bonded and non-bonded atoms. Nevertheless, bearing this point in mind, it is still convenient to consider the *net* attractive energy as the sum of the bond energies.

A problem arises when considering a molecule of two or more different types of bond, for example in the molecule AB_nC_m, containing n(A–B) and m(A–C) bonds. For any one molecule the heat of atomization provides only one datum and can give only the sum of the bond energies of the A–B and A–C bonds. In order to derive separate values for both bonds, some additional data are required.

The earliest, and simplest assumption, made by Fajans[5], was that for a given bond, the bond energy is constant from one molecule to another. Cottrell[4] points out that for a molecule in which there is more than one type of bond, it is necessary to know the energies of all types except one from other data, and to obtain the remaining bond energy term as the residium. If the assumption of constancy held exactly, this would lead to no difficulty, but if it did not, the procedure would give large differences in the energy of the 'same' bond in different molecules. This would happen because the total effects causing deviations from constancy in the bond energies as a whole are lumped into an effect on the one bond considered last. For example, we might ask the question, what is the value of E(C–Cl) in the molecule CH_3Cl, as compared with the value in CCl_4? We might calculate a value for E(C—H) from $\Delta H_f^a(CH_4)$ and derive a figure for E(C—Cl) in CH_3Cl from the relationship

$$E(\text{C—Cl}) = -\Delta H_f^a(\text{CH}_3\text{Cl,g}) - 3E(\text{C—H}).$$

This derived value for E(C—Cl) is, in fact, 0·8 kcal/mole greater than that found in CCl_4. However, we could equally well derive a value for E(C—Cl) in CCl_4, assume the same value in CH_3Cl, and say that the three carbon–hydrogen bonds are together 0·8 kcal/mole stronger than those found in methane. Only some auxiliary data about the C—Cl and C—H bonds would enable the question to be resolved. With the information available the only unambiguous statement that can be made is that for the gas-phase redistribution reaction

$$\tfrac{3}{4}\,\text{CH}_4 + \tfrac{1}{4}\,\text{CCl}_4 \rightarrow \text{CH}_3\text{Cl}$$

we have a value $\Delta H = -0·8$ kcal/mole.

A simple application of the transferability of bond energies from one molecule to another is the derivation of E(C—C) and E(C—H) in the normal alkanes. Taking any pair of alkanes, and assuming that E(C—C) and E(C—H) are the same in both molecules, values for these two can be obtained. For example from the relationships

$$-\Delta H_f^a(C_2H_6,g) = 6E(C-H) + E(C-C) = +674{\cdot}58 \text{ kcal/mole},$$

and

$$-\Delta H_f^a(C_3H_8,g) = 8E(C-H) + 2E(C-C) = +954{\cdot}24 \text{ kcal/mole},$$

we obtain $E(C-H) = 98{\cdot}72$, and $E(C-C) = 82{\cdot}2$ kcal/mole. Other values for successive pairs of hydrocarbons are shown in Table 1, from which it is apparent that these bond energies are by no means constant from one molecule to another for the lower alkanes. Only after n-hexane do these values become constant at $E(C-H) = 98{\cdot}7$ and $E(C-C) = 82{\cdot}6$ kcal/mole.

TABLE 1

Bond energies[a] E (C—H) *and* E (C—C) *in the alkanes at 25°C in kcal/mole*

Alkanes	E (C—H)	E (C—C)
CH_4	99·29	—
CH_4/C_2H_6	99·29	78·84
C_2H_6/C_3H_8	98·73	82·20
C_3H_8/C_4H_{10}	98·35	83·70
C_4H_{10}/C_5H_{12}	98·70	82·50
C_5H_{12}/C_6H_{14}	98·60	82·82
C_6H_{14}/C_7H_{16}	98·64	82·72
C_7H_{16}/C_8H_{18}	98·64	82·70
C_8H_{18}/C_9H_{20}	98·68	82·63

[a] Based on ΔH_f^0 values; C, 170·9; H, 52·09; and those for alkanes given in ref. 6.

It is these departures from constancy of bond energies which are interesting, in that reasons may be sought why a particular molecule, containing apparently the 'same' bonds as another has a greater or lesser bond energy content.

In these examples we have considered structures involving carbon atoms the valency or hybrid state of which is the same, in general terms. Although the introduction of a chlorine atom into methane may slightly alter the hybrid character of the bonds, in both this and the other molecules mentioned so far the carbon atom is using essentially sp^3 hybrid bonding.

However, it may be that the bond energies of C—C, and C—H bonds vary with the state of hybridization of the carbon atom, and that $E(\mathrm{C}sp^2\text{—H})$ is not the same as $E(\mathrm{C}sp^3\text{—H})$, for example. Thus, in the hydrogenation of ethylene,

$$CH_2{=}CH_2 + H_2 \rightarrow CH_3\text{—}CH_3,$$

not only is a $\mathrm{C}sp^2{=}\mathrm{C}sp^2$ bond converted to a $\mathrm{C}sp^3\text{—}\mathrm{C}sp^3$ bond, but in addition, where there were four $\mathrm{C}sp^2$—H bonds in ethylene, there are now six $\mathrm{C}sp^3$—H bonds. For the analogous hydrogenation of propylene,

$$CH_3CH{=}CH_2 + H_2 \rightarrow CH_3CH_2\text{—}CH_3,$$

the $\mathrm{C}sp^2{=}\mathrm{C}sp^2$ bond is also converted to a $\mathrm{C}sp^3\text{—}\mathrm{C}sp^3$ bond, and three $\mathrm{C}sp^2$—H bonds become five $\mathrm{C}sp^3$—H bonds. In this case, however, a $\mathrm{C}sp^3\text{—}\mathrm{C}sp^2$ bond is changed to a $\mathrm{C}sp^3\text{—}\mathrm{C}sp^3$ bond. According to Dewar[(7)] the difference between the heats of hydrogenation of ethylene and propylene, $\Delta H'$, can be equated to variations in bond energies on hybridization changes, i.e.,

$$\Delta H' = [E(\mathrm{C}sp^2\text{—H}) - E(\mathrm{C}sp^3\text{—H})] - [E(\mathrm{C}sp^3\text{—}\mathrm{C}sp^2) - E(\mathrm{C}sp^3\text{—}\mathrm{C}sp^3)].$$

Large deviations from constancy of bond energies are found in compounds for which two or more equally acceptable valence bond structures can be written. Such compounds usually have higher heats of atomization than those calculated on the basis of the sum of bond energy terms for any one of these structures. This extra stability is usually ascribed to 'resonance' between valence bond structures, and the excess heat of atomization above that calculated for the most stable valence bond structure is referred to as the resonance energy.

2. *Bond Dissociation Energies*

The concept of bond energy considered so far is an abstract one, and it is an attempt to give a value to the strength of a bond as it is in the molecule, with respect to dissociation to the atoms. It is impossible to verify experimentally that a value ascribed to a particular bond is correct (except in the restricted case of a molecule containing only one type of bond) and the only criterion of correctness is that the sum of the bond energies shall be equal to the heat of atomization of the gaseous molecule, or $\Sigma E(\text{b}) = -\Delta H_f^a(\text{g})$.

The *dissociation energy* $D(\text{A—B})$ of a bond A—B is a quantity which can be measured, at least in principle. It refers to the reaction $AB \rightarrow A + B$, in the ideal gas state at 0 °K, where the products A and B are in their ground states. Dissociation energies which have been calculated from spectral data refer to this temperature, but those which have been derived from kinetic and equilibrium data often refer to room temperature or higher. The bond dissociation energy measured at normal temperature does not differ greatly from the value at the absolute zero of temperature, and often data obtained at room temperature are not sufficiently precise to warrant the correction, for which the necessary heat capacity data are often lacking in any case.

For a diatomic molecule the bond energy and bond dissociation energy (at 25 °C) are the same. For a polyatomic molecule this is not usually so. The dissociation energy $D(CH_3\text{—H})$ refers to the process $CH_4 \rightarrow CH_3 + H$, in which the methyl radical will "reorganize" from its sp^3, tetrahedral arrangement in methane to one which is probably planar, involving the use of sp^2 hybrids. The second "stepwise" dissociation energy, $D(CH_2\text{—H})$, would include the reorganization energy of the CH_2 radical, and the third dissociation energy, $D(\text{CH—H})$ would incorporate the reorganization energy of the CH radical, whilst the last dissociation energy $D(\text{C—H})$ would include the valence-state energy of the carbon atom in the CH radical, since in this last process the carbon atom would fall back to the ground state.

However, we can write

$$-\Delta H_f^a(CH_4,\text{g}) = D(CH_3\text{—H}) + D(CH_2\text{—H}) + D(\text{CH—H}) + D(\text{C—H}) = 4\bar{D}(\text{C—H}).$$

This leads to the idea of a *mean* bond dissociation energy $\bar{D}(\text{C—H})$, which in this particular case is identical with the bond energy. In a molecule containing more than two different atoms, the two terms would not be synonymous.

For diatomic molecules, A_2, which are gases at room temperature such as H_2, O_2, Cl_2, etc., bond dissociation energies give the heat of formation of the free atom directly from the expression $D(\text{A—A}) = 2\Delta H_f^0(\text{A,g})$, since the heat of formation of the molecule is zero, by definition. For a molecule RA, in which R might be an organic radical, we can write

$$D(\text{R—A}) = \Delta H_f^0(\text{R,g}) + \Delta H_f^0(\text{A,g}) - \Delta H_f^0(\text{RA,g}),$$

so that if the dissociation energy D(R—A) is known, together with the heats of formation of A and RA, the heat of formation of the free radical R can be calculated. For example, from a knowledge of the dissociation energy $D(CH_3\text{—}H)$ and the heats of formation of gaseous methane and the hydrogen atom, it is possible to calculate the heat of formation of the methyl radical from the relationship

$$D(\text{CH}_3\text{—H}) = \Delta H_f^0(\text{CH}_3\text{,g}) + \Delta H_f^0(\text{H,g}) - \Delta H_f^0(\text{CH}_4\text{,g}).$$

The bond dissociation energy for some other process in which a methyl radical appears can now be calculated if the relevant heats of formation are known. Thus D(C—Br) in methyl bromide might be derived using the equation

$$D(\text{CH}_3\text{—Br}) = \Delta H_f^0(\text{CH}_3\text{,g}) + \Delta H_f^0(\text{Br,g}) - \Delta H_f^0(\text{CH}_3\text{Br,g}).$$

It is most useful to know the heats of formation of radicals, and also of atoms, because bond dissociation energies can then be calculated from heats of formation of stable compounds. It should be emphasized, however, that the thermochemical approach gives the *heat* of a dissociation process. Whilst this will generally be rather close to the bond dissociation energy, the condition for equality is that the reverse process $R + X \rightarrow RX$ should proceed without activation energy.

The fragments produced on dissociation of a bond in a polyatomic molecule are frequently different in shape and valence-description from their form in the undissociated molecule (e.g. the flattening of $\text{—}CH_3$ on dissociation of $CH_3\text{—}X$). One can therefore speak of a "reorganization" of the fragments, and of the "energy of reorganization". In compounds containing metal-carbon or metal-halogen bonds the valence-state excitation energy of the metal atom can make a large contribution to the reorganization energy. For the dissociation of mercury dimethyl into methyl radicals and mercury atom, viz.

$$\text{HgMe}_2 \rightarrow \text{Hg} + 2\text{Me},$$

the mean dissociation energy $\bar{D}$(Hg—Me) is given by the equation

$$2\bar{D}(\text{Hg—Me}) = \Delta H_f^0(\text{Hg,g}) + 2\,\Delta H_f^0(\text{Me,g}) - \Delta H_f^0(\text{HgMe}_2\text{,g}).$$

In this dissociation process, the mercury atom falls from the valence state to the ground state, and this energy, together with the reorganization energy of the methyl radicals, is included in the overall dissociation energy. To make a fair comparison between metal-carbon bond dissociation energies, D(M—C), Long[8] has suggested that it would be preferable to consider a mean dissociation energy for the process in which the metal atom remains in the excited valence state. This he calls the mean *intrinsic* bond energy, $\overline{D}_i$. The idea of mean, intrinsic bond dissociation energy is very close to that of bond energy—both are attempts to express the strength of a bond as it is found in the molecule. In both cases the heat required to dissociate the molecule into its constituent atoms is the sum of the bond strengths in the molecule. However, bond energies refer to dissociation to unexcited atoms, whereas mean intrinsic bond dissociation energies refer to dissociation to atoms in an excited valence state. For example, for the dissociation of mercury dimethyl the intrinsic dissociation energy is defined by the expression

$$2\overline{D}_i(\text{Hg—Me}) = \Delta H_f^0(\text{Hg}^*,\text{g}) + 2\Delta H_f^0(\text{Me,g}) - \Delta H_f^0(\text{HgMe}_2,\text{g}),$$

where Hg* represents the mercury atom in its divalent state.

Cotton[9] has taken this idea a step further for the metal carbonyl compounds, where a mean, intrinsic bond dissociation energy is calculated for the process

$$\text{Ni(CO)}_4 \rightarrow \text{Ni}^* + 4\text{CO}^*,$$

where both the nickel atom and the CO group remain in the states in which they are supposed to exist in the nickel tetracarbonyl molecule. The C—O bond length in the carbonyl compound is different from that in a free carbon monoxide molecule, and an attempt is made to calculate the reorganization energy involved in the change.

Heats of Reaction

The concept of bond energy can be very useful where a comparison is being made between two dissimilar molecules, for example to calculate the values for E(Si—N) in the two compounds Me_3SiNEt_2 and $(Me_3Si)_2NH$, where there are a number of different types of bond. Often, however, it is not necessary to press the idea of transferability of bond strength to this extent, especially when similar molecules are being compared. An extreme example of this situation is the comparison of the bonding in two geometrical isomers, such as *cis*- and *trans*-dimethylcyclopentane. Any difference between the heats of formation of the two isomers can be attributed to changes in repulsions between non-bonded atoms, since the number and type of bonds are the same in both cases and the intrinsic bond strengths are the same in the two isomers.

Likewise with the homologous series of cycloalkanes, $(CH_2)_n$, which are built up of —CH_2— units. In this case it is not even necessary to derive the heats of formation to show up variations in bond strengths and non-bonded repulsions, since the heat of combustion *per* CH_2 *group* is a measure of the strength of two carbon-carbon bonds and two carbon–hydrogen bonds. For example, the heats of combustion of cyclopentane and cyclohexane are −158·7 and −157·5 kcal/CH_2 group, respectively. This compares with a value of −157·5 kcal/CH_2 group for the normal higher alkanes. Since the energy content of the products of these oxidations is the same in each case, this must mean that the energy content of cyclopentane, per CH_2 group, is higher than that of cyclohexane. The interpretation of this is that the bonding in cyclopentane is weaker than in cyclohexane, by about 1·2 kcal/CH_2 group, although for the moment it is left open whether this is due to weaker carbon–carbon or carbon–hydrogen bonds, to increased repulsions, or to all three of these factors. Suffice it to say that the cyclopentane molecule has a "strain" energy of some 6 kcal/mole, as compared with cyclohexane.

In this example, comparison of heats of combustion have led directly to information about relative bond strengths. This simple comparison cannot be made between the unsaturated cycloalkenes, say cyclopentene and cyclohexene, because the numbers of different bonds are not the same. In cyclopentene the numbers of C—C, C—H and C=C bonds are 4,4,1, whereas in cyclohexene they are 5,5,1. An elegant way round this difficulty which prevents making a direct comparison of heats of combustion, was introduced by Kistiakowsky.[10, 11] This was to compare the heats of hydrogenation of the two unsaturated compounds, of cyclopentene to cyclopentane, and of cyclohexene to cyclohexane.

The heat of hydrogenation is a measure of the difference between the chemical bonding energy in the unsaturated and saturated cyclic compounds, so that to make a useful comparison between cyclopentene and cyclohexene allowance must be made, in the heat of hydrogenation of cyclopentene, for the strain which appears in cyclopentane, but not in cyclohexane. This strain energy of $\sim$6·0 kcal/mole has been evaluated from a comparison of the heats of combustion of the cycloalkanes with the higher, normal straight-chain alkanes.

Resonance energies may also be calculated from heats of hydrogenation. For example, in the gas phase, the heat of hydrogenation of pyrrole to pyrrolidine, calculated from heats of formation of the gaseous compounds, is $-31{\cdot}6$ kcal/mole. This may be compared with a value of $-50{\cdot}9$ kcal for the heat of hydrogenation of cyclopentadiene. As a first approximation one might say that the resonance energy of pyrrole is 19·3 kcal/mole greater than that of cyclopentadiene. This figure must be modified for two reasons. Firstly, because the heats of hydrogenation depend on the differences of strain energy in the saturated and unsaturated compound. Secondly, the contribution to the heat of hydrogenation of pyrrole due to the change from two Csp^2—Nsp^2 bonds to two Csp^3—Nsp^2 bonds may not be the same as the contribution to the heat of hydrogenation of cyclopentadiene due to the change of bond type Csp^2—Csp^3 to Csp^3—Csp^3. Whilst it is comparatively easy to allow for the first effect of strain energy, the energy change due to altered hybrid states is uncertain.

Heats of hydrogenation have been measured for a wide variety of unsaturated organic compounds, to give information about strain and stabilization (resonance) energies. However, this is only one type of addition reaction for which thermochemical data have been accumulated. Lacher and his co-workers[12, 13] have measured heats of halogenation of ethylenic compounds, for example the chlorination of the homologous series of perfluoroalkenes, viz.,

$$CF_2{=}CF(CF_2)_nCF_3 + Cl_2 \rightarrow CF_2(Cl)CF(Cl)\,(CF_2)_nCF_3.$$

A comparison of these heats of chlorination with those of the alkenes gives information about the effects of fluorine atoms on the ethylenic linkage.

Heats of addition of one ethylene derivative to another, or of one ring compound to another have also been measured. These reactions are, of course, self-polymerization when the compounds are the same, and co-polymerization when they differ. Here again, the interest lies in variations within homologous series. Thus, we may hope to relate the heat of addition polymerization of ethylene derivatives to substitution effects, or of cyclic compounds to ring size and strain energies. Heats of polymerization will necessarily give only a *difference* between the bonding energy in the monomer and polymer.

These particular examples, taken from Chapters 2, 3, 4 and 5, indicate the type of information which can be drawn from the heats of combustion, hydrogenation, halogenation and polymerization reactions involving organic compounds.

Another, though very different type of addition reaction for which a great deal of thermochemical information is available is that in which a so-called "molecular addition compound" is formed. An example is the reaction

$$BCl_3 + Me_3N \rightarrow Cl_3B \cdot NMe_3$$

in which a co-ordinate bond is formed between the Group III acceptor atom, boron, and the Group V donor atom, nitrogen. In these cases the heat of the addition reaction, or of the reverse process of dissociation of the addition compound into its two constituent molecules, is a direct measure of the strength of the co-ordinate bond between donor and acceptor atoms. A large amount of reorganization may occur in both donor and acceptor molecules when the bond is broken, and to calculate the intrinsic strength of the co-ordinate bond the reorganization energies must be estimated.

These heats of dissociation of molecular addition compounds are considered in Chapter 6, the first of four chapters which deal with dissociation energies, derived from calorimetric data. Chapter 7 is concerned with the heats of dissociation of organic molecules, where one of the dissociation products is a free radical, and with the way in which the derived heats of formation of radicals can be used to calculate other dissociation energies from calorimetric data. In Chapter 8 these derived heats of formation of alkyl and aryl radicals are used to calculate dissociation energies of metal–carbon bonds, in organo-metallic compounds. Lastly, the dissociation, or ionization energies of organic acids and bases in aqueous solution are reviewed in Chapter 9.

With the exception of the molecular addition compounds and the organo-metallic derivatives, most of the data considered in these chapters are for organic compounds, and the majority of the bonds are between two elements of the first Period, e.g. carbon–hydrogen, carbon–oxygen, carbon–halogen, etc. Where a second-period element such as silicon, phosphorus or sulphur is involved in a bond, there is a striking difference in that the possibility of multiple bonding is much greater, because of the use of $3d$-orbitals. This is reflected in variations in bond strengths and heats of reactions. The final chapter, Chapter 10, reviews some of the thermochemical data which are available for silicon, phosphorus and sulphur where this type of multiple bonding may occur.

Experimental Methods

Before turning to these topics in more detail, some of the experimental methods which are currently being used to measure heats of reaction will be briefly described. Recent developments in experimental methods have been reviewed by Skinner[14] and the details of techniques used in combustion calorimetry, in particular, have been very fully described in *Experimental Thermochemistry*[15]. What follows here is intended, therefore, to give only an idea of the types of apparatus which have been used to obtain the data presented in subsequent chapters.

Generally, heats of reaction are measured calorimetrically, and the particular design of the calorimeter may vary considerably, depending on the type of reaction involved, the amount of heat change, and the duration of the reaction.

The reaction which has been most widely studied thermochemically is oxidation, and this because organic compounds in general can be burnt in an atmosphere of oxygen with comparative ease. The flame calorimeter, designed by Rossini[16] in 1930 has been used to a limited extent to measure the heats of combustion of gases or vapours in oxygen, at constant pressure. Amongst the compounds investigated were the lower alkanes, alkenes and alcohols.

The apparatus used to measure the heat of combustion of hydrogen is shown schematically in Fig. 2. It is made from Pyrex glass, except for the silica burner tube. The inlet tubes lead the hydrogen and oxygen gases, at controlled rates, into the reaction

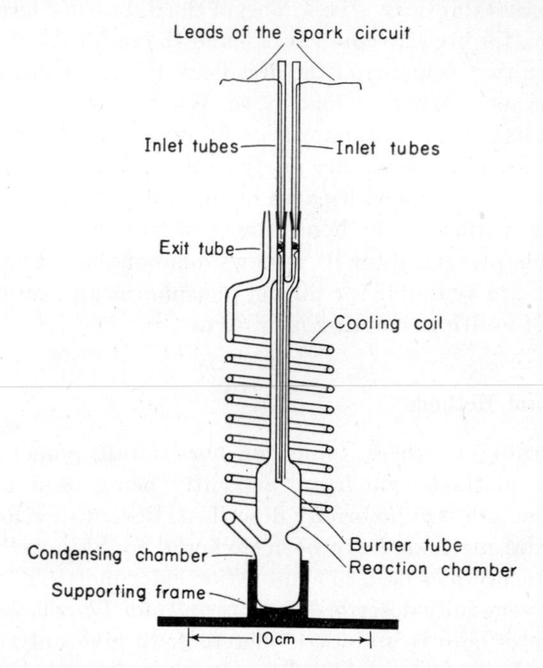

FIG. 2. The flame calorimeter (taken from Rossini, ref. 16).

chamber. The flame, ignited by a spark, is about 5 mm long. The water produced by the reaction condenses and is collected as a liquid in the chamber. The whole apparatus is immersed in water contained in a calorimeter can, and it is the temperature rise of this water which is measured. To ensure uniform heat losses the calorimeter can is surrounded by an isothermal jacket, not shown in the diagram.

The bomb calorimeter, introduced in 1869 by Berthelot, has found a more widespread application than the flame calorimeter. In bomb calorimetry oxidation of the solid or liquid compound is carried out at constant volume, under a pressure of oxygen from 25 to 35 atmospheres. The bomb itself, of about 350 ml internal volume, is usually made from corrosion-resistant steel, or is platinum lined, and has a cap which can be screwed down to withstand the pressure. There are normally two valves in this cap, inlet and outlet, so that the gaseous contents of the bomb can be swept out and analysed. The bomb is immersed in a can of water (often about 3,000 g) the temperature of which rises when the sample is burnt. The bomb and calorimeter can are usually surrounded by an isothermal jacket. If the substance to be burnt is solid, it is pelleted, and if liquid filled into ampoules of thin glass or plastic compound, and placed in a shallow platinum crucible. The charge is fired electrically by a small fuse and combustion of simple organic compounds normally occurs instantly.

To obtain accurate results the design of the apparatus is critical, and recently marked improvements have been made in techniques of combustion calorimetry; for compounds containing only carbon, hydrogen, oxygen and nitrogen, it is possible to obtain heats of combustion to within $\pm 0{\cdot}05$ per cent, in favourable cases. In general terms the reaction here is of the type

$$C_nH_mO_pN_q + (n + \tfrac{1}{4}m - \tfrac{1}{2}p)\, O_2 \rightarrow nCO_2 + \tfrac{1}{2}mH_2O + \tfrac{1}{2}qN_2.$$

With a well-designed calorimeter, such accuracy can be achieved only by attention being paid to three important points. (1) The high purity of the substance under investigation; an obvious need, though one often difficult to meet. (2) Analysis of the combustion products, to establish the stoichiometry of the combustion process. Incomplete combustion sometimes occurs, particularly of liquid samples contained in glass ampoules, and a most satisfactory check of this is to absorb the carbon dioxide produced, and compare the mass with that calculated for complete combustion of the mass of substance introduced into the bomb. For compounds containing halogens, and for organo-metallic compounds, the analysis of the combustion products may be difficult because often a complex mixture of products is formed in the bomb. Thus, in the combustion of an organo-metallic compound the products may contain unchanged metal, carbon and oxides of the metal. (3) Thermal corrections to standard conditions must be made. These are necessary because the reaction occurs over a range of temperature; there may be an appearance or disappearance of a number of moles of gas; and also because the energy of the combustion process with the products and reactants in their standard thermodynamic states will not necessarily be the same as the energy of the bomb process, which takes place at 30 atmospheres pressure.

Where the products of oxidation are liquid or solid, for example sulphuric acid from sulphur-containing compounds, or silica from organo-silicon compounds, it is necessary to ensure that the final mixture of reaction products is homogeneous, since unless this is done large thermal errors may be introduced. With the introduction of rotating-bomb calorimetry these conditions are largely achieved, so that the heats of combustion of organo-metallic, halogen- and sulphur-containing compounds can now be measured with considerable accuracy. Recently, for example, the heat of combustion of dimanganese deca-carbonyl has been measured.[17] The bomb contained a dilute solution of nitric acid and the reaction which took place was

$$Mn_2(CO)_{10} + 4\,HNO_3 + 6\,O_2 \rightarrow 2\,Mn(NO_3)_2 + 10\,CO_2 + 2\,H_2O.$$

Figure 3 is a diagrammatic representation of a rotating-bomb calorimeter described by Good, Scott and Waddington.[18] The bomb, which is made of stainless steel, and platinum lined, with the internal fittings of platinum, is shown in the firing position in the calorimeter can, which is water filled. This can is surrounded by anisothermal jacket, with a lid. A drive shaft can be turned, at 10 r.p.m., by motors which are shown above the constant-temperature lid. By means of the mitred gear inside the calorimeter can, this shaft gives the bomb an end-over-end motion, and also turns the bomb round the two axes shown. The bomb is used in the calorimeter in the inverted position. The hot gases come into contact only with the platinum lining. The aqueous solution, on the floor of the bomb, protects the valves and sealing gaskets. After combustion, when the rotation is started, the crucible falls into the bomb liquid and is thoroughly washed by it.

Catalytic hydrogenation occupies an important place in reaction calorimetry. This technique was introduced by Kistiakowsky[19] and his co-workers in 1935, and since then Lacher,[20, 24] Turner[21] and Skinner[22] have extended its range of usefulness in thermochemistry. The heats of hydrogenation of mono-olefins, dienes, acetylenes and also some bicyclic hydrocarbons have been measured both in the gas phase and in solution. An example of a solution reaction for which the heat has been determined is the hydrogenation of dodeca-3,9-diyne, i.e.,

$$CH_3CH_2C{\equiv}C(CH_2)_4C{\equiv}CCH_2CH_3 + 4H_2 \rightarrow CH_3(CH_2)_{10}CH_3.$$

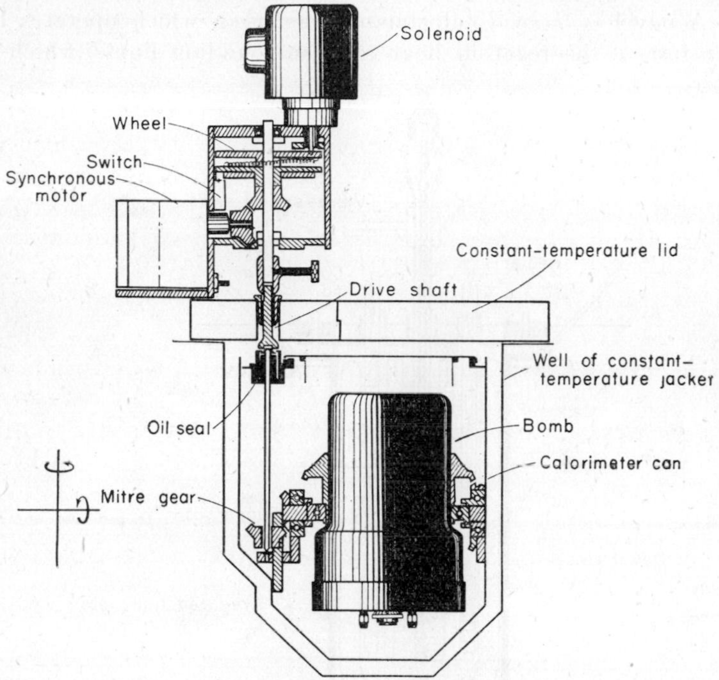

FIG. 3. The rotating-bomb calorimeter (taken from Good, Scott and Waddington, ref. 18).

The calorimeter which was used to measure this heat of hydrogenation, described by Flitcroft, Skinner and Whiting,[23] is shown in Fig. 4. The reaction vessel, totally immersed in water inside a Dewar vessel, is attached by an arm to an external vibroshaker. This device allowed very vigorous agitation of the contents of the reaction vessel, enabling the hydrogenation experiments to be completed in a very short time. These workers used a catalyst of reduced palladium oxide, and either acetic acid or ethanol as solvent.

In contrast to this *addition* hydrogenation, some of Lacher's work has been concerned with the heats of reaction in which halogens are *displaced* by hydrogen to form the hydrocarbon and halogen acids, e.g.,

$$CH_3CH_2CH_2F + H_2 \rightarrow C_3H_8 + HF.$$

A novel *isothermal* calorimeter was used, which operates by transferring the reaction heat to a surrounding liquid which is

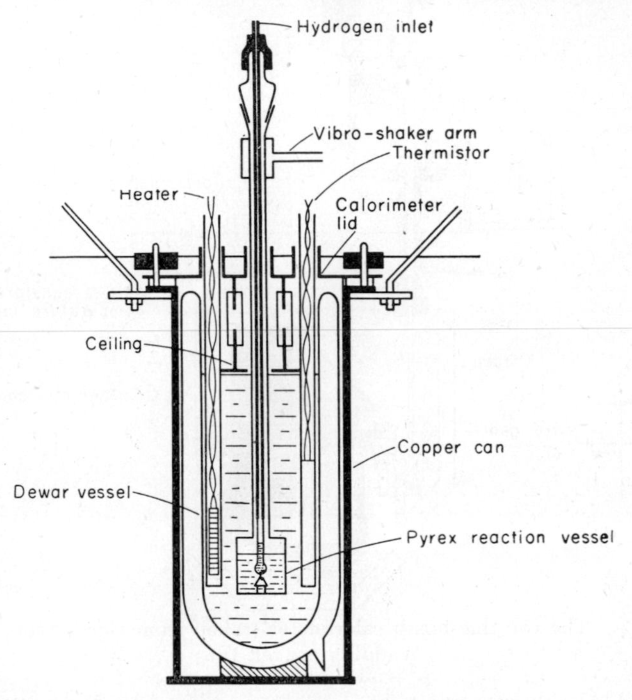

FIG. 4. Calorimeter for measuring heats of hydrogenation (in the liquid phase, at 25°C) (taken from Flitcroft, Skinner and Whiting, ref. 23).

simultaneously being cooled by bubbling an inert gas through it. A steady state is obtained when this cooling just balances the heat produced by the reaction.

A diagram of the hydrogenation chamber and calorimeter is shown in Fig. 5, taken from a paper by Lacher, Kianpour, Oetting and Park.[24] The chamber containing the palladium-on-carbon catalyst is suspended centrally. The reactant gases enter the bottom of this chamber, and leave from the top, passing then through a heat exchanger coiled round the reaction chamber, before finally leaving the calorimeter. The entire unit is enclosed in a Dewar vessel filled with volatile liquid, kept at constant temperature by the flow of inert gas through it.

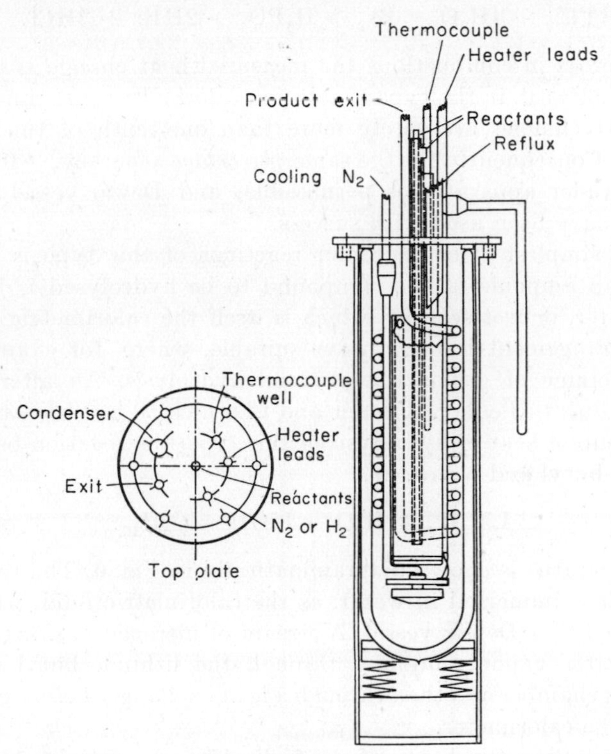

Fig. 5. Calorimeter for measuring heats of hydrogenation (in the gas phase, at high temperatures.) (taken from Lacher, Kianpour, Oetting and Park, ref. 24).

The calorimeter is capable of being operated at high temperatures, for example at 248 °C using tetra-2-ethylhexyl orthosilicate as the calorimetric fluid. It is calibrated electrically, by determining the electrical energy which is required to just balance the cooling which obtained for a particular hydrogenation experiment.

Hydrolysis reactions both of inorganic and organic substances have been extensively studied by thermochemists. Typical inorganic hydrolysis reactions which have been studied thermochemically include the hydrolysis of certain inorganic halides and oxyhalides, an example of which is the hydrolysis, under oxidizing conditions, of phosphorus trichloride to phosphoric acid,[25]

$$PCl_3 + 4H_2O + Br_2 \rightarrow H_3PO_4 + 2HBr + 3HCl.$$

Whereas in combustions the measured heat change is usually about 5,000 cal, in the type of solution calorimetry just considered the heat changes are rarely more than one-tenth of this, some 500 cal. Consequently for the same *percentage* accuracy, $\pm 0{\cdot}05$ per cent, cruder apparatus is permissible, and Dewar-vessel calorimeters have been used with success.

The simplest calorimeter for reactions of this type is one in which an ampoule of the compound to be hydrolysed is broken into water, or wet solvent, which is itself the calorimetric liquid. This arrangement is not always suitable, where, for example, a large volume of gas is liberated on hydrolysis. An alternative design, due to Pedley, Skinner and Chernick[26] has been used[27] to measure a heat of hydrolysis of this type, the reaction between lithium butyl and water, i.e.,

$$LiC_4H_9 + H_2O \rightarrow LiOH + C_4H_{10}.$$

The apparatus is shown diagrammatically in Fig. 6. The reaction chamber is immersed in water, as the calorimetric fluid, which is contained in a Dewar vessel. A stream of nitrogen gas, saturated with water vapour, bubbles through the lithium butyl in the reaction chamber and then through a heat exchanger before passing out of the calorimeter.

To measure the heats of neutralization of acids by bases in dilute solution, where heat changes of about 0·5 cal are involved, a more sophisticated calorimetric arrangement must be used. The calorimeters developed by Calvet[28] are capable of measuring these and much smaller heat changes to an accuracy of $\pm 0{\cdot}5$ per cent.

One of the cells used in this type of calorimeter is shown in Fig. 7. It consists of a cylindrical glass cell, in which the reaction occurs, which fits closely into a silver socket. The socket is situated in a cavity in a large metal block maintained at constant temperature. One set of junctions of a thermoelectric pile is in thermal contact with the cell and the other set is in contact with the metal

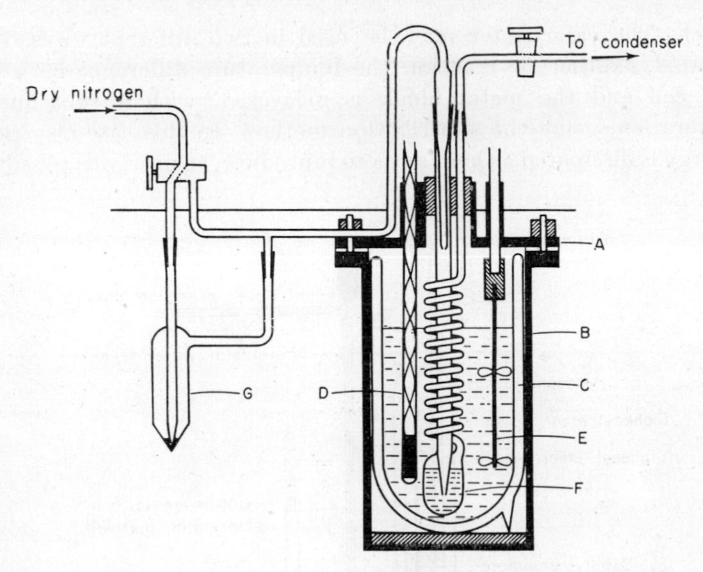

Fig. 6. Calorimeter for measuring heats of hydrolysis (with water vapour, at 25°C) (taken from Pedley, Skinner and Chernick, ref. 26). A, lid; B, can; C, Dewar-vessel; D, thermistor; E, stirrer; F, reaction chamber; G, water-saturator.

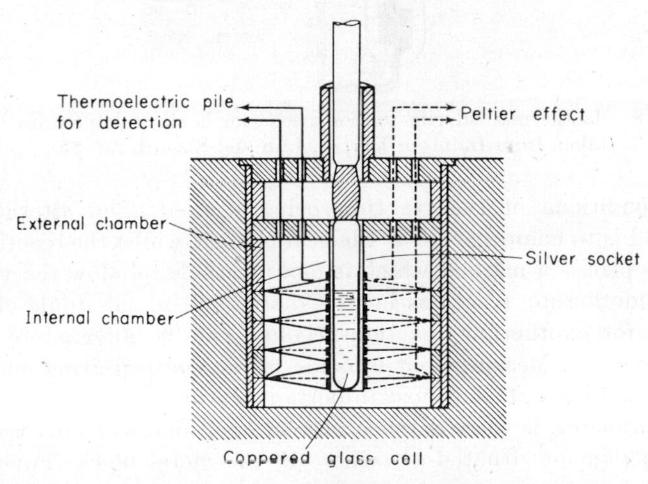

Fig. 7. Reaction cell of a 'Calvet' calorimeter (for measuring very small heats) (taken from Calvet, ref. 28).

block. The calorimeter may be used in two different ways. For a rapid, exothermic reaction the temperature difference between the cell and the metal block is measured, with a subsequent calibration, using the substitution method. In this case electrical energy is dissipated as heat so as to reproduce, as nearly as possible,

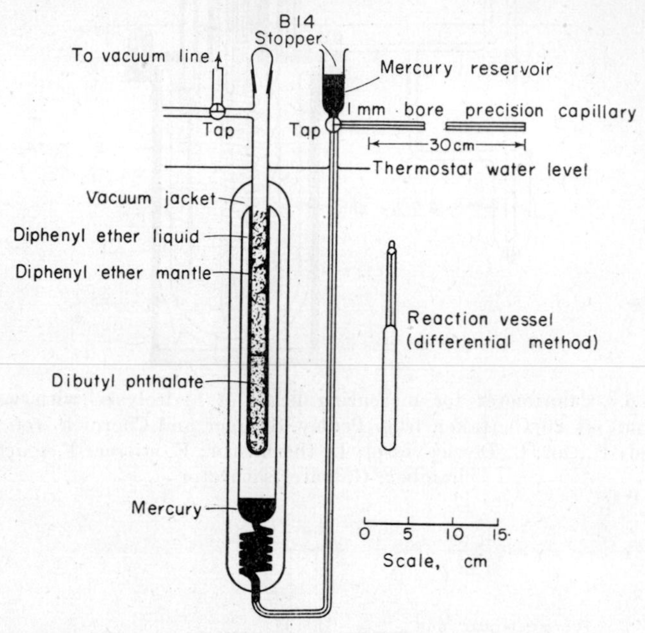

FIG. 8. **Isothermal calorimeter for measuring heats of polymerization. (taken from Dainton, Diaper, Ivin and Sheard, ref. 29).**

the conditions of the reaction being studied. The alternative method is to compensate for the heat change, whilst the reaction is taking place—a method which is more suitable for slow reactions. For endothermic reactions heat is dissipated by the Joule effect, whilst for exothermic reactions cooling can be affected by the Peltier effect. Measurement is made of the compensating energy.

The additional, and most important feature of the Calvet type of calorimeter, is the existence of a second, identical microcalorimetric element situated elsewhere in the metal block. For temperature measurements the two cells are connected *in opposition*, which means that it is the *difference* in thermoelectric e.m.f. between the two cells which is measured. Any temperature fluctuations in the metal block as a whole will affect the two cells equally, and will therefore not be reflected in the measured reaction heat. This elegant arrangement provides, in practice, the effect of the extremely steady thermostat, which is necessary for measurement of small heats. In addition, in measuring heats of neutralization, where the phial of acid is broken into a solution of alkali in the microcalorimetric cells, a "blank" experiment can be carried out in the second cell. In the blank run a phial of water is broken into the alkali solution, and this compensates for heats of dilution and of breaking the phials.

Most of the reactions mentioned so far, combustion, hydrogenation, hydrolysis, and halogenation are completed in a short time. In contrast, many polymerization reactions, for which heats have been determined, are much slower. Although a simple, Dewar-vessel calorimeter has been used with some success to measure the heats of polymerization, an isothermal fusion calorimeter, with diphenyl ether (m.p. 26·9 °C) is capable of giving more accurate results. The type shown in Fig. 8 has been described by Dainton, Diaper, Ivin and Sheard.[29]

The calorimeter has a central well, filled with butyl phthalate, containing a glass dilatometer, in which the polymerization takes place. The contraction of reactants in the dilatometer is used as a measure of the degree of the polymerization reaction. Simultaneously the movement of the mercury thread of the fusion calorimeter (caused by melting of the diphenyl ether mantle) is used as a measure of the heat evolved in the polymerization reaction. The calorimeter can be calibrated electrically.

CHAPTER 2

STRAIN ENERGIES IN SATURATED AND UNSATURATED ORGANIC COMPOUNDS

Saturated Cyclic Compounds

1. Cyclo-alkanes

The strain energies in cycloalkanes have already been referred to and this topic will now be considered in more detail. In the higher acyclic normal alkanes, the heat of combustion per CH_2 group is — 157·5 kcal/mole,[30] whilst in the gaseous cycloparaffins it is as follows: cyclopropane, —166·5; cyclobutane, —163·8; cyclopentane, —158·7; cyclohexane, —157·5; cycloheptane, —158·2; cyclo-octane, —158·5; cyclononane, —158·7 kcal/mole.[31] In so far as a greater heat of combustion reflects a more positive heat of formation, and therefore a molecule with weaker bonding, these data show the presence of strain in the three- and four-membered rings. In the five-membered ring this strain is reduced, and is at a minimum for cyclohexane, after which increase in ring size causes increased strain, at least up to the nine-membered ring. As the series is further ascended, the strain energy decreases and the heat of combustion of gaseous C_{14}, C_{15}, C_{16} and C_{17} cycloalkanes is probably the same as that of the acyclic normal alkanes.[32]

The strain in cyclopropane and cyclobutane is largely a result of *angular* strain due to compression of the tetrahedral angle of 109° 28′ in the carbon-carbon bonding. In cyclopentane and cyclohexane this angular strain is reduced by the molecule adopting a puckered conformation. Thus, the conformation of the cyclopentane molecule is that of four carbon atoms in a plane, with one carbon atom some 0·5 Å below this plane; Fig. 1 (a). This is a mean value about which the puckering oscillates, and in addition there is a pseudo, one-dimensional rotation, in which the phase of the puckering rotates round the ring.

In adopting such puckered conformations another type of strain is introduced, caused by interaction of non-bonded atoms. In puckered ring systems of six to ten carbon atoms the hydrogens

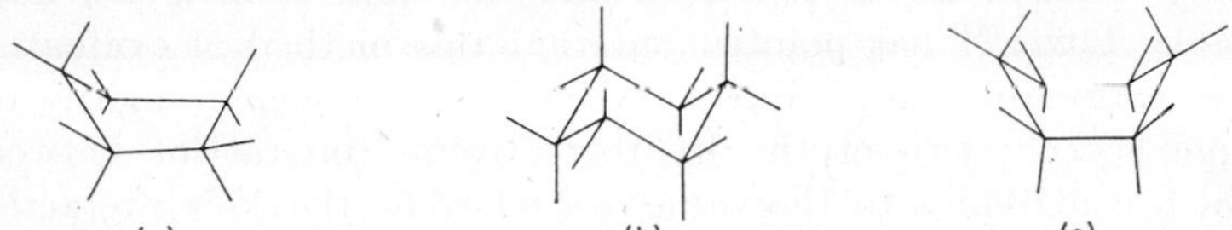

FIG. 1.

are especially crowded together within the ring, and *interaction* strain results.

Angular strain in the cyclohexane molecule can be relieved by its adopting either the chair (*b*) or the boat (*c*) conformation (Fig. 1), and various attempts have been made to calculate the energy difference between these two conformations. In one empirical method, Turner[33] compares the boat and chair conformations with the n-butane molecule.

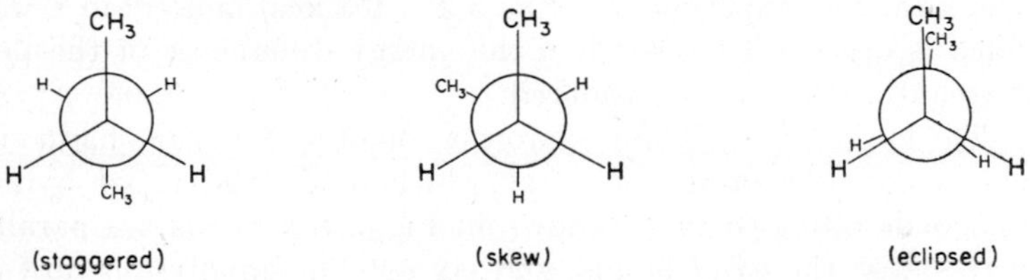

FIG. 2.

Allowing for rotation about the central C-C bond, there are three conformations of n-butane which might be considered, and these are shown in Fig. 2, as Newman projections along the central C-C bond.

The conformation of minimum energy, arbitrarily assigned zero, is the *staggered* one. The *skew* conformation has been estimated to have an energy of 0·8 kcal, due to interaction of non-bonded atoms, whilst the *eclipsed* conformation has a much higher interaction energy, estimated at between 4·4 and 6·1 kcal.

Turner considers the cyclohexane molecule as consisting of six n-butane structures, i.e. $C_1C_2C_3C_4$, $C_2C_3C_4C_5$, etc. round the ring to C_1. Thus, the chair form has six skew butane interactions (4·8 kcal), and the boat form involves four skew and two eclipsed interactions (8·8–12·2 kcal). Hence the energy difference between the two forms is 7·2–10·6 kcal, and the chair form is the more stable. Pitzer[34] has pointed out that this method of evaluating the energy difference is likely to give a value which is slightly too large because two of the hydrogen atoms (interaction between which contributes to the value of 0·8 kcal for the skew interaction in n-butane) have been replaced by carbon atoms in cyclohexane.

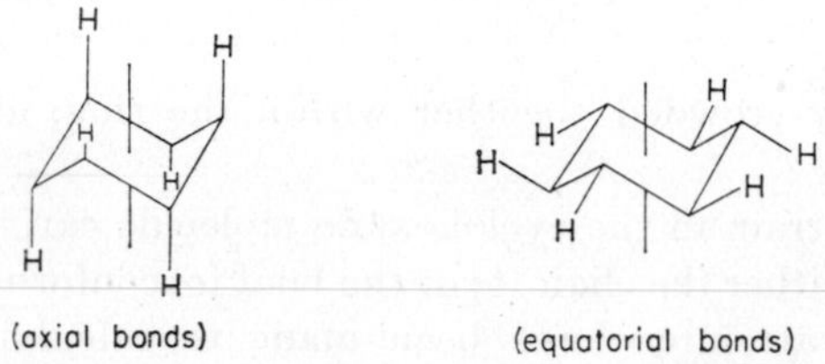

(axial bonds) (equatorial bonds)

FIG. 3.

The energy difference between the chair and boat forms has been measured experimentally as 5·3 ± 0·3 kcal/mole[35] in a way which is described later, when the energy differences of the perhydroanthracenes are considered.

The lower-energy, chair conformation of cyclohexane has a six-fold axis of alternating symmetry, which divides the carbon-hydrogen bonds into two types, shown in Fig.3. Six bonds are parallel to the axis: the *axial* bonds, and six extend radially outward at angles of 109·5° to the axis: the so-called *equatorial* bonds. This fact, that the carbon-hydrogen bonds divide into two types is important in considering energy differences between substituted cyclohexanes, referred to later.

2. *Heterocyclic Compounds*

In the cyclopentane molecule there is interaction between the hydrogen atoms, which in this case are eclipsed, leading to a strain energy of some 6 kcal/mole. Replacement of a ring carbon atom of cyclopentane by an oxygen atom is expected to reduce the strain energy considerably. The oxygen and carbon atoms are of similar size, so that the structure of the ring will not be markedly affected, although interaction between the non-bonded atoms will be reduced by the removal of two hydrogen atoms. With the replacement of a carbon atom by sulphur, the strain should be further reduced, since the larger sulphur atom will allow relief of angular strain with less puckering of the ring, and consequently less interaction strain, than is found in the oxygen-substituted compound.

The comparatively strainless chair form of cyclohexane will be less influenced by "conversion" to the corresponding heterocyclic compounds.

TABLE 1

Heats of formation of five- and six-membered ring systems (kcal/mole)

Compound	ΔH_f^0(g)	$\Delta [\Delta H_f^0$(g)]
cyclohexane	−29·43[30]	11·0
cyclopentane	−18·46[30]	
tetrahydropyran	−50·7[36]	7·6
tetrahydrofuran	−43·1[36]	
thiacyclohexane	−15·1[37]	
thiacyclopentane	− 8·1[38]	7·0
piperidine	−10·4[39]	
pyrrolidine	− 0·8[40]	9·6

In Table 1, the heats of formation of some of these five- and six-membered rings are given, together with the differences between the two values. The difference is 11·0 kcal for cyclohexane and cyclopentane, but this decreases when a CH_2 group is replaced by either on O or an S atom. When a CH_2 group is replaced by an NH group to give either piperidine or pyrrolidine, the difference between the heats of formation of the five- and six-membered ring is slightly greater than for the corresponding oxygen and sulphur compounds. However, this difference of 9·6 kcal is not too reliable as it is based on a heat of combustion made by Deléphine as early as 1898.

3. *Decalins*

Because of the non-planar structure of the cyclohexane ring, the fusion of two cyclohexane rings, to form decalin, can give rise to either a *cis* or a *trans* configuration. Calculation of the interaction energy, made by Barton,[41] indicates that the most stable conformations of the decalins are the two chair forms (*a*) and (*b*) shown in Fig. 4. The difference in energy between the *cis* and *trans* isomers is due to three *skew* interactions. These are seen in Fig. 4 (*b*), as the interaction between pairs of hydrogen atoms which may be identified by the carbon atoms to which they are bonded, i.e. the atoms C_1C_7, C_1C_5 and C_3C_5. Following Turner's method, and taking

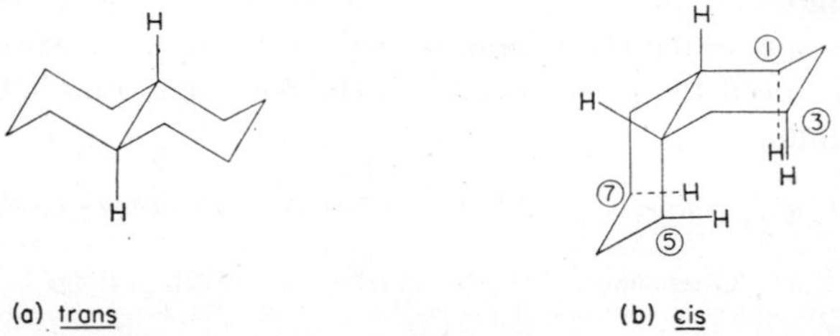

(a) trans (b) cis

FIG. 4.

0·8 kcal as the energy due to a *skew* interaction, the energy difference between the two isomers should be 2·4 kcal/mole. The heats of formation at 25 °C, were determined by Davies and Gilbert,[42] from heats of combustion, as ΔH_f^0(l), — 52·75 for *cis*-decalin, and — 54·87 kcal/mole for *trans*-decalin, and these values have been substantially confirmed by Rossini's[43] more recent work. For the gaseous compounds Rossini derives ΔH_f^0(g), — 40·38 for *cis*-decalin and — 43·57 kcal/mole for *trans*-decalin, giving an energy difference for the gaseous isomers of 3·19 kcal/mole. Agreement with the calculated difference is good, although a value of 1·0 kcal for a *skew* interaction energy would be more correct.

When a methyl group is introduced into the 9-position to give 9-methyldecalin, a greater additional interaction energy results in the *trans* compound than in the *cis*. Turner[33] calculates that although the *trans* isomer will still be more stable than the *cis* isomer, it will be so by only 0·8 kcal/mole. This prediction has been largely confirmed by Speros and Rossini[44] who obtain a heat of *trans* → *cis* isomerization of 1·39 ± 0·64 kcal/mole from combustion data.

4. *Perhydroanthracenes*

When three cyclohexane rings are fused together to form the perhydroanthracenes, the number of stable isomers which can be isolated increases to five, and these are shown in Fig. 6. The configurations of the rings A and C are designated *cis* if the hydrogen atoms on C_{13} and C_{14} (Fig. 5) are on the same side of the molecule, or *trans* if they are on opposite sides. The same applies to the carbon atoms C_{11} and C_{12}. The configuration is also designated *syn* if the two hydrogen atoms on C_{11} and C_{13} are on the same side of the molecule, and *anti* if they are on opposite sides. These structures can be represented in perspective, or following Johnson's[45] diagrammatic form, in which a black circle is used to indicate a hydrogen atom above the plane of the molecule, and an unshaded circle for a hydrogen atom below the plane of the molecule.

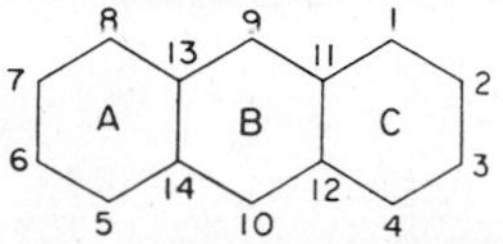

FIG. 5.

The most stable of these isomers is the *trans-syn-trans*, since all ring junctures are equatorial and there are no *skew* interactions, (apart from those found in the chair form of cyclohexane, to which we have arbitrarily assigned a zero energy of interaction).

(a) The *trans-syn-trans* isomer is, therefore, assigned a zero energy, $E = 0$.

(b) The *cis-syn-trans* isomer has three equatorial and one axial juncture, and this results in three *skew* interactions, just as in the decalin series, to which we assigned an energy, $E = 2{\cdot}4$ kcal.

(c) The *cis-anti-cis* isomer has two equatorial and two axial linkages, which imposes two *cis*-decalin types of interaction, to give $E = 4{\cdot}8$ kcal.

(d) The *cis-syn-cis* isomer will have a comparatively large interaction energy between the axial hydrogen atoms bonded to C_{13} and C_{11} in the central ring. This interaction is comparable with the 1,3 interaction between axial bonds in *cis*-1,3-dimethylcyclohexane, estimated at 5·4 kcal/mole by Pitzer.[47, 48] In the present case Johnson[45] estimates the interaction of two methylene groups to be about 8/9 parts of the interaction between two methyl groups, or 4·8 kcal. In addition, two *skew* interactions bring the total energy to $E \sim 6{\cdot}4$ kcal.

(e) The *trans-anti-trans* isomer differs from the *trans-syn-trans* in that the central ring assumes a boat conformation. This accounts for a difference of 5·3 kcal, i.e. the difference be-

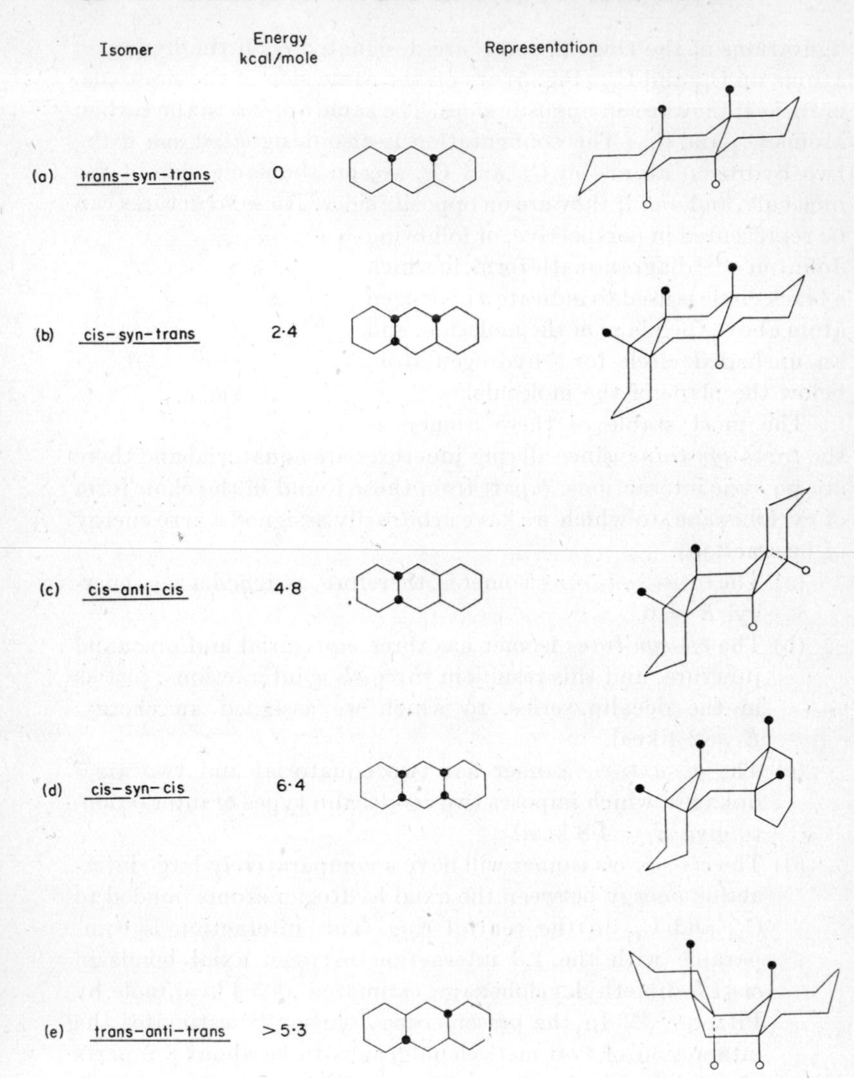

FIG. 6. Perhydroanthracenes. Energy differences between isomers (taken from Orloff, ref. 46).

tween the boat and chair forms of cyclohexane. In addition, there are two other small interactions, the magnitudes of which are uncertain, so that the value of 5·3 is a minimum.

The energy difference between the chair and boat forms of cyclohexane has been determined experimentally by measurement of the heats of combustion of the two isomeric lactones shown in Fig. 7. These are the *trans-syn-trans* (I) and the *trans-anti-trans* (II)

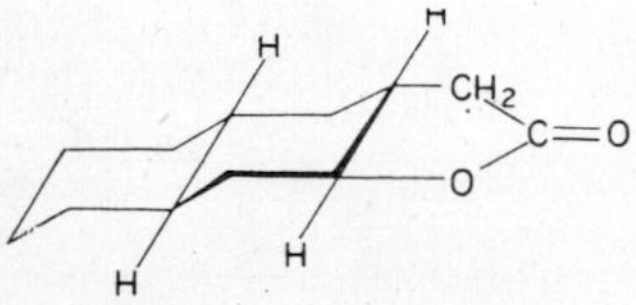

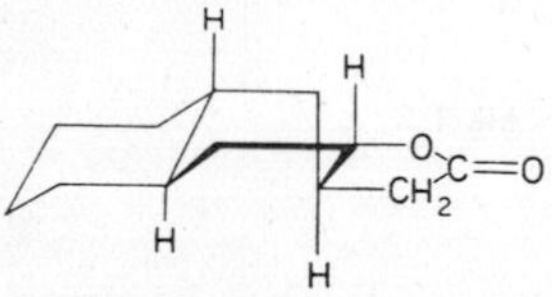

Fig. 7

isomers which differ in that the central ring assumes the chair conformation in the former and a boat in the latter. Johnson *et al.*[35] have shown that the heat of formation of gaseous (I) is less than that of (II) by 5·3 ± 0·3 kcal/mole. This value is considered to represent ΔH for the conversion chair → boat form of cyclohexane, since the difference in other interactions in the two isomeric lactones is probably small.

Unfortunately, as yet there are no combustion data for the isomeric perhydroanthracenes, against which to check the calculations experimentally.

5. *Dimethylcyclohexanes*

When two hydrogen atoms of cyclohexane are substituted by two methyl groups, to give the dimethylcyclohexanes, the possibility of *cis-trans* isomerism arises, in much the same way as substitution of two hydrogen atoms by "ring fusion" causes *cis-trans* isomerism in the decalins.

In Fig. 8, the conformations of *cis*-1,2, *trans*-1,3 and *cis*-1,4 isomers are shown, and it is seen that owing to the alternation of the equatorial and axial bonds on the same side of the ring, if one group is equatorial, the other is axial.

In the chair form of cyclohexane, the carbon atoms are in two planes (Fig. 9), each plane containing three carbon atoms. Owing to the flexibility of the chair conformation the two planes may interchange positions and the molecule will assume a second chair form, when all the bonds which were axial in the former will be equatorial in the latter, and vice versa.

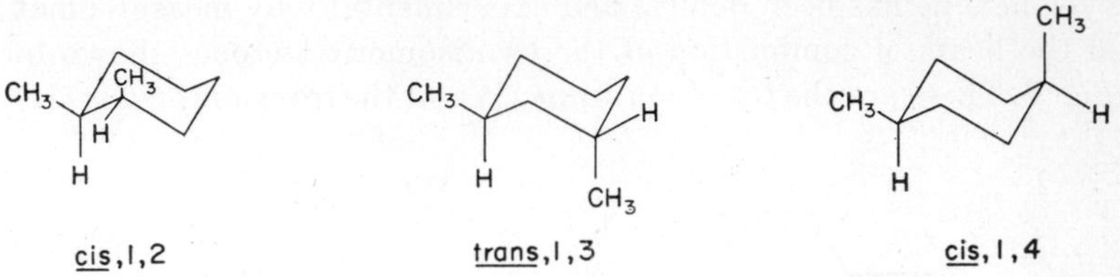

cis, 1,2 trans, 1,3 cis, 1,4

FIG. 8

For these *cis*-1,2, *trans*-1,3 and *cis*-1,4 isomers such inversion will produce identical conformations. On the other hand, with the

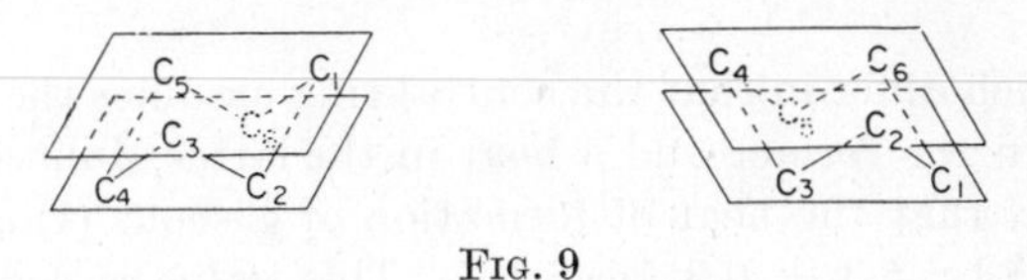

FIG. 9

trans-1,2, *cis*-1,3 and *trans*-1,4 isomers, two conformations of different energy exist for each isomer, corresponding to either diequatorial or diaxial substitution. When a methyl group is in an axial

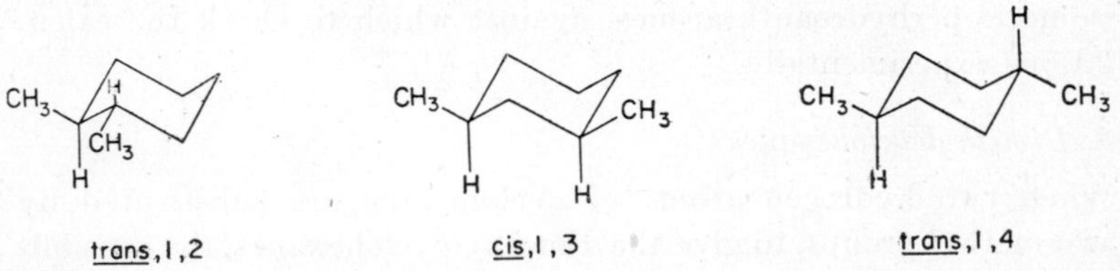

trans, 1,2 cis, 1,3 trans, 1,4

FIG. 10.

position, two *skew* n-butane interactions are introduced, whereas in an equatorial position no such interactions result. Hence the diequatorial conformations, shown in Fig. 10, have the lower energy.

Since the placing of any group into an axial conformation produces two *skew* n-butane energy values, diequatorial substitution will also be more stable than axial-equatorial substitution. Consequently of the *cis*/*trans* pairs, the ones with lower energy values will be *trans*-1,2-, and *trans*-1,4-dimethylcyclohexanes, whilst for 1,3 compounds, the *cis* isomer will have a lower energy than the *trans* isomer.

From this type of consideration, Beckett, Pitzer and Spitzer[47] drew up energy relationships of the type shown in Table 2, which gives the conformations (equatorial or axial) of the substituents, the number of n-butane *skew* interaction energies, x, the calculated energy differences between isomers, and finally the observed values. The observed and calculated values show the same trend, although the value for x, the n-butane *skew* interaction, again seems nearer to 1·0 kcal/mole.

TABLE 2

Energy differences between dimethylcyclohexane isomers

Compound	Conformations of methyl groups	Interaction Energy[a] (calculated)[b]		ΔH_f^0(g)[c]	Interaction Energy (observed)
		x	kcal/mole	kcal/mole	kcal/mole
cis-1,2	ea	$3x$	2·4	−41·15	3·01
trans-1,2	ee	x	0·8	−43·02	1·14
cis-1,3	ee	0	0	−44·16	0
trans-1,3	ea	$2x$	1·6	−42·20	1·96
cis-1,4	ea	$2x$	1·6	−42·22	1·94
trans-1,4	ee	0	0	−44·12	0·02

[a] x = n-butane *skew* interaction energy, 0·8 kcal.
[b] Arbitrarily taking *cis*-1,3 as of zero interaction energy.
[c] Taken from ref. 30.

6. *Dimethylcyclopentanes*

Using a method similar to that applied to the dimethylcyclohexanes, Haresnape[49] has calculated the energy difference between the *cis* and *trans* isomers of the dimethylcyclopentanes. For the 1,3 compounds the *cis* isomer should be more stable than the *trans* by 0·5 kcal/mole, whereas for the 1,2 compounds it is the *trans* which should be more stable than the *cis* isomer by 1·7 kcal/mole. The experimental values, derived from the heats of formation of the gaseous compounds, are shown in Table 3. The correlation between calculated and experimental values is good.

7. Hydrindanes

A five-membered ring may be fused to a cyclohexane ring in a chair conformation either through a *cis* or a *trans* ring juncture. The *cis* fusion involves one equatorial and one axial bond; the *trans* fusion involves two equatorial bonds. Following the ideas developed

TABLE 3

Energy differences between dimethylcyclopentane isomers

Compound	Interaction Energy (calculated) kcal/mole	ΔH_f^0(g)[a] kcal/mole	Interaction Energy (observed) kcal/mole
cis-1,2	1·7	−30·96	1·71
trans-1,2		−32·67	
cis-1,3	0·5	−32·47	0·54
trans-1,3		−31·93	

[a] Following Haresnape's suggestion that the lower boiling isomer is *cis* and the higher boiling isomer is *trans*.

for the decalins, the isomer with two equatorial bonds *(trans)* would be expected to have the lower energy. This was found experimentally by Rossini,[50] who obtained heats of formation differing by $1{\cdot}04 \pm 0{\cdot}53$ kcal/mole, the *trans* isomer having the lower enthalpy.

Unsaturated Compounds

1. Cyclic Olefins

The interaction and angular strain energies considered so far have been derived from heats of combustion, i.e. heats of oxidation to carbon dioxide and water. Such data are not always available for olefinic compounds, but a considerable amount of work has been carried out on the heats of hydrogenation of these unsaturated compounds. The products of such reactions, the hydrogenated compounds, generally differ in each case. Here the heat of hydrogenation is a measure of the *difference* between the heats of formation of the saturated and unsaturated compounds, as shown in Fig. 11.

The heat of hydrogenation will therefore reflect strain energies in *both* the saturated and unsaturated compounds. Thus the expected (standard) heat of hydrogenation will be *increased* if (*a*) the saturated molecule is more stable, i.e. ΔH_f^0 (saturated) is more ne-

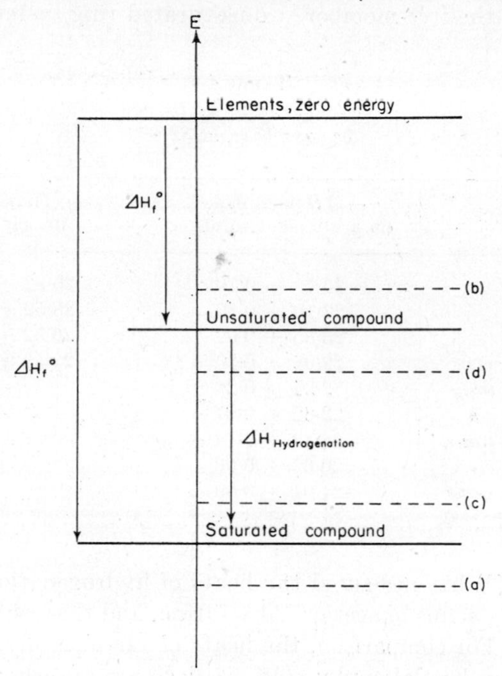

FIG. 11. Energy diagram relating heats of formation and heats of hydrogenation.

gative; or if (*b*) the unsaturated molecule is less stable, i.e. ΔH_f^0 (unsaturated) is more positive. On the other hand, the expected heat of hydrogenation will be *reduced* if (*c*) the saturated molecule is less stable, i.e. ΔH_f^0 (saturated) is more positive; or if (*d*) the unsaturated molecule is more stable, i.e. ΔH_f^0 is more negative.

An example of this is seen in the heat of hydrogenation of cyclopentene, in the gas phase, which is 1·7 kcal/mole *lower* than that of cyclohexene, (Table 4). This despite the fact that the strain of the cyclopentene double bond is clearly *greater* than that of the olefinic linkage in cyclohexene, so that the heat of hydrogenation cyclopentene might be expected to be higher than that of cyclohexene. The explanation of this presumably lies in the greater strain in the saturated product cyclopentane than in cyclohexane, causing the heat of formation of cyclopentane to be more positive than would be otherwise anticipated. This lowers the heat of hydrogenation of the five-membered unsaturated ring system.

TABLE 4

Heats of hydrogenation of cyclo-olefins in acetic acid solution, at 25 °C, and in the gas phase, at 82 °C

Compound	$-\Delta H$ (kcal/mole) (in acetic acid solution)	$-\Delta H$ (kcal/mole) (in gas phase)
cyclopentene	25·7 ± 0·10[51]	26·92 ± 0·01[10]
cyclohexene	27·10 ± 0·10	28·59 ± 0·01[11]
cycloheptene	25·85 ± 0·09	26·52 ± 0·02[52]
cyclo-octene, *cis*	22·98 ± 0·10	23·53 ± 0·04[52]
trans	32·24 ± 0·21	—
cyclononene, *cis*	23·62 ± 0·07	—
trans	26·49 ± 0·14	—
cyclodecene, *cis*	20·67 ± 0·08	—
trans	24·01 ± 0·09	—

Turner[51] has measured the heats of hydrogenation of a number of cyclo-olefins in acetic acid solution, and the results are shown in Table 4. For comparison, the heats of gas phase hydrogenation, measured by Kistiakowsky *et al.*,[10, 11, 52] are also shown.

Two main points may be singled out for comment from these results. Firstly, the values obtained for the *cis*-olefins show a decrease of 6·4 kcal in passing from cyclohexene (−27·1 kcal) to *cis*-cyclodecene (−20·7 kcal). The general trend, established for the series cyclohexene to *cis*-cyclo-octene from the gas phase hydrogenation heats, is projected at least as far as the ten-membered ring derivative. Whilst it appears that increased steric compression of the higher hydrocarbons plays a dominant role in lowering the heats of hydrogenation of the larger cyclo-olefins, the differences of strain in the unsaturated compounds do play some part. In addition to the *angular* and *interaction* strains considered so far for the saturated compounds, there is in the cyclic olefins the additional possibility of *torsional* strain, the twisting of the olefinic link to permit ring formation. Thus, the heat of hydrogenation of *cis*-cyclononene is higher than that of *cis*-cyclo-octene, although if the value were to depend solely on strain energy in the saturated hydrocarbons, the reverse relationship would be expected, since the cyclononane ring has a greater strain energy than cyclo-octane, to the extent of some 1·7 kcal/mole.

In each case the *trans* isomer has a higher heat of hydrogenation, and therefore a less negative heat of formation than the corresponding *cis* isomer. The heats of isomerization (*trans* → *cis*) calculated for the eight-, nine- and ten-membered cyclo-olefins are −9·2, −2·9, and −3·3 kcal/mole, as compared with +1·0 kcal/mole for the heat of isomerization of *trans*- to *cis*-butene. The difference of 9 kcal observed in the heats of hydrogenation of *cis*- and *trans*-cyclo-octene is the largest yet observed for any pair of *cis*/*trans* isomers and reflects the severe strain that accompanies incorporation of a *trans* double bond in the eight-membered ring. Thus, in the cyclic olefins the *cis* isomers are the more stable, the reverse of the situation with the chain olefins, where it is the *trans* isomer which is the more stable. In the cyclic compounds, less angular and torsional strain are introduced when the *cis* bonds are used in ring formation.

2. *Cyclic* ortho-*Substituted Benzene Derivatives*

It is interesting to compare the heats of hydrogenation of some cyclic *ortho*-substituted benzene derivatives of the type shown in Fig. 12, which though not strictly olefinic compounds, do contain a double bond in the benzene ring.

The heat of hydrogenation of benzene to cyclohexane, in the gas phase, is −49·7 kcal/mole.[11] The heat of hydrogenation of tetralin to *trans*-decalin, in the gas phase, can be calculated as −46·2 kcal/mole from heats of combustion which give ΔH_f^0 (tetralin, g) = + 2·6 kcal/mole,[53] and ΔH_f^0 (*trans*-decalin, g) = −43·57 kcal/mole.[43] For hydrindene to hydrindane the value for the gas phase is −45·8 kcal/mole, measured directly by Kistiakowsky.[10] The hydrogenation product was most probably *trans*-hydrindane.

Again, these values are probably less influenced by strain in the unsaturated compound than in the hydrogenation product. If this is so, the similar heats of hydrogenation of tetralin and hydrindene suggest that the interaction strains in *trans*-decalin and *trans*-hydrindane are about the same.

3. *Acyclic Olefins*

We consider now the effects of steric interaction in the acyclic olefins. Table 5 shows the heats of hydrogenation of *cis*- and *trans*-pairs of compounds, and the difference between these heats, the heat of *cis* → *trans* isomerization.

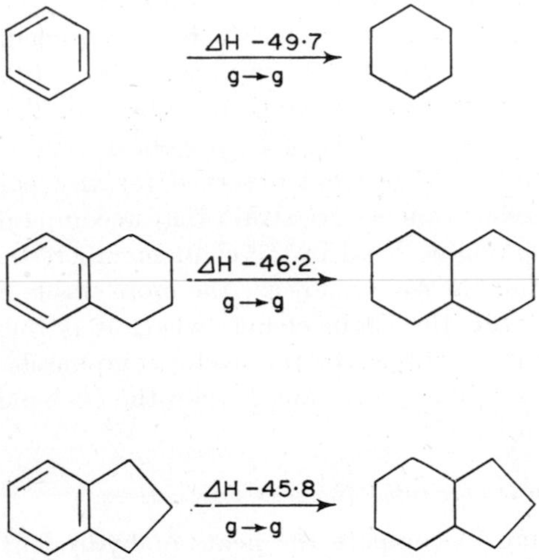

ΔH −49·7
g→g

ΔH −46·2
g→g

ΔH −45·8
g→g

FIG. 12. Heats of hydrogenation of cyclic *ortho*-substituted benzene derivatives (kcal/mole).

In these olefins,the conflicting requirements of the *cis*-substituents make the heat of formation of the *cis* isomer more positive than the corresponding *trans* isomer, so increasing the heat of hydrogenation of the *cis* compound. This is the reverse of the situation found for the cyclo-olefins. The *cis/trans* difference for methylisopropylethylene, −0·9 kcal/mole, is much the same as that for the butene-2 isomers, suggesting that the isopropyl group adopts a configuration which has sterically much the same effect as a methyl group. For methyl-t-butylethylene, the difference is increased to −4·3 kcal/mole, whilst the large steric requirements of two t-butyl groups in di-t-butylethylene cause the *cis* isomer to be some 9·3 kcal/mole more strained than the *trans* isomer.

TABLE 5

Heats of cis → trans *isomerizsation from heats of hydrogenation of non-cyclic olefinic and acetylenic compounds*

Compound		$-\Delta H$ hyd. (kcal/mole)	ΔH isom. (kcal/mole)
butene–2			
$CH_3CH-CHCH_3$	*cis*	28·57[a]	−1·0
	trans	27·62	
methylisopropylethylene			
$CH_3CH=CHCH(CH_3)_2$	*cis*	27·32[b]	−0·9
	trans	26·38	
methyl-t-butylethylene			
$CH_3CH=CHC(CH_3)_3$	*cis*	30·80[b]	−4·3
	trans	26·51	
di-t-butylethylene			
$(CH_3)_3CCH=CHC(CH_3)_3$	*cis*	36·24[b]	−9·3
	trans	26·87	
maleic acid			
fumaric acid			
$COOHCH=CHCOOH$	*cis*	36·29[c] (36·21[d])	−5·1 (−5·4)
	trans	31·15[c] (30·78[d])	
dec-3-en-1-yne			
$CH\equiv CCH=CH(CH_2)_5CH_3$	*cis*	95·62[e]	+0·3
	trans	95·92	
pent-3-en-1-yne			
$CH\equiv CCH=CHCH_3$	*cis*	95·6[e]	+0·4
	trans	96·0	

[a] Gas phase, at 82°(19)
[b] Acetic acid solution at 25°(54)
[c] Solid phase, direct measurement, at 25°(23, 55)
[d] Solid phase, calculated from heats of combustion(56)
[e] Liquid phase, at 25°(22)

The heat of *cis* → *trans* isomerization of butene-2, in the vapour phase, is also available from Lacher's(57) data on the hydrobromination of these isomers, at 100 and 110 °C. The difference between the two heats is again −1·0 kcal/mole.

$$CH_3CH=CHCH_3(cis) + HBr \rightarrow CH_3CH_2CH(Br)CH_3 \qquad \Delta H = -18{\cdot}34 \pm 0{\cdot}16$$

$$CH_3CH=CHCH_3(trans) + HBr \rightarrow CH_3CH_2CH(Br)CH_3 \qquad \Delta H = -17{\cdot}34 \pm 0{\cdot}14$$

Skinner and Snelson[22] have measured the heats of hydrogenation of two pairs of *cis/trans* isomers of compounds containing an olefinic and an acetylenic bond (Table 5). For the dec-en-ynes, and pent-en-ynes the *cis* isomers are slightly more stable than the *trans* isomers. The difference in the heat of hydrogenation is small, and the errors attached to the results are large, so that the order of stability may not be as it appears. However, it appears that the steric requirements of the acetylenic group are less than the alkyl or carboxylic groups.

Polycyclo-alkanes and Alkenes

A combination of two strain effects so far mentioned, hydrogen-hydrogen repulsion and torsional strain probably operates in some bi-cyclo-unsaturated compounds. Figure 13 shows diagrammatically the hydrogenation of bi-cyclo-heptene (*a*), and of bi-cyclo-heptadiene (*b*) to bi-cycloheptane (*c*), and of bi-cyclo-octene (*d*) to bi-cyclo-octane (*e*). The heats of hydrogenation, in solution, measured by Turner[58], are also included in the diagram. Whereas the heat of hydrogenation of cyclohexene is *greater* than that of cyclopentene, the heat of hydrogenation of cyclo-octene, with its two six-membered ring system, is *less* than that of the corresponding five-membered ring system, bi-cycloheptene.

Turner[58] has suggested that the strain energies of the saturated products bi-cyclo-octane and bi-cycloheptane will be similar, since both of these compounds are extensively eclipsed (in contrast to the simple ring systems, where cyclopentane suffers more strain energy than cyclohexane). The larger heat of hydrogenation of bi-cycloheptene cannot be traced to strain in the products, and the reason for it doubtless lies in the unsaturated compound. Very probably the bi-cycloheptene molecule suffers *angular* strain, because of the constraint imposed by the bridge of only one carbon atom; a strain which is not to be found in bi-cyclo-octene with its two-carbon atom bridge.

Two comments are made on the greater heat of hydrogenation of bi-cyclo-octene than that of cyclohexene. These are:

(i) that the structure of bi-cyclo-octane may be twisted about the central axis to reduce hydrogen-hydrogen repulsion, which would make the heat of formation of the saturated compound more negative, and increase the heat of hydrogenation, and,

(ii) bi-cyclo-octene may be more twisted about the olefinic bond than is cyclohexene, and this torsional strain, not present in cyclohexene, would again lead to an increased heat of hydrogenation.

The heat of hydrogenation of bi-cycloheptadiene, has been measured as 68·1 kcal/mole,[59] in solution. If the value were the

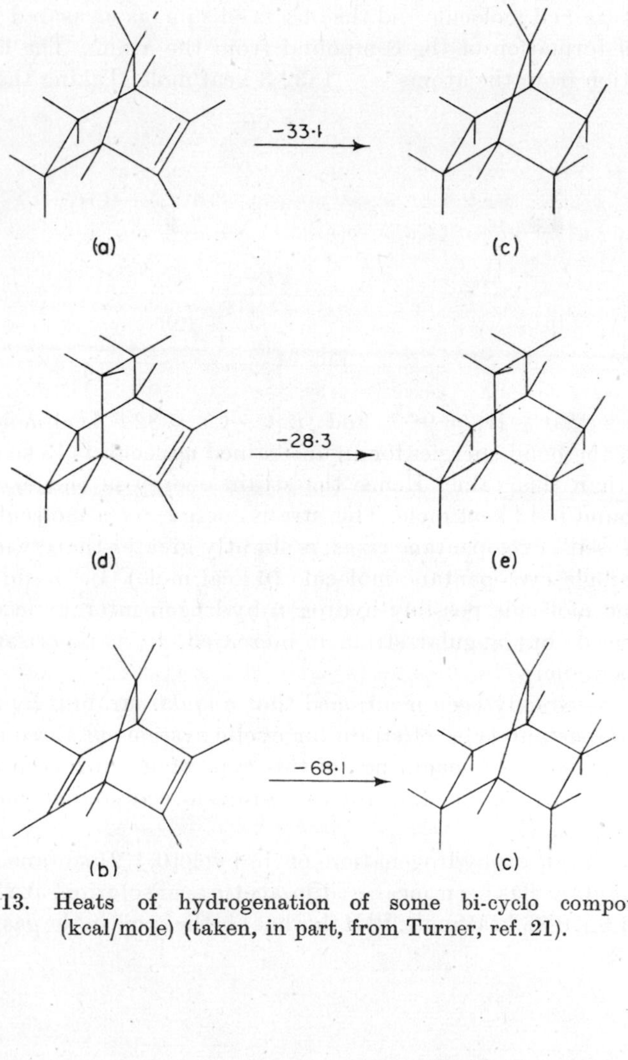

−33·1

(a) (c)

−28·3

(d) (e)

−68·1

(b) (c)

FIG. 13. Heats of hydrogenation of some bi-cyclo compounds (kcal/mole) (taken, in part, from Turner, ref. 21).

same in the gas phase, (an assumption which might introduce an error of about ± 2 kcal/mole), then from the heat of formation of gaseous bi-cyclo[2,2,1]heptadiene, $+57{\cdot}1 \pm 0{,}5$ kcal/mole,[60] we derive ΔH_f^0 (bi-cyclo[2,2,1]heptane, g) $= -11{\cdot}0 \pm 2{\cdot}5$ kcal/mole. The strain energy, *Es*, in this saturated compound, can be obtained from the relationship

$$Es = \Sigma E(\mathrm{b}) - (-\Delta H_f^a),$$

the difference between the calculated sum of the bond energies for the unstrained molecule and the observed sum, as measured by the heat of formation of the compound from the atoms. The heat of formation from the atoms is $-1832{\cdot}3$ kcal/mole. Taking the bond

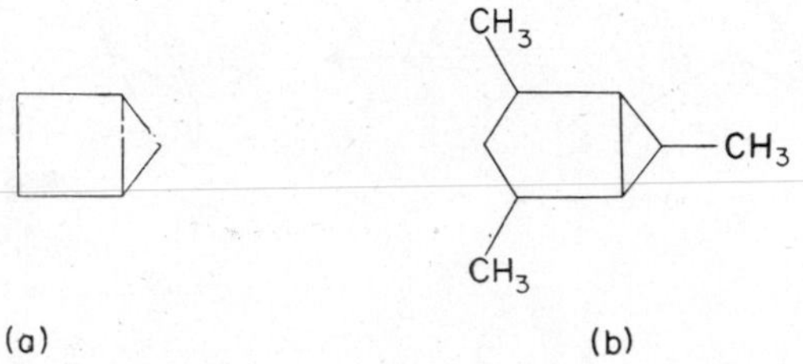

CH_3 CH_3 CH_3

(a) (b)

FIG. 14.

energies E(C—H) $= 98{\cdot}7$ and E(C—C) $= 82{\cdot}6$ kcal/mole, the sum of the bond energies for an unstrained molecule is 13 kcal/mole more than this value. Hence the strain energy in this saturated compound is 13 kcal/mole. This strain energy, for a molecule with two "fused" cyclopentane rings, is slightly greater than twice that for a single cyclopentane molecule (6 kcal/mole). In the bi-cyclo-heptane molecule possibly hydrogen-hydrogen interaction energy is reduced, but angular strain is increased, by comparison with cyclopentane.

It has already been mentioned that *angular* strain is by far the most important type of strain for cyclic systems of three or four carbon atoms. The magnitude of this type of strain is seen clearly from thermochemical data for two bi-cyclo compounds shown in Fig. 14.

The heat of hydrogenation of bi-cyclo[0,1,2]pentane (*a*) to cyclopentane has been measured in acetic acid solution, at 25 °C, as $-55{\cdot}14 \pm 0{\cdot}36$ kcal/mole.[21] If this heat is the same in the gas phase, then from the heat of formation of cyclopentane we calculate the heat of formation of the gaseous bi-cyclopentane as $+36{\cdot}7$ kcal/mole. Incorporating heats of atomization and bond energies given previously, the strain energy for this molecule is calculated as 51 kcal/mole. This is approximately the sum, 52 kcal/mole, of the separate strain energies of cyclobutane and cyclopropane which are 25 and 27 kcal/mole, respectively.

Other thermochemical data for bi-cyclo compounds include the heat of combustions of liquid 1, 3, 5-trimethylbi-cyclo[0, 1, 3]hexane (*b*), for which a value has been given[61] of $-1369{\cdot}5 \pm 0{\cdot}5$ kcal-mole.

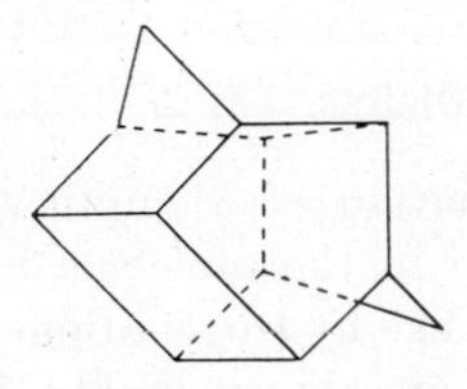

FIG. 15.

This leads to a heat of formation of the gaseous compound of about $-15{\cdot}5$ kcal/mole. It would be more useful to have a heat of formation of the unsubstituted bi-cyclo[0, 1, 3]hexane. This may be estimated in the following way. The substitution of a hydrogen atom by a methyl group in cyclohexane makes the heat of formation more negative by $7{\cdot}6$ kcal/mole. The introduction of a second methyl group, to give the *cis*-1,3-compound lowers the heat of formation by a further $7{\cdot}2$ kcal/mole. The total effect of three methyl groups in the 1,3,5-positions will probably be about -22 kcal/mole. We therefore estimate the heat of formation of the unsubstituted bi-cyclo[0, 1, 3]hexane to be about $+6{\cdot}5$ kcal/mole. Again incorporating heats of atomization and bond energies, a strain energy of 30 kcal/mole is derived. This compares with a sum of the separate strain energies of 33 kcal/mole, being 6 kcal/mole for cyclopentane and 27 kcal/mole for cyclopropane. In both of these cases the angular strain energy appears to be additive.

Another saturated, polycyclic hydrocarbon for which a heat of formation is available is hexa-cyclo$[7, 2, 1, 0^{2,5}, 0^{4,8}, 0^{6,12}]$dodecane, the "cage" molecule shown in Fig. 15. From combustion data[62] the value has been obtained $\Delta H_f^0(\mathrm{c}) = +12{\cdot}06 \pm 0{\cdot}27$ kcal/mole, and taking a somewhat arbitrary heat of sublimation of 12 kcal/

mole, then $\Delta H_f^0(g) = +24$ kcal/mole. Incorporating the heats of atomization of the elements and the bond energies given above, a strain energy of 35 kcal/mole is calculated. Of this figure soma 25 kcal/mole is probably due to angular strain in the cyclobutane ring, and perhaps 5 kcal/mole each for the two cyclopentane rings, which are constrained to be almost planar. In the other four cyclopentane rings, where the conformation is much the same as in a free cyclopentane molecule, angular strain will be slight. Hydrogen-hydrogen interaction strain will be much reduced because of the fewer number of hydrogen atoms.

Exo-endo Isomerism in Olefins

The heats of hydrogenation of a number of other ring systems having an olefinic bond in the molecule have been measured by Turner and Garner.[59] The hydrogenations were carried out in solution, and the results are shown in Fig. 16. The figures written under the compounds refer to heats of hydrogenation to the equivalent saturated compounds. Those above the arrows are the heats of isomerization of the *exo* to the *endo* compound, the difference between the heats of hydrogenation of the two compounds, since the hydrogenation product is the same in both cases. Finally, the figure in parentheses under the arrow is the heat of isomerization "corrected" for substitution effects. In each case conversion from the *exo* to the *endo* compound involves a change in the degree of substitution of the double bond, from di- to tri-substitution, i.e.

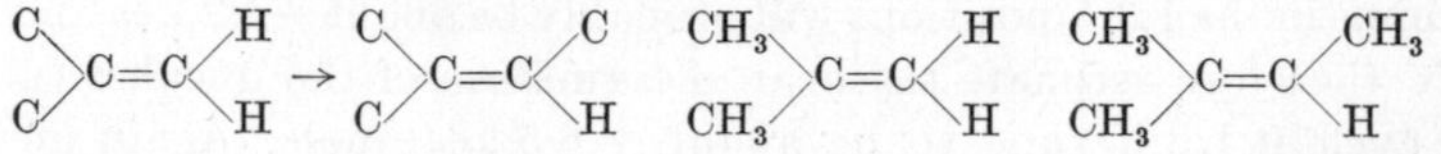

$$\begin{matrix}C\\C\end{matrix}\!\!>\!C{=}C\!<\!\!\begin{matrix}H\\H\end{matrix} \rightarrow \begin{matrix}C\\C\end{matrix}\!\!>\!C{=}C\!<\!\!\begin{matrix}C\\H\end{matrix} \qquad \begin{matrix}CH_3\\CH_3\end{matrix}\!\!>\!C{=}C\!<\!\!\begin{matrix}H\\H\end{matrix} \qquad \begin{matrix}CH_3\\CH_3\end{matrix}\!\!>\!C{=}C\!<\!\!\begin{matrix}CH_3\\H\end{matrix}$$

exo- *endo-* isobutene trimethylethylene

Since the heat of hydrogenation of isobutene is 1·5 kcal/mole greater than that of trimethylethylene, this factor is added to the heat of *exo* → *endo* isomerization in each case.

Turner[21] makes some comments on these values:

1. The heat of hydrogenation of methylenecyclopentane (*c*) is 0·9 kcal/mole less than that of the equivalent six-membered ring, methylenecyclohexane (*e*). This probably arises from two causes. (i) A greater strain in the six-ring unsaturated compound, because the methylene hydrogens are eclipsed by adjacent ring hydrogens,

which is not the case in the five-ring compound. (ii) In the five-ring, saturated product, methylcyclopentane, there is strain, since the methyl group is eclipsed by interaction with ring hydrogens, whereas in the six-ring, methylcyclohexane, the corresponding interactions are staggered. These factors increase the heat of hydrogenation for the methylenecyclohexane, and reduce that of the methylenecyclopentane.

(a) CH_2 −29·4 → −0·9 (+0·6) → (b) CH_3 −28·5

(c) CH_2 −26·9 → −3·9 (−2·4) → (d) CH_3 −23·0

(e) CH_2 −27·8 → −2·4 (−0·9) → (f) CH_3 −25·4

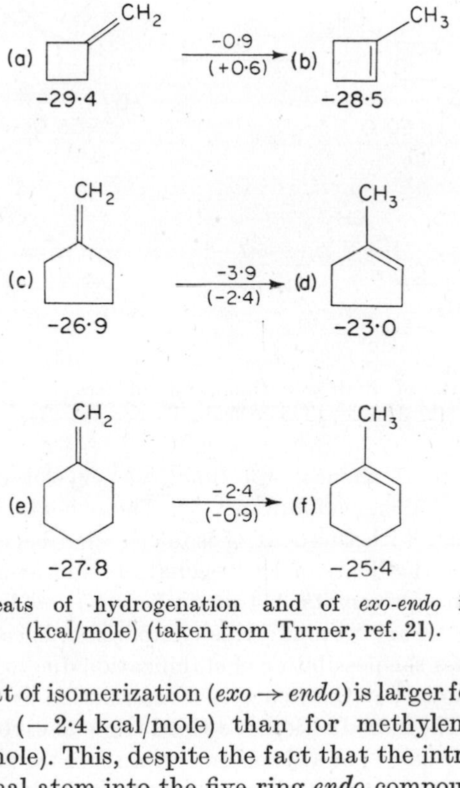

FIG. 16. Heats of hydrogenation and of *exo-endo* isomerization (kcal/mole) (taken from Turner, ref. 21).

2. The heat of isomerization (*exo* → *endo*) is larger for methylenecyclopentane (−2·4 kcal/mole) than for methylenecyclohexane (−0·9 kcal/mole). This, despite the fact that the introduction of a second trigonal atom into the five-ring *endo* compound will introduce more angular strain than into the six-ring *endo* compound. This increased angular strain in the five-ring system must be more than offset by a stabilization resulting from reduction in non-bonded repulsions.

The very small heat of *exo* → *endo* isomerization of methylenecyclobutane (*a*) to 1-methylcyclobutene (*b*) suggests that the strain produced by introducing a second trigonal carbon atom into the ring is offset by reduction in atom-atom repulsions. The angular strain which is introduced by a second trigonal carbon atom should be appreciable since it is now a trigonal angle of 120° which is reduced to 90°, whereas previously for a tetrahedral carbon atom the reduction is only from 109° to 90°.

Turner[21] has also measured the heats of hydrogenation of the

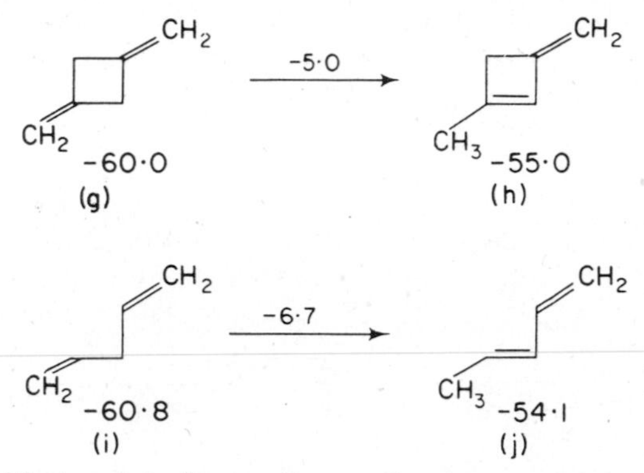

FIG. 17. Heats of hydrogenation and of *exo-endo* isomerization (kcal/mole) (Taken from Turner, ref. 21).

"four-ring system" dienes, 1,3-dimethylenecyclobutane (*g*) and 1-methyl-3-methylenecyclobutene (*h*). These heats are shown in Fig. 17, together with the heat of isomerization between the two. Also shown are the heats of hydrogenation, and isomerization, of the open-chain equivalents, 1,4-pentadiene (*i*) and 1,3-pentadiene (*j*)[63]. It is necessary to make this comparison, because isomerization introduces the possibility of stabilization due to conjugation. The figures show that the heats of isomerization are very similar in both cases. The introduction of a third trigonal carbon atom produces very little effect; or at least any strain so introduced is largely counterbalanced by removal of 1,3 transannular hydrogen-hydrogen repulsions in 1,3-dimethylenecyclobutane.

Conclusion

These examples show how heats of combustion and of hydrogenation of isomeric compounds, or of a homologous series, can be used to determine the relative strain energies which exist in the compounds. Strain energies can be divided, somewhat artificially, but usefully into three different types; *angular* strain, due to compression of the angle normal to the particular type of carbon hybridization; *interaction* strain, due to repulsion between non-bonded atoms; and, finally, *torsional* strain of double bonds out of the plane where the greatest p_π-p_π-orbital overlap can occur.

CHAPTER 3

STABILIZATION ENERGIES IN NON-AROMATIC COMPOUNDS

Introduction

Of late, there has been a revival of interest in the problem of conjugation effects in butadiene and other unsaturated hydrocarbons, and it has been suggested[7] that the apparent stabilization or resonance energies found in these molecules are not due to electron delocalization between the conjugated double bonds.

Cook,[64] Dewar,[65] and Stoicheff[66] have all focused attention on the length of the C—C single bond and its dependence on hybridization. It has been pointed out[67] that the length of the central C—C bond in butadiene is that expected of a single bond, involving sp^2 hybrid carbon atoms, and that it is not a bond shortened by conjugation effects.

We shall look at the experimental thermochemical data for some conjugated molecules, firstly from the point of view of conjugation and hyperconjugation, and polar effects, and secondly to see how they can be explained in terms of differing hybridization of the carbon atoms.

Conjugation and Hyperconjugation

1. Olefins

It is to be expected that the total heat of hydrogenation of a compound containing more than one double bond would be approximately the sum of the heats of hydrogenation of the individual bonds, as found in closely related compounds. Thus, the heat of hydrogenation of 1,5-hexadiene, −60·53 kcal/mole,[68] is very close to twice the value of −30·34 kcal/mole found for butene-1.[10] This is taken for comparison, since it contains the $CH_2CH{=}CH_2$ grouping, as does 1,5-hexadiene. With limonene,

(*I*) (Fig. 1), the observed value of $-54 \cdot 11$ kcal/mole is still close to the sum of the values for mono-olefins with the most closely analogous double bonds, trimethylethylene, (*II*), and *unsym*-methylisopropylethylene, (*III*). The heats of hydrogenation are $-26 \cdot 92$ and $-28 \cdot 00$ kcal/mole,[11] respectively, giving a sum of $-54 \cdot 92$ kcal/mole.

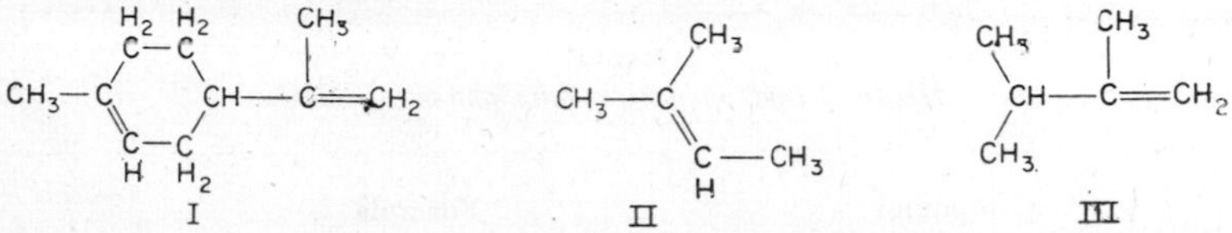

Fig. 1.

However, when the double bonds are conjugated with each other, the heats of hydrogenation are lower than predicted. The heat of hydrogenation of 1,3-butadiene, $-57 \cdot 1$ kcal/mole, is less than twice the value for butene-1, by $3 \cdot 5$ kcal/mole.

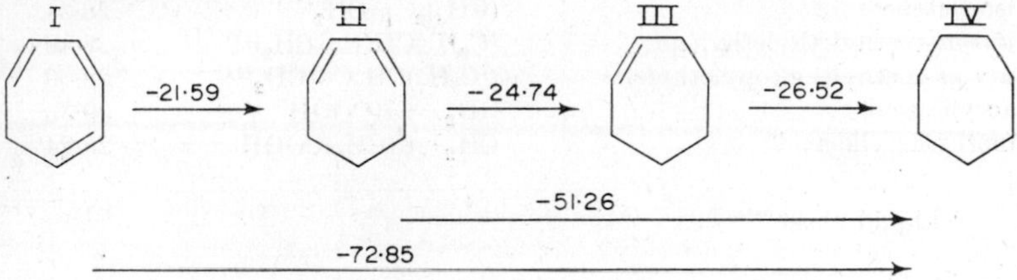

Fig. 2. Heats of hydrogenation of 1,3,5-cycloheptatriene (gas phase, in kcal/mole).

The heat of hydrogenation of 1,3,5-cycloheptatriene, $I \rightarrow IV$ in Fig. 2, has been measured by Kistiakowsky *et al.*,[69] and confirmed from heats of combustion of *I*[60] and *IV*.[31] The heats of gas phase hydrogenation $II \rightarrow IV$, and $III \rightarrow IV$ have also been measured, so that the step-wise heats for the three processes can be calculated. These heats of hydrogenation increase from $-21 \cdot 59$, through $-24 \cdot 74$ to $-26 \cdot 52$ kcal/mole. This case is complicated by the change in strain energies on hydrogenation, but since it appears that interaction strain in the saturated product is more important than angular and torsional strain in the cyclic olefins, the reverse trend would be expected, a decrease in heats of successive hydrogenations.

The lowered heats in the cases where conjugated double bonds are involved have been generally attributed to stabilization of the conjugated olefin, due to interaction between the two double bonds, or "π-conjugation".[70]

The data in Table 1 show that the heats of hydrogenation of substituted ethylenes are some 2·7 kcal/mole less than that of

TABLE 1

Heats of hydrogenation (gas phase, at 82°C)

Compound	Formula	$-\Delta H$ (kcal/mole)
ethylene	$CH_2{=}CH_2$ [19]	32·82
propylene	$CH_3CH{=}CH_2$ [71]	30·12
butene-1	$CH_3CH_2CH{=}CH_2$ [71]	30·34
heptene-1	$CH_3(CH_2)_4CH{=}CH_2$ [11]	30·14
iso-propylethylene	$(CH_3)_2CHCH{=}CH_2$ [10]	30·34
t-butylethylene	$(CH_3)_3CCH{=}CH_2$ [10]	30·34
iso-butene	$(CH_3)_2C{=}CH_2$ [71]	28·34
unsym-methylethylethylene	$(C_2H_5)CH_3C{=}CH_2$ [11]	28·49
unsym-methylisopropylethylene	$({}^iC_3H_7)CH_3C{=}CH_2$ [11]	28·00
acrylic acid[a]	$CH_2{=}CHCOOH$	30·35
methylacrylic acid[a]	$CH_2{=}C(CH_3)COOH$	28·24

[a] Liquid phase[22]

ethylene itself and that this increase is virtually independent of the nature of the alkyl radical substituent. This is the case even when two hydrogen atoms of the same carbon atom in ethylene are substituted by alkyl groups, for although the heat of hydrogenation is further reduced, by some 2 kcal/mole, it is virtually constant for the different substituents.

A similar reduction also occurs when the already substituted ethylene, acrylic acid, has a further hydrogen atom replaced by a methyl group, to give methylacrylic acid. Here the reduction in the heat of hydrogenation is 2·1 kcal/mole.

These reduced heats of hydrogenation have generally been attributed to stabilization of the unsaturated compound, due to "hyperconjugation",[72] involving some delocalization of the bonding electrons of the alkyl group and the π-electrons of the double bond.

2. *Acetylenes*

Recently, Skinner *et al.*[22, 23, 55] have made a series of measurements of the heats of hydrogenation of acetylenic compounds. The heats of hydrogenation of some of these compounds containing two acetylenic bonds (diynes) are shown in Table 2. The measurements were made in solution, but have been corrected to the *liquid* phase, for both reactants and products.

The values may be compared with the heats of hydrogenation in the *gas* phase of monoacetylenes, calculated from heats of formation,[30] and shown in Table 3. As in the olefin series, a reduction in the heat of hydrogenation occurs when a hydrogen is substituted; again the lowering is virtually independent of the particular alkyl group.

TABLE 2
Heats of hydrogenation, (liquid reactant to liquid product, at 25 °C)

Compound	Formula	$-\Delta H$ (kcal/mole)
dodeca-3, 9-diyne	$CH_3CH_2C{\equiv}C(CH_2)_4C{\equiv}CCH_2CH_3$	131·15 ± 0·5
dodeca-5, 7-diyne	$CH_3(CH_2)_3C{\equiv}C{-}C{\equiv}C(CH_2)_3CH_3$	127·24 ± 0·7
octa-1, 7-diyne	$CH{\equiv}C(CH_2)_4C{\equiv}CH$	139·7 ± 1·2
hexa-1, 5-diyne (dipropargyl)	$CH{\equiv}C(CH_2)_2C{\equiv}CH$	139·4 ± 1·0

TABLE 3
Heats of hydrogenation, (gas phase at 25°C). Calculated from ΔH_f^0 data.[30]

Compound	Formula	$-\Delta H$ (kcal/mole)
acetylene,	$CH{\equiv}CH$	74·43
methylacetylene	$CH_3C{\equiv}CH$	69·14
1-butyne	$CH_3CH_2C{\equiv}CH$	69·63
1-pentyne	$CH_3(CH_2)_2C{\equiv}CH$	69·50
1-hexyne	$CH_3(CH_2)_3C{\equiv}CH$	69·51
dimethylacetylene	$CH_3C{\equiv}CCH_3$	65·12
2-pentyne	$CH_3CH_2C{\equiv}CCH_3$	65·80
3-hexyne	$CH_3CH_2C{\equiv}CCH_2CH_3$	65·80

The heat of hydrogenation of octa-1,7-diyne might be expected to be twice that of 1-butyne, which is in effect "one half" of the molecule. The difference is only 0·5 kcal/mole. The heat of hydrogenation of hexa-1,5-diyne (− 139·4) compares closely with that found for octa-1,7-diyne, as might reasonably be anticipated. Also, the heat of hydrogenation of dodeca-3,9-diyne (− 131·15) is close to that estimated for two moles of 3-hexyne, (*ca.* − 131·6). In octa-1,7-diyne, hexa-1,5-diyne, and dodeca-3,9-diyne, the —C≡C— groups are separated from one another by a chain of four —CH_2— groups, so that there is little reason to expect any interaction, or conjugation between them.

In dodeca-5,7-diyne, in which the —C≡C— groups are adjacent to each other, the molecule can be considered to be stabilized by the π-electron conjugation energy of the —C≡C—C≡C— system, and the smaller heat of hydrogenation of the —5,7— relative to the —3,9— isomer measures the increased energy content of the conjugated diyne. The difference of 3·9 kcal/mole between the heats of hydrogenation of the two isomers is not, however a direct measure of the overall conjugation energy of the —C≡C—C≡C— system, since the stability of both isomers is unequally influenced by the hyperconjugation effect of the alkyl groups adjacent to the —C≡C— bonds.

Theoretical calculations by Mulliken *et al.*,[72] by Roberts and Skinner[73] and by Coulson and Crawford,[74] indicated that in a compound of the type RC≡CR, in which there is an alkyl substituent on both of the acetylenic carbon atoms, the *hyperconjugation* energy is about 6·5 kcal/mole. Where an alkyl group is attached to only one acetylenic carbon atom, as in RC≡CH, the hyperconjugation energy is only 3·5 kcal/mole. Now dodeca-3,9-diyne, represented by the formula RC≡CR′R′C≡R, can be thought of as an acetylene of the first type, with twice the hyperconjugation energy of RC≡CR, i.e. 13 kcal/mole. In contrast, the -5,7 isomer, represented by RC≡C—C≡CR, is more nearly like two molecules of a monosubstituted acetylene, and the hyperconjugation energy will be only 7 kcal/mole, some 6 kcal/mole less than the -3,9-isomer. Thus the overall *conjugation* energy in the -5,7-diyne will be some 6 kcal/mole greater than the observed difference in the heats of hydrogenation of the two isomers, 3·9 kcal/mole, a total of some 9·9 kcal/mole.

TABLE 4
Heats of hydrogenation[a], *at 25 °C*

Substituent	Acetylene	$-\Delta H$ (kcal/mole)	$\Delta(\Delta H)$ (kcal/mole)
phenyl	$HC\equiv CH$[b]	74·4	
			3·7
	$C_6H_5C\equiv CH(l)$[c]	70·7	
			6·6
	$C_6H_5C\equiv CC_6H_5(c)$[c]	64·1	
vinyl	$HC\equiv CC_4H_9(l)$[b]	69·5	
			6·2
	$CH_2=CHC\equiv CC_4H_9$[c]	63·3	
methyl	$HC\equiv CH$[b]	74·4	
			5·3
	$CH_3C\equiv CH$[b]	69·1	
			4·0
	$CH_3C\equiv CCH_3$[b, d]	65·1	

[a] Gas phase, except where otherwise stated.
[b] Calculated from ΔH_f^0 data.(30)
[c] Ref. 55. [d] Ref. 75.

Substituent	Ethylene[d]	$-\Delta H$ (kcal/mole)	$\Delta(\Delta H)$ (kcal/mole)
phenyl	$H_2C=CH_2$	32·8	
			4·2
	$C_6H_5CH=CH_2$	28·6	
			8·0
	$C_6H_5CH=CHC_6H_5$	20·6	
vinyl	$H_2C=CHC_4H_9$	30·1	
			6·2
	$CH_2=CHCH=CHC_4H_9$	23·9	
methyl	$H_2C=CH_2$	32·8	
			2·7
	$CH_3CH=CH_2$	30·1	
			2·5
	$CH_3CH=CHCH_3$	27·6	

[d] From Wheland,(70) section 3·2.

As would be expected, substitution of the hydrogen in acetylene by phenyl, vinyl or methyl groups reduces the heat of hydrogenation. Table 4 shows some values obtained by Flitcroft and Skinner,[55] and also comparable values for corresponding ethylenes. In the ethylenes, phenyl and vinyl substitution bring about similar reductions. Whilst vinyl substitution has much the same effect in acetylenes as in ethylenes, phenyl substitution produces a slightly greater effect in the ethylenes. Conversely, methyl substitution has about twice the effect on the acetylenic bond as on the olefinic bond. These effects can be attributed to extra stability in the unsaturated hydrocarbons, due to *conjugation* of the C_6H_5- or $CH_2{=}CH$- groups with the neighbouring unsaturated linkage, or to *hyperconjugation* of H_3C-groups with adjacent acetylenic or olefinic bonds.

Polar Effects

By contrast, the data obtained for the acetylenes substituted with —COOH, —COOMe, and —$CONH_2$ show that these substituents bring about an increase in the heat of hydrogenation, relative to the unsubstituted acetylene (Table 5). Although —CH_2COOH brings about a reduction in the heat of hydrogenation, it is not as great as that for —CH_3.

On this thermochemical evidence, it appears that the conjugating power of the carbonyl group is weak. This is in conflict with the X-ray structural analysis of acetylene dicarboxylic acid dihydrate[76] which shows a coplanar structure and a very short C—C bond length of 1·43 Å, indicating that resonance extends through the whole structure. Skinner[55] suggests that the increased heats of hydrogenation might be attributed to the *polar* character of the substituents: that the more polar carbonyl group may give rise to a resonance stabilization (ionic-covalent resonance energy) in the saturated product of hydrogenation, and that this increased stabilization of the product is greater than the resonance energy due to conjugation in the acetylenic compound.

Support to this idea is given from the heats of hydrogenation of vinyl chloride and vinyl bromide, shown in Table 6, which are about 1·7 kcal/mole greater than for ethylene. Now it is generally accepted that vinyl chloride is stabilized by conjugation (back

TABLE 5

Heats of hydrogenation, at 25 °C

Substituted compound	$-\Delta H$ (kcal/mole)	Reference compound	$-\Delta H$ (kcal/mole)	Substituent	Increment per substituent (kcal/mole)
$HOOCC{\equiv}CCOOH$(c)	86·8 ± 1·1[b]	$HC{\equiv}CH$	74·4[a]	$—COOH$	+ 6·2
$HC{\equiv}CCOOCH_3$(l)	79·1 ± 1·1[b]	$HC{\equiv}CH$	74·4[a]	$—COOCH_3$	+ 4·7
$PrC{\equiv}CCOOCH_3$(c)	71·1 ± 1·2[b]	$PrC{\equiv}CH$	69·5[a]	$—COOCH_3$	+ 1·6
$PrC{\equiv}CCONH_2$(c)	72·9 ± 0·8[b]	$PrC{\equiv}CH$	69·5[a]	$—CONH_2$	+ 3·4
$PhC{\equiv}CCOOH$(c)	72·6 ± 1·1[b]	$PhC{\equiv}CH$	70·7[b]	$—COOH$	+ 1·9
$HC{\equiv}CCH_2COOH$(c)	72·4 ± 1·1[b]	$HC{\equiv}CH$	74·4[a]	$—CH_2COOH$	− 2·0
$MeC{\equiv}CCH_2COOH$(c)	65·8 ± 1·2[b]	$MeC{\equiv}CH$	69·1[a]	$—CH_2COOH$	− 3·3

[a] From ΔH_f^0 data[30].
[b] Ref. 55.

co-ordination) in that the C—Cl bond has a partial double bond character, and hence the heat of hydrogenation should be less than that of ethylene. That it is, in fact, greater suggests a stabilization of the hydrogenation product, ethyl chloride, due to ionic-covalent resonance involving the very electronegative chlorine atom.

The effect on the heat of hydrogenation of the introduction of fluorine atoms into vinyl chloride is also seen from the data in Table 6. The heat of hydrogenation of vinyl chloride to ethane and a molecule of HCl, that is both an addition and a replacement hydrogenation occurring at the same time, is $-51{\cdot}2$ kcal/mole. For the compound CF_2CHCl, in which two hydrogens have been substituted by fluorine atoms, the overall hydrogenation heat is increased by 10 kcal/mole to $-61{\cdot}8$ kcal/mole. If all three hydrogens in vinyl chloride are substituted by fluorines, the heat of hydrogenation of the resulting compound is increased by a further 3 kcal/mole to $-64{\cdot}9$ kcal/mole.

TABLE 6

Heats of hydrogenation and halogenation

Reaction	$-\Delta H$
$CH_2{=}CHCl + H_2 \rightarrow CH_3CH_2Cl$	34·57[24]
$CH_2{=}CHBr + H_2 \rightarrow CH_3CH_2Br$	34·57[20]
$CH_2{=}CHCl + 2H_2 \rightarrow CH_3CH_3 + HCl$	51·19[24]
$CF_2{=}CHCl + 2H_2 \rightarrow CF_2HCH_3 + HCl$	61·77
$CF_2{=}CFCl + 2H_2 \rightarrow CF_2HCFH_2 + HCl$	64·92
$CF_2{=}CCl_2 + Cl_2 \rightarrow CF_2(Cl)CCl_3$	41·1[12]
$CF_2{=}CFCl + Cl_2 \rightarrow CF_2(Cl)CFCl_2$	48·8
$CF_2{=}CF_2 + Cl_2 \rightarrow CF_2(Cl)CF_2Cl$	57·3
$CF_2{=}CFCl + Br_2 \rightarrow CF_2(Br)CF(Cl)Br$	32·1[77]
$CF_2{=}CF_2 + Br_2 \rightarrow CF_2(Br)CF_2(Br)$	38·1

Presumably this reflects an increasing stabilization of the saturated product of the reaction, with greater fluorine content, due to ionic-covalent resonance.

A similar situation holds for the heats of chlorination of some fluoro-olefins. Thus in the series $CF_2{=}CCl_2$, $CF_2{=}CFCl$, $CF_2{=}CF_2$, the heats of chlorination increase from $-41{\cdot}1$, through $-48{\cdot}8$ to

TABLE 7
Heats of chlorination

Compound	Temp. °C	$-\Delta H$
$CH_2{=}CH_2$[78]	82	$43{\cdot}7 \pm 0{\cdot}2$
$CF_2{=}CF_2$[79]	90	$57{\cdot}3 \pm 0{\cdot}2$
$CF_2{=}CF{\cdot}CF_3$[12]	90	$47{\cdot}2 \pm 0{\cdot}2$
$CF_2{=}CF{\cdot}CF_2CF_3$[13]	128	$45{\cdot}0 \pm 0{\cdot}3$
$CF_2{=}CF(CF_2)_2CF_3$[13]	128	$45{\cdot}6 \pm 0{\cdot}4$
$CF_2{=}C(CF_3)_2$[13]	128	$42{\cdot}2 \pm 0{\cdot}5$
CF_2-CF[12] | ‖ CF_2-CF	90	$37{\cdot}4 \pm 1$

$-57{\cdot}3$ kcal/mole. The heats of bromination also increase in the same sense for the two compounds $CF_2{=}CFCl$, $-32{\cdot}1$, and $CF_2{=}CF_2$, $-38{\cdot}1$.

Lacher and his co-workers[12, 13, 79] have also measured the heats of chlorination, in the vapour phase, of a number of fluoro- and fluorochloro-olefins. The heats refer to the reactions of the type $CF_2{=}CFR + Cl_2 \rightarrow CF_2(Cl)CFR(Cl)$. The results are shown in Table 7, together with the heat of chlorination of ethylene, measured by Kistiakowsky *et al.*[78]

The heat of chlorination of tetrafluoroethylene is strongly exothermic ($-57{\cdot}3$ kcal/mole) and is $13{\cdot}6$ kcal/mole greater than that of ethylene ($-43{\cdot}7$ kcal/mole). When one fluorine is replaced by a CF_3 group, the heat of chlorination drops by 10 kcal/mole. The perfluoroethyl group, CF_2CF_3, and the perfluoropropyl group, $CF_2CF_2CF_3$, give about the same drop of 12 kcal/mole. When two fluorine atoms of the *same* carbon atom are replaced by CF_3 groups, the lowering is about 15 kcal/mole.

These changes are qualitatively similar to those already mentioned for alkyl substituted ethylenes (Table 1) in that the lowering of the reaction heat is virtually independent of the particular substituting perfluoroalkyl group, and is greater for two such groups on one carbon atom than it is for only one.

The heat of chlorination of perfluorocyclobutene, $-37{\cdot}4$ kcal/mole refers to the reaction:

$$\begin{array}{l} CF_2\text{—}CF \\ |\quad\quad \| \\ CF_2\text{—}CF \end{array} + Cl_2 \rightarrow \begin{array}{l} CF_2\text{—}CFCl \\ |\quad\quad | \\ CF_2\text{—}CFCl \end{array}$$

This heat is some 20 kcal/mole less than that for tetrafluoroethylene and is twice the decrease of 10 kcal/mole in passing from tetrafluoroethylene to the mono-substituted perfluoropropene, $CF_2{=}CF{\cdot}CF_3$. Although the heat of chlorination is complicated by the change in strain energy in passing from the unsaturated to the saturated ring, it seems likely that compounds of the type $CF_3(CF_2)_nCF{=}CF(CF_2)_nCF_3$ will have a heat of chlorination of about -38 kcal/mole, some 20 kcal/mole less than for tetrafluoroethylene. This substitution effect is qualitatively the same as for the change in heat of hydrogenation on methyl substitution of the ethylenes, viz: $CH_2{=}CH_2$, $-32{\cdot}82$; $MeCH{=}CH_2$, $-30{\cdot}12$; $MeCH{=}CHMe$, *trans*, $-27{\cdot}62$; where the increments are 2·7 and 2·5 kcal/mole.

Hybridization

Recently Dewar and Schmeising[65] have suggested that conjugation and hyperconjugation energies can be attributed to changes in bond strength when alteration of the hybrid state of the carbon atom occurs on hydrogenation.

It has long been recognized[80] that the bonds formed by sp^2 carbon atoms must be shorter than those formed by sp^3 carbon. Hence it seems reasonable to assume that bond energies of bonds formed by sp^2 carbon must be greater than those of analogous bonds formed by sp^3 carbon. The effects of this are seen in a comparison of the hydrogenation of ethylene and 1,3-butadiene.

If x is the heat of hydrogenation of ethylene, E_{AB} the bond energy of a single bond between atoms A and B involving carbon in the sp^3 state and E'_{AB} the bond energy of a single bond, involving carbon in the sp^2 state, we may write

(a) $2CH_2{=}CH_2 + 2H_2 \rightarrow 2CH_3CH_3 + 2x$

(*b*) $2CH_2{=}CH_2 \rightarrow CH_2{=}CH{-}CH{=}CH_2 + H_2 + E'_{CC} + E_{HH} - 2E'_{CH}$

(*c*) $2CH_3{-}CH_3 \rightarrow CH_3CH_2CH_2CH_3 + H_2 + E_{CC} + E_{HH} - 2E_{CH}$,

from which we derive the relationship, $(a - b + c)$,

$$CH_2{=}CH{-}CH{=}CH_2 + 2H_2 \rightarrow CH_3CH_2CH_2CH_3 + 2x - [(E'_{CC} - E_{CC}) - 2(E'_{CH} - E_{CH})].$$

Now if the "conjugation energy" of butadiene is defined as the difference between the heat of hydrogenation of butadiene and that of two moles of ethylene, clearly this will include a term E_h, given by,

$$E_h = (E'_{CC} - E_{CC}) - 2(E'_{CH} - E_{CH}).$$

This term depends on the effect of the different hybridization of the carbon atoms in the saturated and unsaturated hydrocarbons.

A similar situation arises in the case of hyperconjugation, in comparing, say, propene with ethylene. In this case we may write

$$CH_2{=}CH_2 + H_2 \rightarrow C_2H_6 + x$$

$$C_2H_6 + CH_4 \rightarrow C_3H_8 + H_2 + E_{HH} + E_{CC} - 2E_{CH}$$

$$CH_2{=}CH_2 + CH_4 \rightarrow CH_2{=}CHCH_3 + H_2 + E''_{CC} - E'_{CH} - E_{CH} + E_{HH},$$

where E''_{CC} is the bond energy for a σ-bond between an sp^2 carbon atom and an sp^3 carbon atom. Hence, combining these equations:

$$CH_2{=}CHCH_3 + H_2 \rightarrow CH_3CH_2CH_3 + x - [(E''_{CC} - E_{CC}) - (E'_{CH} - E_{CH})]$$

from this it is seen that the apparent hyperconjugation energy in propene contains a term E'_h given by

$$E'_h = (E''_{CC} - E_{CC}) - (E'_{CH} - E_{CH}).$$

The same situation will arise quite generally and experimental delocalization or resonance energies will contain a contribution due to changes in hybridization, given by,

$$\text{Total } E_h = mE_h - nE'_h,$$

where m is the number of single bonds between Csp^2—Csp^2 atoms, and n is the number of bonds between Csp^2—Csp^3 atoms, in the ordinary, classical structure.

On the basis of bond energy being proportional to bond length, Dewar and Schmeising[(65)] propose a set of bond energies (at 25 °C) corresponding to the different hybrid states of the carbon atoms.

Bloor and Gartside[(81)] have also developed this idea by assuming the bond energies to be proportional to the overlap integrals of the bond orbitals. The proportionality constant is evaluated by using the bond energy of the Csp^3—Csp^3 single bond obtained from experimental values of the heats of formation of saturated long-chain hydrocarbons.[30] The bond energies of the five other types of carbon–carbon single bonds are then calculated by using tables of overlap integrals[82] and appropriate bond lengths.[83] Then, by using the Csp^2—H bond energy, obtained from the same set of

TABLE 8

Calculated bond energies[a]

Bond Type	Bond Distance (Å)	Overlap Integral	Bond Energy (kcal/mole)
Csp^3-Csp^3	1·543	0·647	82·76
Csp^3-Csp^2	1·530	0·668	85·48
Csp^3-Csp	1·460	0·715	91·42
Csp^2-Csp^2	1·470	0·716	91·58
Csp^2-Csp	1·420	0·754	96·48
$Csp-Csp$	1·380	0·800	103·60
Csp^3-H			98·67
Csp^2-H			98·69
$Csp-H$			102·38
C=C	1·353		143·10
C≡C			187·23

[a] Using ΔH_f^0(C, g) = 171·0 kcal; and $\Delta H_f^0(H, g)$ = 52·09 kcal/g atom. [Taken from Bloor and Gartside[81]].

data as the tetrahedral C—C bond energy, and the observed heats of formation of ethylene, propylene, acetylene and propyne[30] the bond energies of the C=C and C≡C bonds, the Csp^2—H and the Csp—H bonds are calculated. These are shown in Table 8.

This table of "standard" bond energies can then be used to predict the heats of hydrogenation of any unsaturated hydrocarbon for which steric effects are small. Some of these are shown in Table 9, from which it is seen that the predicted values are quite close to the experimental ones, even in cases where there is usually thought to be considerable conjugation or hyperconjugation stabilization. Most of the results, in fact, show a small destabilization energy, probably due to the simplifying assumption of neglecting polar effects and non-bonding interactions. The close correspondence between predicted and experimental heats of hydrogenation depends on wide variations being allowed in E(C—C), with change in the hybridization of carbon orbitals, whilst E(C—H) is virtually constant. This seems most unlikely.

TABLE 9
Heats of hydrogenation (gas phase)

Compound	Observed $-\Delta H$ (kcal/mole)	Calculated $-\Delta H$ (kcal/mole)	Stabilization energy
ethylene	32·82		
propylene	30·12		
acetylene	75·06		
propyne	69·70		
trans-butene-2	27·62	27·42	−0·20
1,3-butadiene	57·07	55·50	−1·57
1-methyl-1,3-butadiene	54·11	52·80	−1·31
styrene[a]	28·20	26·72	−1·48
trans-stilbene[a]	20·10	20·82	+0·72
1,4-diphenyl-1,3-butadiene	44·00	44·62	+0·62
2-butyne	65·12	64·73	−0·39
diphenylethyne[a]	63·12	59·85	−3·49
diphenylbutadyne[a]	126·99	124·67	−2·32
cyclopentene	26·92	27·38	+0·46
1,3-cyclopentadiene	50·90	51·38	+0·48

[a] Refers to hydrogenation of aliphatic olefinic bonds only.
[Taken from Bloor and Gartside[(81)]].

Conclusion

In the first and older approach, all variations in heats of hydrogenation, apart from those obviously caused by steric effects are ascribed to delocalization involved in a π-bond with either a second π-bond, (conjugation) or an alkyl group (hyperconjugation). In the newer interpretation, these variations are ascribed entirely to bond energies which differ with the hybrid state of the carbon atom.

These are not the only explanations, and Berry[(84)] has concluded that the shortening, and strengthening of the central C—C bond in 1,3-butadiene is due mainly to another cause, that of dipolar attraction. Whilst the largest contribution to the structure comes from *I* (Fig. 3), the next largest is from *VI*, corresponding to two attractive dipoles, and the structure *II*, resulting from 1,3 conjugation contributes only to a small extent. Also this idea of dipole attraction is in keeping with the idea of bond length alternation in the long polyene, and is further supported in a more general way by the results which have been given for the thermochemistry of substituted ethylenic and acetylenic compounds, in which the substituents are very electronegative—for example the halogens.

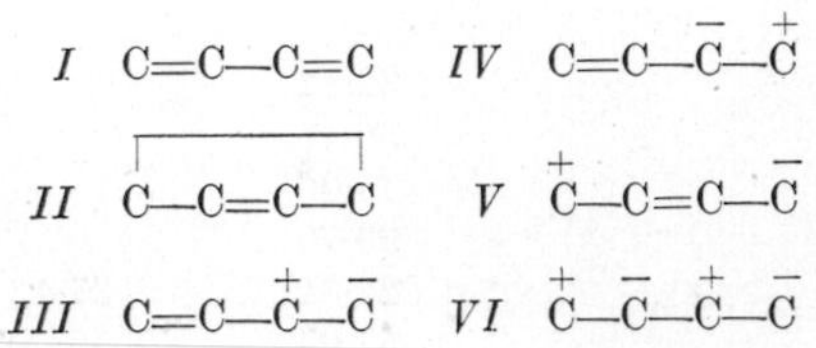

$$I\quad \mathrm{C{=}C{-}C{=}C} \qquad IV\quad \mathrm{C{=}C{-}\overset{-}{C}{-}\overset{+}{C}}$$

$$II\quad \mathrm{C{-}C{=}C{-}C}\ \text{(first and last C joined)} \qquad V\quad \mathrm{\overset{+}{C}{-}C{=}C{-}\overset{-}{C}}$$

$$III\quad \mathrm{C{=}C{-}\overset{+}{C}{-}\overset{-}{C}} \qquad VI\quad \mathrm{\overset{+}{C}{-}\overset{-}{C}{-}\overset{+}{C}{-}\overset{-}{C}}$$

Fig. 3

At present then, it is uncertain to what extent these three factors: conjugation/hyperconjugation, hybridization, and polar attractions, (in addition to small steric interaction energies) are responsible for variations in hydrogenation heats.

CHAPTER 4

STRAIN AND RESONANCE ENERGIES IN AROMATIC COMPOUNDS

Introduction

With the development of quantum-mechanical theory, the significance of representing a molecule such as benzene by multiple structure (Fig. 1, I and II) took shape in the concept of resonance. The theory of resonance is based on the idea that "if we have a set of wave functions for a molecule, each of which may be regarded as a reasonable approximation to the true wave function of the ground state, then a suitably chosen combination of these will be an even better approximation to the true wave function".[85] In addition, if we estimate the energy of the molecule for a mixture of the functions, this will be less than an estimate based on any one of the separate functions comprising the mixture. The difference between these two quantities is taken as the resonance energy.

These ideas were introduced by Hückel,[86] who used a molecular orbital approach to calculate the energy of cyclic polyenes. According to this theory, the molecular π-orbitals of a regular m-sided polygon of carbon atoms may be classified by a quantum number j which may take any of the values $j = 0, \pm 1, \pm 2, \ldots$ The binding energy of the orbital is determined by j and has the value

$$E_j = 2\beta \cos\left(\frac{2j\pi}{m}\right),$$

where 2β is the energy of the π-bond in ethylene.

For $m = 5$, 6, and 7, the situation is shown in Fig. 2. There are three bonding orbitals which can house six electrons, whilst the remaining orbitals are antibonding. The benzene molecule, the cyclopentadienate ion ($C_5H_5^-$), and the cycloheptatrienyl ion (the tropylium ion, $C_7H_7^+$) all have six electrons which will fill the bonding orbitals. The reason for their particular stability is associated with the closed shells.

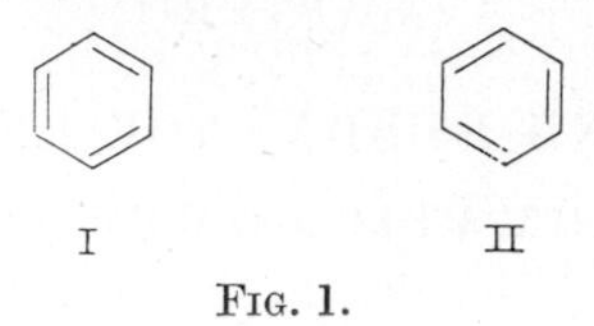

Fig. 1.

The stability of six-electron systems of this type is an illustration of the "$4n + 2$" rule. This rule is based on the fact that in a cyclic system of $2p_\pi$ atomic orbitals, all the molecular π-orbitals, except the one of lowest energy, are doubly degenerate. This means that $4n + 2$ electrons are required to fill all the orbitals with energy less than or equal to a certain value.

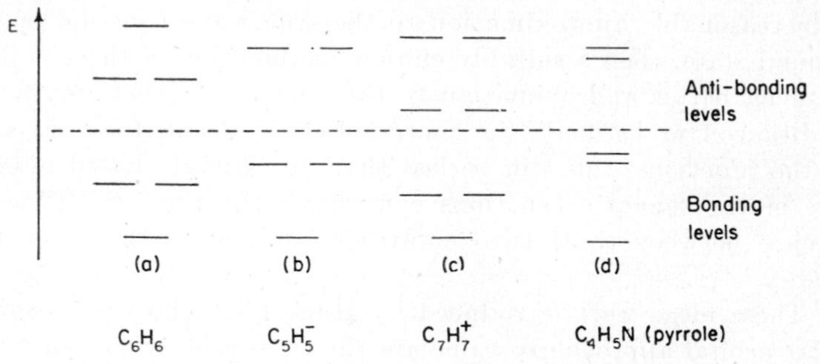

Fig. 2. Molecular-orbital energy levels (Taken from Coulson, ref. 87).

In contrast, the eight-electron system, exemplified by the planar cyclo-octatetraene molecule, would have as configuration of lowest energy one in which the bonding orbitals are all doubly occupied, the remaining two electrons occupying the two degenerate non-bonding orbitals. This molecule would not possess a closed shell ground state and consequently would not be expected to possess particular stability.

Ascending the series, planar conjugated molecules of ten, fourteen and eighteen carbon atoms would be expected to be aromatic in so far as they would have large resonance energies. Of these, the only one in which planarity is likely is the eighteen-membered ring system, cyclo-octadecanonaene. This compound has been prepared,[88] but as yet there are no thermochemical data available for it.

Experimental Determination of Resonance Energies

Experimentally it is possible to obtain a value for the energy of a molecule (the heat of formation), but calculation of the energy of a non-resonating, reference structure introduces a number of complications.

For example, the resonance energy of benzene might be calculated from the reported heat of hydrogenation to cyclohexane, $-49{\cdot}8$ kcal/mole.[68] The heat of hydrogenation of cyclohexene is known to be $-28{\cdot}6$ kcal/mole, and three times this value could be assigned to the heat of hydrogenation of the hypothetical, non-resonating molecule 1,3,5-cyclohexatriene, viz. $-85{\cdot}8$ kcal/mole. This molecule might be taken as a reference standard against which to measure the resonance energy of benzene. The difference, 36 kcal/mole, between this calculated hydrogenation heat, and that actually measured for benzene, is then taken as the resonance energy of the benzene molecule.

An alternative, and widely used method of calculating resonance energies is from bond energies. By taking a standard set of bond energies the heat of formation of the non-resonating reference structure (i.e. *one* of the resonance structures) can be calculated, and compared with that of the actual molecule. The resonance energy of benzene, E_r, would be calculated from the relationship

$$E_r = -\Delta H_f^a(C_6H_6,g) - [3E(C{=}C) + 3E(C{-}C) + 6E(C{-}H)],$$

where ΔH_f^a denotes the heat of formation of the molecule from the atoms, and E the bond energy as calculated from the paraffins and olefins. Here again the resonance energies will depend on the particular set of bond energies chosen, so that the resonance energy is not an intrinsic property but depends entirely on the reference adopted.

More important than the need to define the reference state, is an appreciation that the resonance energies calculated by either method include not only delocalization energies, but also energy terms for (1) bond compression; (2) hybridization changes; (3) work of charge separation; (4) steric effects; (5) heat capacity differences; and so on. The last of these terms has already been considered with reference to bond energies, and it has been suggested that the effect is not great in most cases. The other effects will be considered in more detail here.

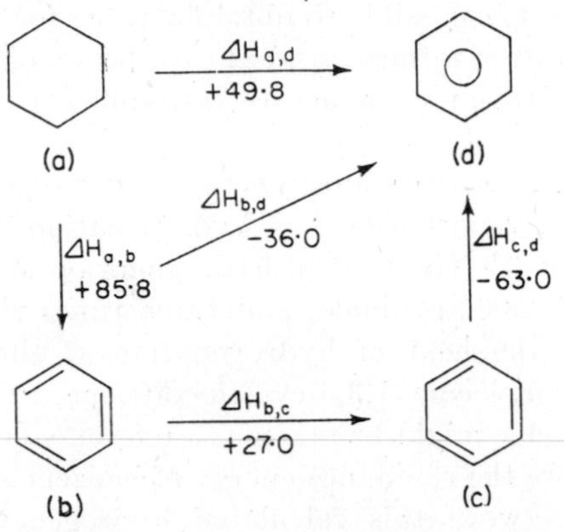

Fig. 3. Heat of hydrogenation of hypothetical 1,3,5-cyclohexatriene to benzene (kcal/mole); (a) cyclohexane; (b) non-resonating cyclohexatriene; (c) non-resonating benzene; (d) normal (resonating) benzene. (Taken from Turner, ref. 21).

1. Bond Compressional Energy

A treatment of compressional energy for the benzene case was given by Coulson and Altman[89] in 1952, and this is summarized diagrammatically in Fig. 3.

The cyclohexatriene model is represented by structure (*b*), in which the double and single bonds are of unequal length. The transformation of this hypothetical molecule to benzene may be split into two processes. The first involves the readjustment of the bond lengths from the alternating double and single bonds in (*b*) to bonds of equal length (1·39 Å as in benzene) in (*c*). By using known force constants of ethane and ethylene an approximate value of +27·0 kcal/mole is calculated for this compressional energy. This process is followed by delocalization of the electrons to give the benzene molecule (*d*). Since the energy for the overall process is −36 kcal/mole, the true resonance energy must be −63 kcal/mole.

2. *Hybridization Changes*

Considering again the case of benzene, we note that in the 1,3,5-cyclohexatriene molecule the single bonds are formed by overlap of sp^2—sp^2 orbitals of carbon atoms. In the cyclohexene molecule, which is taken as a standard for the heat of hydrogenation, the single bonds adjacent to the double bonds are formed by sp^3—sp^2 orbitals. In so far as the strengths of bonds vary with the state of hybridization of the carbon atoms, the calculated heat of hydrogenation of 1,3,5-cyclohexatriene should be corrected for this hybridization effect.

This may be calculated by taking the bond energies obtained by Bloor and Gartside,[81] and given in Table 8, Chapter 3, of $E\,(\mathrm{C}sp^2\text{—}\mathrm{C}sp^2) = 91{\cdot}58$ and $E\,(\mathrm{C}sp^3\text{—}\mathrm{C}sp^2) = 85{\cdot}48$ kcal/mole. The correction for the hybridization effect would therefore be 6·10 kcal (91·58–85·48 kcal) for each carbon–carbon bond involved, or 18·3 kcal/mole for the 1,3,5-cyclohexatriene molecule. Thus the observed resonance energy should be reduced by this amount from 36·0 to 17·7 kcal/mole, or from 63·0 to 44·7 kcal/mole if the compressional energy is included.

3. *Charge Separation*

Tropone, I (*a*), and azulene, II (*a*), shown in Fig. 4 have resonance energies, of 12 and 28 kcal/mole, respectively. The theoretical implication of a stable system being achieved by six π-electrons, is that the structures are closer to those shown in I (*b*) and II (*b*); certainly this is in keeping with the observed physical and chemical properties.

In both of these cases a certain amount of energy is expended, relative to the classical structures, in separation of the charges. Hence the true resonance energies will be increased by this amount from the figures calculated either by bond energies or from heats of hydrogenation.

4. *Steric Effects*

The heat of hydrogenation, ΔH_h, of a cyclic, unsaturated compound, say benzene to cyclohexane, includes not only an energy term corresponding to loss of resonance energy, E_r, but also a term $[E_s$ (benzene) $- E_s$(cyclohexane)$]$. This is due to an alteration in energy caused by change in steric interactions in the two molecules.

Likewise, in the reference compound, which in this case is cyclohexene, the heat of hydrogenation, $\Delta H_h'$, also includes a term, $[E_s(\text{cyclohexene}) - E_s(\text{cyclohexane})]$, corresponding to steric inter-

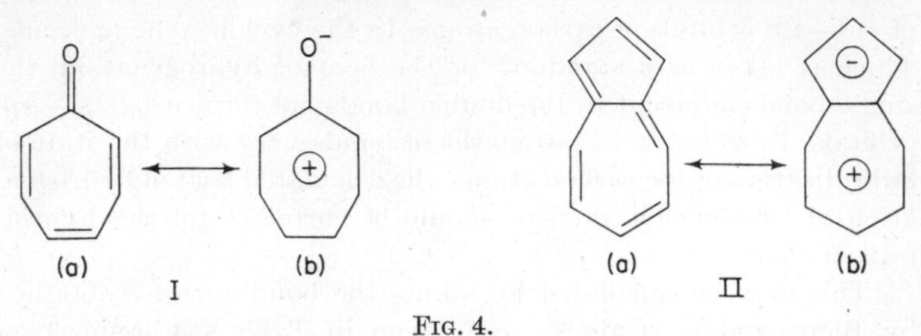

FIG. 4.

action energy differences in these two molecules. In so far as the product is the same in both cases, a difference in hydrogenation heats can be represented by,

$$\Delta H_h - 3\,\Delta H_h' = E_r + E_s(\text{benzene}) - 3\,E_s(\textit{cyclo}\text{hexene}) + 2\,E_s(\textit{cyclo}\text{hexane})$$

and this difference includes a term due to steric interaction energies in the molecules. In this particular case these terms are small, and are usually neglected. However, in some cases these steric interaction energies can be appreciable.

Generally, the "resonance" energies which are used in future discussions are the gross figures, and except in a few cases will not be analysed to account for the effects mentioned under the headings *1* to *4*. However, it is well to bear in mind that the true π-electron delocalization energies may be considerably different from these gross "resonance" energies, due to these factors.

Five- and Seven-membered Ring Systems

Hückel's rule leads one to expect resonance stabilization in the cyclopentadienate and cycloheptatrienyl (tropylium) ions. With a view to determining the resonance energy of the latter, Turner[21] has measured the heat of hydrogenation of tropylium chloride to cycloheptane and hydrogen chloride, in acetic acid solution, as $-86{\cdot}23 \pm 0{\cdot}08$ kcal/mole. An energetic comparison of the relative stabilities of tropylium chloride and the isomeric benzyl chloride has been made by Turner, using the heat of hydrogenation data, in the following way, which is shown diagrammatically in Fig. 5.

The heats of formation of liquid cycloheptane (—37·7 kcal/mole) and of gaseous hydrogen chloride (—22·1 kcal/mole) can be used in conjunction with their respective heats of solution in acetic

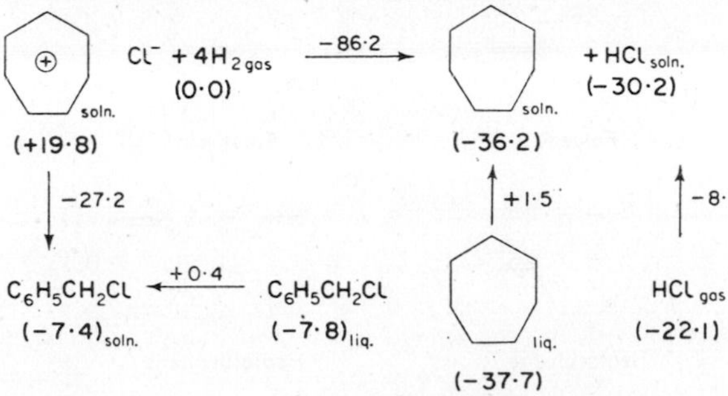

FIG. 5. Heat of isomerization of tropylium chloride to benzyl chloride (kcal/mole) (taken from Turner, ref. 21).

acid (+1·5 and —8·1 kcal/mole) to derive the heats of formation of these compounds in solution. They are —36·2 and —30·2 kcal/mole, respectively. Combined with the heat of hydrogenation of —86·2 kcal/mole, these give +19·8 kcal/mole for the heat of formation of tropylium chloride in solution. The heat of formation of liquid benzyl chloride is —7·8 kcal/mole and its heat of solution in acetic acid, +0·4 kcal/mole, so that the heat of formation is —7·4 kcal/mole, in solution. Consequently the heat of isomerization in solution, of tropylium chloride to benzyl chloride is —27·2 kcal/mole. For comparison, the heat of isomerization of cycloheptatriene (tropylidene) to toluene (as calculated from the heats of formation)[90, 30] is —31·5 kcal/mole. That the two heats of isomerization are so similar shows that the resonance energy of tropylium chloride is close to that of cycloheptatriene, which is quite small. Although these figures are complicated by undetermined heats of solution, it appears that most of the stability achieved by cycloheptatriene losing an electron to give a six-electron aromatic system is counterbalanced by the electrostatic work required for the ionization.

The molecular orbital theory has been applied to many other hypothetical systems of conjugated double bonds, as a test of

Hückel's ideas. Amongst these is a group of compounds containing five- and seven-membered rings, shown in Fig. 6.

Fulvene was prepared in 1956 by Thiec and Wiemann,[91] and although there are no thermochemical data available for this parent compound, the heat of combustion of the dimethyl deriv-

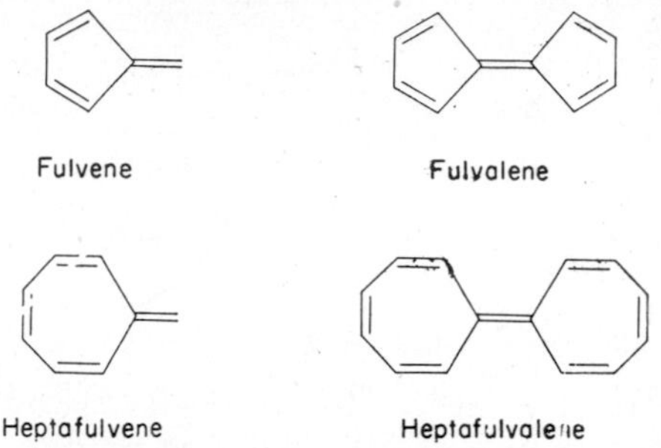

Fulvene Fulvalene

Heptafulvene Heptafulvalene

FIG. 6.

ative has been measured as $-1125{\cdot}0$ kcal/mole.[92] The heat of formation of gaseous dimethyl fulvene is calculated as $+31{\cdot}0$ kcal/mole. Unfortunately, the heat of formation of gaseous isopropylcyclopentane, the hydrogenation product of dimethyl fulvene, appears not to have been recorded. However, if the difference between the heats of formation of gaseous cyclopentane and isopropylcyclopentane is the same as that between pentane and 2-methylheptane, 16·5 kcal/mole, then the heat of formation of gaseous isopropylcyclopentane would be $-34{\cdot}96$ kcal/mole. Hence, the heat of hydrogenation of dimethyl fulvene is calculated as $-66{\cdot}0$ kcal/mole. This may be compared with the heats of hydrogenation of cyclopentadiene, $-50{\cdot}87$ kcal/mole, and of tetramethylethylene, $-26{\cdot}63$ kcal/mole, the sum of which is $-77{\cdot}5$ kcal/mole. The dimethylfulvene molecule therefore has a resonance energy some 11·5 kcal/mole greater than that of cyclopentadiene. Unfortunately there are, as yet, no thermochemical data available for fulvalene, in which two fulvene rings are joined.

The heats of hydrogenation of both heptafulvene and heptafulvalene have been measured in solution as $-92{\cdot}63 \pm 0{\cdot}4$ and $-130{\cdot}77 \pm 3{\cdot}1$ kcal/mole, respectively.[93] From these, resonance energies of 13·2 and 28·0 kcal/mole have been calculated. Whilst none of these resonance energies is large, in comparison with six-membered ring systems, they are nevertheless greater than those found in straight-chain conjugated systems.

Four- and Eight-membered Ring Systems

Hückel's rule suggests that no especial resonance stability or aromatic character is to be expected of a planar cyclo-octatetraene molecule. There is, therefore, little to be gained by the molecule becoming planar, at the expense of introducing a certain amount of strain energy, in order to permit increased $p_\pi - p_\pi$ overlap between conjugated carbon atoms. In fact an arrangement of minimal strain is adopted, in which the molecule has a tub structure with

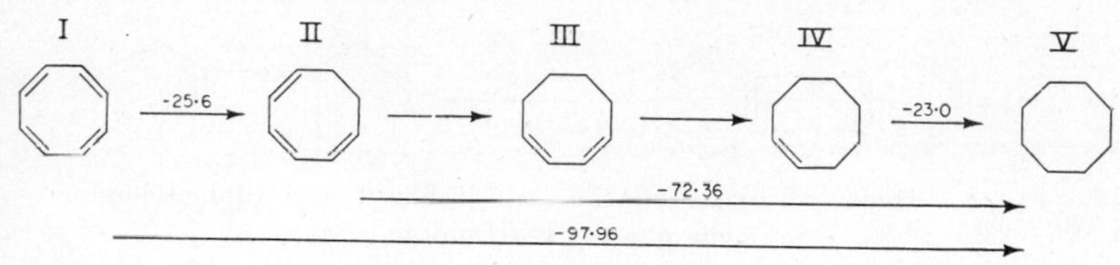

FIG. 7. Heats of hydrogenation of cyclo-octenes (in acetic acid solution) (kcal/mole).

C=C—C angles of approximately 120°, and with angles between adjacent double bonds of nearly 90°, owing to rotation about the intervening single bonds.

To confirm the prediction that cyclo-octatetraene would have little resonance energy, experimental approaches have been made to calculate the stabilization energy from heat of hydrogenation data in the gas phase,[94] and also in solution.[21] Since other relevant heats of hydrogenation are known only in solution, we shall consider only the solution data.

As in all calculations of resonance energy, the difficulty lies in finding a suitable reference against which to compare the heat of hydrogenation. A comparison has been suggested by Turner[21] which is shown diagrammatically in Fig. 7. Three separate heats have been measured $I \rightarrow V$, $II \rightarrow V$, and $IV \rightarrow V$. From the first two the difference can be derived from the reaction $I \rightarrow II$. One might take as a reference the heat of hydrogenation of cyclo-octene, $IV \rightarrow V$, $-23{\cdot}0$ kcal/mole. Four times this value. -92 kcal, is *less* than the heat of hydrogenation of cyclo-octatetraene, $-97{\cdot}96$ kcal, which implies a *negative* resonance energy of 6 kcal! However, we know that the heat of hydrogenation of cyclo-octene, $IV \rightarrow V$, is low because of strain in the cyclo-octane molecule, V. The heat of the reaction $I \rightarrow II$, $-25{\cdot}6$ kcal is slightly less than that for the hydrogenation of cyclohexene, $-27{\cdot}1$ kcal, which implies a certain amount of stabilization of

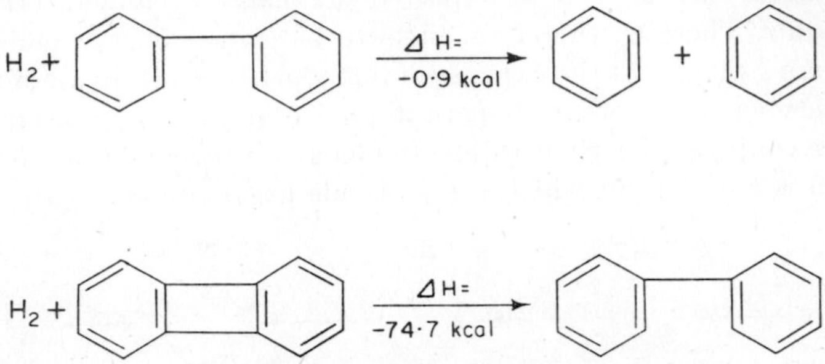

H_2 + diphenyl $\xrightarrow[-0{\cdot}9\ \text{kcal}]{\Delta H=}$ benzene + benzene

H_2 + diphenylene $\xrightarrow[-74{\cdot}7\ \text{kcal}]{\Delta H=}$ diphenyl

FIG. 8. Heats of hydrogenation of diphenyl and diphenylene (gas phase) (kcal/mole).

cyclo-octatetraene. Turner chooses an intermediate value of $-25{\cdot}0$ kcal as a mean for each of the four stages $I \rightarrow V$, to allow for repulsion effects, and this leads to a calculated stabilization energy of only 2 kcal ($100{\cdot}0 - 97{\cdot}96$ kcal) for the cyclo-octatetraene molecule. It should be emphasized, however, that these calculations are made on data obtained in solution, and do not allow for any differences in heats of solution, or in heats of vaporization of cyclo-octatetraene and cyclo-octane.

Cyclobutadiene would have as its configuration of lowest energy one doubly occupied bonding orbital, but also two electrons occupying two degenerate non-bonding orbitals. The molecule would not possess a closed shell ground state, in a regular planar configuration, and it is likely to be an unstable molecule with little or no resonance energy.

Although cyclobutadiene itself has not been prepared, the "derivative" diphenylene was first synthesized in 1941 by Lothrop,[95] and its heat of combustion has been measured recently as $\Delta H_c^0(\text{g}) = -1517{\cdot}1 \pm 0{\cdot}7$ kcal/mole.[60,96] This leads to $\Delta H_f^0(\text{g}) = +115{\cdot}2$ kcal/mole. For the compound in which two benzene rings are joined by only one carbon–carbon bond, diphenyl, Parks and Vaughan[97] have obtained $\Delta H_f^0(\text{g}) = +40{\cdot}5$ kcal/mole. From these values, and $\Delta H_f^0(\text{benzene, g}) = +19{\cdot}82$ kcal/mole it is possible to calculate the heats of the hydrogenation reactions shown in Fig. 8.

The hydrogenation heat of diphenyl to two benzene molecules will be affected by (*a*) conjugation energy and (*b*) strain energy in the diphenyl molecule, although the magnitude of this is unlikely to exceed 0·8 kcal/mole (see below). Likewise these two factors will affect the heat of hydrogenation of diphenylene to diphenyl. The very much larger value of $-74{\cdot}7$ kcal/mole, indicates that any increased resonance energy, due to the cyclobutadiene ring formation is more than offset by the strain incurred in closing the ring, to an extent of some 74 kcal/mole.

Cata-condensed Hydrocarbons

The "$4n + 2$" rule appears to apply not only to monocyclic systems, but also to "cata-condensed" hydrocarbons, in which every unsaturated carbon atom lies on the perimeter of the molecule. An example is the azulene molecule which may be regarded as a conjugated cycle of ten bonds with a relatively unimportant cross-link.

Although the heat of combustion of azulene has been measured,[98] the heat of formation of the corresponding saturated product bi-cyclo[0,3,5]nonane is unknown. It is, therefore, not possible to calculate the heat of hydrogenation in the vapour phase. In solution, the heat of hydrogenation has been determined as $-99{\cdot}0 \pm 0{\cdot}1$ kcal/mole,[21] which compares with the *gas* phase heat of hydrogenation of naphthalene to *trans*-decalin, of $-80{\cdot}0$ kcal/mole. If we neglect any differences in strain energy between *trans*-decalin and bi-cyclo[0,3,5]nonane, and assume that the gas phase heat of hydrogenation of azulene is the same as that in solution, then the resonance energy of azulene is 19 kcal/mole (99·0–80·0) less than that of naphthalene. The electrostatic work involved in charge transfer, to give the two six-electron ring systems, presumably accounts, in part, for this lower resonance energy.

Polycyclic Hydrocarbons

1. Stabilization Energies

The heat of hydrogenation of acepleiadylene has been measured by Turner.[21] This hydrogenation is shown diagrammatically in Fig. 9. Two heats of hydrogenation were measured, $I \rightarrow III$, $\Delta H = -88{\cdot}35 \pm 0{\cdot}45$ kcal/mole, and $II \rightarrow III$, $\Delta H = -29{\cdot}75 \pm 0{\cdot}13$ kcal/mole, so that the heat of hydrogenation for the process $I \rightarrow II$ is calculated by difference as $-58{\cdot}6$ kcal/mole.

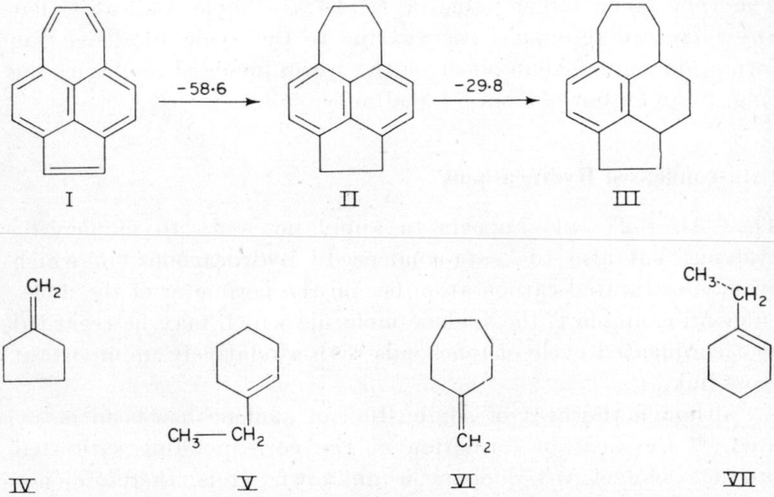

FIG. 9. Heat of hydrogenation of acepleiadylene (in acetic acid solution) (kcal/mole)(taken, in part, from Turner, ref. 21).

A reference model for the hydrogenation of acepleiadane, $II \rightarrow III$, was constructed by taking the sum of (*a*) the average heats of hydrogenation of ethylidenecyclopentane (*IV*) and 1-ethylcyclohexene (*V*), $-25{\cdot}0$ kcal, and (*b*) the average for ethylidenecycloheptane (*VI*) and 1-ethylcyclohexene (*VII*) $-24{\cdot}9$ kcal. The heat of hydrogenation calculated for this model is $-49{\cdot}9$ kcal/mole, so that acepleiadane has a resonance energy some 20 kcal/mole greater than that of the hydrogenation product (*III*). Assuming the resonance energy of this molecule to be about 36 kcal/mole, as in benzene, then the resonance energy of acepleiadane is about 56 kcal/mole.

A reference standard against which the heat of hydrogenation of acepleiadylene ($I \rightarrow II$) may be compared is a heat equal to the cyclopentene value (−25·7 kcal) plus twice the heat of hydrogenation of cyclohexene (−27·10 kcal). This gives a calculated heat of hydrogenation ($I \rightarrow II$) of −79·9 kcal/mole, which compares with the actual value of −58·6 kcal/mole, so that acepleiadylene is some 21·3 kcal/mole more stable than acepleiadane, and the total resonance energy of acepleiadylene is about 77 kcal/mole.

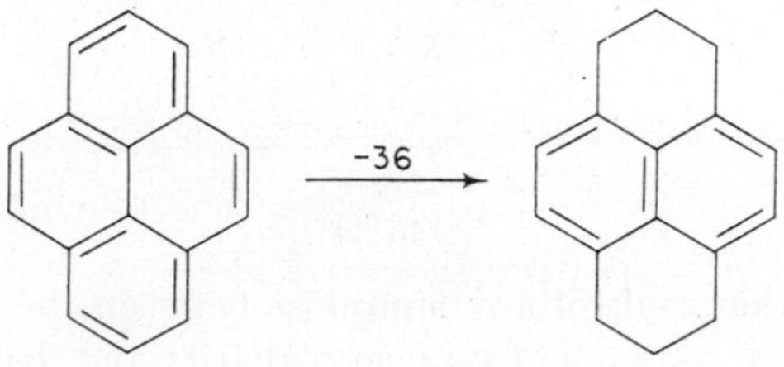

-36

I II

FIG. 10. Heat of hydrogenation of pyrene (gas phase) (kcal/mole).

It is interesting to compare the heat of hydrogenation of acepleiadylene with that of pyrene, with which it is isomeric. This is shown in Fig. 10. The heats of combustion of pyrene (*I*) [99] and *sym*-hexahydropyrene (*II*) [100] have been measured and the heats of formation of the gaseous compounds are +52·3 and +16·3 kcal/mole, respectively. The heat of hydrogenation $I \rightarrow II$, −36 kcal/mole, is less than for the corresponding hydrogenation of acepleiadylene, −58·6 kcal/mole. Strictly, this figure refers to hydrogenation in solution, but the gas-phase value will be much the same. If we assume that the resonance energy of the two hydrogenation products acepleiadane (Fig. 9, *II*) and *sym*-hexahydropyrene (Fig. 10, *II*) are the same, and also that the change in strain energy on hydrogenation is the same in the two cases, then the resonance energy of pyrene is greater than that of acepleiadylene by 22 kcal/mole. This is simply the difference between the two heats of hydrogenation. Whilst the first of these assumptions is probably true, it is unlikely that the difference in strain energy between acepleiadane and acepleiadylene is the same as that between *sym*-hexahydropyrene and pyrene. However, corrections due to these strain energies are likely to be small.

2. Strain Energies

Some polycyclic hydrocarbons in which steric interactions are likely to be important are shown in Table 1. These are particularly interesting compounds in which exact planarity of the molecule is impossible, on steric grounds. The observed shape of the mole-

1·8 Å

H---H

H---H

FIG. 11.

cule is then the result of a compromise between the increased resonance energy consequent on near planarity and the increased repulsion if atoms are too close together.[104]

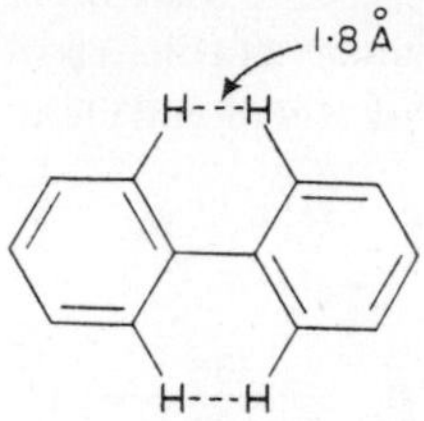

TABLE 1

Heats of combustion, formation and hydrogenation of some aromatic hydrocarbons which are sterically-hindered

Compound	$-\Delta H_c^0$ (c)	ΔH sub.	ΔH_f^0(g)	$\Delta H_{hydrog.}$
benzene	780·98 (l) [30]	8·1 (vap)	19·82	
naphthalene	1231·9 [101]	17·8 [101]	35·9	
anthracene	1684·75 [99]	22·3	48·2	
diphenyl	1493·3 [97]	17·4 [102]	40·5	− 0·9
9,9′-dianthryl	3326·2 [103]	35·4 [103]	113·3	−16·6
9,10-diphenylanthracene	3131·4 [103]	32·0 [103]	103·2	−15·4
perylene	2336·5 [101]	30·0 [101]	85·6	−13·8

An example of this is diphenyl, which, if the molecule were planar would have the four *ortho*-hydrogens closer together (1·8 Å) than the usual sum of their van der Waals' radii (2·3 Å), as shown in Fig. 11.

One of the ways in which repulsion between these hydrogen atoms can be reduced is by rotation of the two phenyl groups about the 1-1′ bond. As rotation increases, repulsion energy decreases, but so does the additional resonance energy, due to conjugation of the two phenyl groups. The energy of the molecule will be the sum of these two quantities, and twist will occur until a balance is reached between opposing energy requirements.

The heat of the hydrogenation reaction

$$C_6H_5-C_6H_5 + H_2 \rightarrow C_6H_6 + C_6H_6,$$

$\Delta H_{hydrog.}$, can be used as a measure of the two energy quantities, since in this reaction both steric interference and additional stabilization due to conjugation are removed. The heat of hydrogenation, — 0·9 kcal/mole may be compared with the value of — 1·3 kcal/mole for the corresponding hydrogenation of 1,3-butadiene, viz.

$$CH_2{=}CH{-}CH{=}CH_2 + H_2 \rightarrow CH_2{=}CH_2 + CH_2{=}CH_2.$$

Compared with 1,3-butadiene, therefore, diphenyl has a greater conjugation energy, to the extent of 0·4 kcal/mole, plus any strain energy introduced by joining two benzene rings in this way. Adrian[105] has estimated this strain energy, due to twist of the molecule, as 0·4 kcal/mole. On this value the additional conjugation energy is 0·8 kcal/mole greater than that in 1,3-butadiene.

For 9,9′-dianthryl, steric interaction is expected to be greater than in the diphenyl case, and here the corresponding hydrogenation reaction, to two molecules of anthracene, has a heat, — 16·6 kcal/mole. This indicates that the compound is much more sterically hindered than diphenyl. For 9,10-diphenylanthracene the heat of hydrogenation to give a molecule of anthracene and two benzene molecules is — 15·4 kcal/mole, so that the comparable figure is half this value, or — 7·7 kcal/mole, to replace one carbon-carbon bond by the two carbon-hydrogen bonds. This steric interaction energy of 7·7 kcal/mole caused by attaching one phenyl group to the anthracene molecule, is more than that found in diphenyl, but less than that found in 9,9′-dianthryl.

The heat of hydrogenation of perylene to two molecules of naphthalene is — 13·8 kcal/mole, as compared with twice the heat

$$\text{perylene} + 2\,H_2 \rightarrow 2\ \text{naphthalene} \quad \Delta H = -13.8\ \text{kcal/mole}$$

of hydrogenation of diphenyl, — 1·8 kcal/mole. The difference, — 12 kcal/mole, is a minimum value for the strain energy imposed by the central, planar six-membered ring system, and will be larger than this if there is any increased resonance in perylene as compared with two naphthalene molecules.

Hetero-aromatics

The six-electron, conjugated cyclic compound is particularly stable, and this condition is found not only in hydrocarbons, but also in the hetero-aromatic compounds, such as pyrrole. As with benzene, the cyclopentadienate and cycloheptatrienyl ions, here again there are three bonding orbitals which can accommodate six electrons, as shown in Fig. 2.

In the case of pyrrole, furan and thiophen, the six π-electrons derive four from the carbon atoms and two (the "lone pair") from the hetero atom. For this reason Albert [106] has termed these heterocyclic compounds π-excessive, in contrast to pyridine, and related compounds, which are referred to as π-deficient, because the hetero atom tends to withdraw π-electrons from the molecular orbitals and thus reduce the resonance energy.

In recent years, with the development of rotating-bomb calorimetry and the refinement of thermodynamic corrections for the combustion process for nitrogen and sulphur containing organic compounds, a number of accurate heats of combustion of heterocyclic compounds have been determined.

The heats of hydrogenation of some five-membered rings, calculated from the difference between the heats of formation of the gaseous, unsaturated and saturated compounds are listed in Table 2.

It has already been shown, however, that the saturated five-ring systems have considerable strain energy, E_s, so that the heats of hydrogenation to the hypothetical, unstrained saturated rings would be greater by these strain energies. These calculated heats, $\Delta H'_{hydrog.}$ are also shown.

These heats of hydrogenation should be compared with twice the heat of a *trans*, unstrained alkene, e.g. *trans*-hexene-3 to hexane, $-27{\cdot}4$ kcal/mole, viz., $-54{\cdot}8$ kcal/mole. The resonance energies, E_r, calculated in this way are shown in the last column of Table 2. The negative value for cyclopentadiene reflects the strain energy in the unsaturated compound, which has not been accounted for.

The resonance energies of pyrrole, thiophen and furan, which range from 15 to 18 kcal/mole are considerably greater than for the

TABLE 2

Heats of formation and hydrogenation of hetero-aromatic compounds

	ΔH_f^0(g)		ΔH_f^0(g)	$\Delta H_{hydrog.}$	E_s	$\Delta H'_{hydrog.}$	E_r
cyclopentadiene	+ 32·41 [30]	cyclopentane	− 18·46 [30]	− 50·87	5·1	− 56·0	− 1·2
pyrrole	+ 30·8[a] [107]	pyrrolidine	− 0·8 [40]	− 31·6	4·7	− 36·3	18·5
thiophen	+ 27·5 [108]	thiacyclopentane	− 8·1 [38]	− 35·6	2·1	− 37·7	17·1
furan	− 5·9[b] [70]	tetrahydrofuran	− 43·08 [36]	− 37·2	2·7	− 39·9	14·9

[a] ΔH vap. taken as 10·0 kcal/mole.
[b] ΔH vap. taken as 6·6 kcal/mole.

corresponding carbon compound cyclopentadiene, and this might be ascribed to the availability of p_{π}-electrons associated with the nitrogen, sulphur and oxygen atoms, which permits greater electron delocalization, a situation not found with carbon.

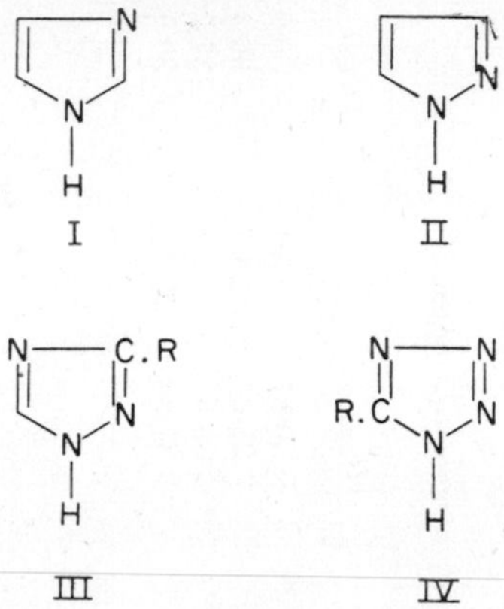

Fig. 12.

There are very few thermochemical data for five-membered hetero-aromatics containing more than one hetero atom, and these are confined to nitrogen compounds. The heats of formation of gaseous imidazole, Fig. 12 (*I*), and pyrazole (*II*), have been derived

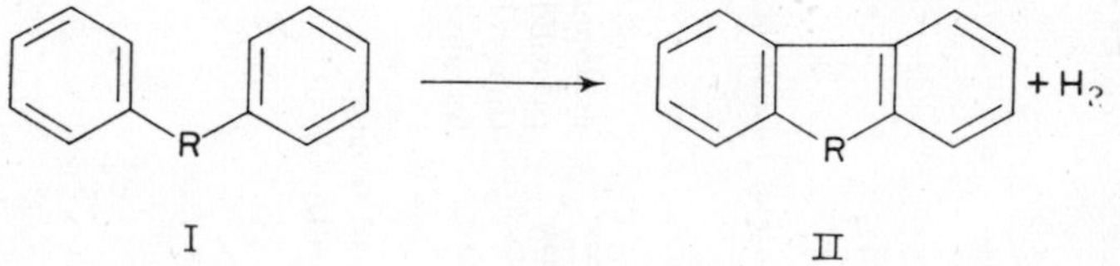

Fig. 13.

from combustion data[111] as $+28{\cdot}0$ and $+41{\cdot}6$ kcal/mole, respectively. The difference between the bonding in the two molecules is that whereas imidazole has two C—N bonds, pyrazole has one C—C bond and one N—N bond. Taking the bond energies E(C—N) = 72·8, E(C—C) = 82·7, and E(N—N) = 39·0 kcal/mole[4] the difference $2E$(C—N)$-$[E(C—C) + E(N—N)] is 23·9 kcal/mole. The bonding in pyrazole should be weaker than that in imidazole by 23·9 kcal/mole, whereas in fact it is only some 13·6 kcal/mole less. Hence the resonance energy of pyrazole must be 10 kcal/mole greater than that in imidazole. The heats of formation of some substituted 1,2,4-triazoles, Fig. 12 (*III*) and 1,2,3,4-tetrazoles (*IV*) have also been calculated from combustion data[110]. The resonance energies of these hetero-aromatics could be determined by using bond energy data for the particular bonds involved, i.e. E(C—C), E(C=C), E(C—H), E(N—N) and E(C—N).[4] Values for E(N=N) and E(C=N) are also available[109] but the value for E(C=N) is based on a heat of combustion of n-butylisobutylideneamine, $CH_3(CH_2)_3N{=}CHCH(CH_3)_2$ and is rather doubtful. Until some independent confirmation of E(C=N) has been made these resonance energies cannot be calculated with any degree of certainty.

There are a few thermochemical data available for the five-membered ring systems in which two benzene molecules are fused to the ring, the fluorene derivatives. It is possible to calculate the heat of the dehydrogenation reaction shown in Fig. 13. The values are shown in Table 3.

TABLE 3

Heats of dehydrogenation (in kcal/mole, at 25 °C)

R	ΔH_f^0(I, c)	ΔH sub.	ΔH_f^0(I, g)
CH_2	$+17{\cdot}3 \pm 0{\cdot}3$	15·3	$+32{\cdot}6 \pm 1{\cdot}0$ [112]
NH	$+27{\cdot}5 \pm 0{\cdot}2$	[20·5]	$+48{\cdot}0 \pm 1{\cdot}0$ [113]
O	$-9{\cdot}1 \pm 0{\cdot}9$	15·2 [102]	$+6{\cdot}1 \pm 0{\cdot}9$ [36]
PPh	$+54{\cdot}3 \pm 2{\cdot}3$	18·1	$+72{\cdot}4 \pm 2{\cdot}5$ [114]

[ ], estimated.

R	ΔH_f^0(II, c)	ΔH sub.	ΔH_f^0(II, g)	ΔH
CH_2	$+20{\cdot}8 \pm 2{\cdot}0$	15·3	$+36{\cdot}1$ [115]	$+3{\cdot}5 \pm 2{\cdot}3$
NH	$+22{\cdot}3 \pm 2{\cdot}0$	[20]	$+42{\cdot}3$ [116]	$-5{\cdot}7 \pm 2{\cdot}2$
O	$-1{\cdot}4 \pm 1{\cdot}0$	15·8	$+14{\cdot}4$ [36]	$+8{\cdot}3 \pm 1{\cdot}9$
PPh	$+44{\cdot}3 \pm 1{\cdot}5$	[18·0]	$+62{\cdot}3$ [117]	$-10{\cdot}1 \pm 4{\cdot}0$

A standard against which to compare these dehydrogenation heats is the heat of the gas phase reaction considered previously, in which two benzene rings join to form diphenyl,

$$C_6H_6 + C_6H_6 \rightarrow C_6H_5{-}C_6H_5 + H_2, \quad \Delta H = +0{\cdot}9 \text{ kcal/mole}.$$

Hence in fluorene, R = CH_2, the five-membered ring has a strain energy of some 2·6 kcal/mole, and in dibenzofuran, R = 0, it is about 8 kcal/mole. Whilst this last figure is probably reliable to within ±2 kcal/mole, the thermochemical data for R = CH_2 are based on very early work which may not be too reliable.

However, the striking fact remains that when R = PPh, closure of the ring system causes a *stabilization* of at least 10 kcal/mole (ΔH is negative) compared with fluorene. This is presumably to be associated with increased resonance energy which is made possible by the availability of the 3*p*-orbitals of the phosphorus atom, which permit additional electron delocalization. Carbazole, R = NH, is also stabilized, though to a lesser extent than the phosphafluorene.

Finally, we turn to the molecule thianthrene, in which two benzene molecules are joined by sulphur atom bridges, to give a central six-membered ring. The heat of formation of gaseous thianthrene is +63·0 kcal/mole.[118] The resonance energy of this molecule, in excess of that of two benzene nuclei, is obtained from the following formal reaction:

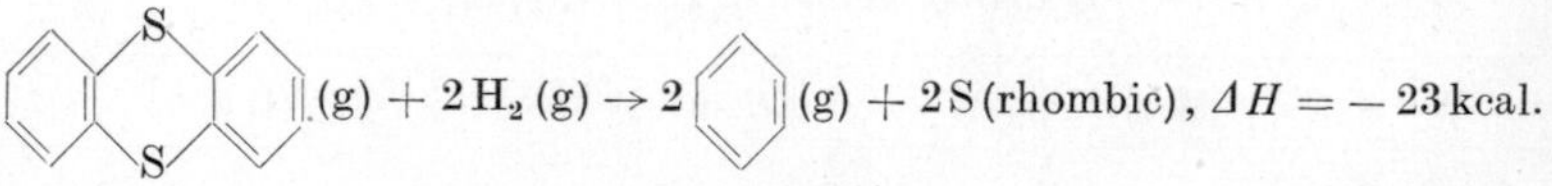

$$\text{(thianthrene)}(g) + 2H_2(g) \rightarrow 2\,\text{(benzene)}(g) + 2S(\text{rhombic}), \Delta H = -23\,\text{kcal}.$$

For comparison we chose the reaction

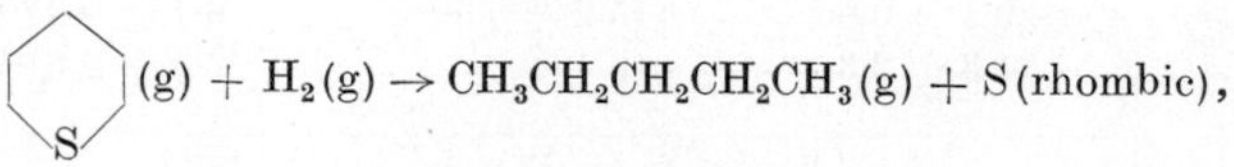

$$\text{(thiane)}(g) + H_2(g) \rightarrow CH_3CH_2CH_2CH_2CH_3(g) + S(\text{rhombic}),$$

$$\Delta H' = -19.9\,\text{kcal}.$$

Hence the resonance energy of thianthrene, in excess of the resonance energy of two benzene nuclei, is $(2\Delta H' - \Delta H) = 16{\cdot}8$ kcal/mole.

Conclusion

In this chapter we have examined briefly how resonance energies can be calculated from heats of hydrogenation. One of the main difficulties lies in the choice of a standard, non-resonating model against which to compare the experimentally determined heat of hydrogenation. This has been shown in detail for the two cases of cyclo-octatraene and also for acepleiadylene.

Even having derived these resonance energies, it must be remembered that they are "gross" figures, which may be complicated by effects of strain and hybridization differences. Strain caused by the interaction of non-bonded atoms in diphenyl and similar molecules are particular cases of this.

However, for the hydrocarbons, heats of hydrogenation support Hückel's "$4n + 2$" rule for aromatic character, although the resonance energies, in some cases, are considerably reduced by the energy of charge separation.

CHAPTER 5

POLYMERIZATION ENERGIES

So far we have been concerned with strain energies and stabilization energies due to electron delocalization changes and polar character. One of the ways in which these effects can be demonstrated in cyclic and unsaturated compounds is by a comparison of heats of hydrogenation. To a large extent, it is these same factors which influence the heats of self-polymerization of ethylenic and cyclic compounds. For some of these compounds heats of both hydrogenation and polymerization are available, and it is interesting to find the same trends in the heats of both of these types of reaction. For a number of heterocyclic compounds, for which other thermochemical data are scanty, polymerization heats can be used to indicate relative strain energies.

A considerable amount of work on the thermodynamics of polymerization has been carried out by Dainton and his co-workers, and this, together with much other data, has been reviewed.[119] For many polymerization reactions the entropy changes have been either measured or calculated, and from these, combined with the measured heats of reaction, the free energies of polymerization can be calculated. From these data it is possible to determine the extent to which polymerization occurs, and the relative influence of the heat and entropy effects on the reaction equilibrium.

We shall look first at the heats and entropies of self-polymerization of some ethylene derivatives, and then at similar data for co-polymerization of these derivatives, especially with sulphur dioxide. Finally, we shall mention the influence of strain on the extent of polymerization of heterocyclic compounds.

Heats of Self-polymerization Reactions

The heats of self-polymerization of a number of derivatives are shown in Table 1. They refer to the polymerization of liquid monomer to polymer in a condensed phase, either liquid or amorphous solid, in liquid monomer. The heats have been either measured directly or calculated from heats of combustion of monomer and polymer (marked ΔH_c). Although the reaction temperature is not the same in every case, the ΔH values would not be much altered by correction to 25 °C.

TABLE I

Heats of polymerization of ethylene derivatives

Derivative	Temp. °C	$-\Delta H$ (kcal/mole)
$CH_2{=}C(CH_3)_2$, isobutene	20·0	12·6 [120]
$CH_2{=}CHC_6H_5$, styrene	25·0	16·7 (ΔH_c) [121]
	76·8	16·4 [122]
	76·8	16·1 [123]
$CH_2{=}CHC_6H_2(CH_3)_3$, vinyl mesitylene	76·8	16·7 [122]
$CH_2{=}CHC_6H_4Cl$, *o*-chlorostyrene	76·8	16·4 [123]
p-chlorostyrene	76·8	16·0 [123]
$CH_2{=}CHC_6H_3Cl_2$, 2,5-dichlorostyrene	76·8	16·5 [123]
$CH_2{=}C(CH_3)C_6H_5$, α-methylstyrene	25·0	8·4 (ΔH_c) [124]
$CH_2{=}CHCOOCH_3$, methyl acrylate	76·8	18·7 [125]
$CH_2{=}C(CH_3)COOCH_3$, methyl methacrylate	76·8	13·0 [126]/13·9 [127]
$CH_2{=}C(CH_3)COOC_4H_9$, butyl methacrylate	76·8	13·5 [127]
$CH_2{=}CHCl$, vinyl chloride	25·0	26·0 (ΔH_c) [128]
$CH_2{=}CCl_2$, vinylidene chloride	25·0	18·0 (ΔH_c) [128]
$CF_2{=}CF_2$, tetrafluoroethylene	25·0	33·0 (ΔH_c) [129, 130, 131, 132]
$CH_2{=}CHCN$, acrylonitrile	76·8	17·3 [125]
$CH_2{=}CHCONH_2$, acrylamide	76·8	19·8[a] [122]
CH=CH, acenaphthylene	76·8	24·0[a] [122]

[a] refers to process: monomer, solution → polymer, solution.

Generally, the values obtained from combustion data are less reliable than those measured directly, because the calculation involves taking a difference between two comparatively large heats of combustion. Where these heats of combustion are known within small limits of error, an accurate heat of polymerization can be obtained. For styrene, the value obtained from combustion data, $-16 \cdot 7$ kcal/mole, is in fair agreement with the directly measured value of $-16 \cdot 1$, and quite close to the more recently measured value of $-16 \cdot 4 \pm 0 \cdot 3$ kcal/mole.

Accurate heats of combustion are difficult to obtain for halogen-containing compounds, especially where the halogen is fluorine. Although the heats of polymerization of vinyl chloride and vinylidene chloride have been derived, from combustion data, within quite small limits of error, the same is certainly not true for tetrafluoroethylene. There are three values for the heat of formation of gaseous tetrafluoroethylene, $-151 \cdot 3$,[129] -162[130] and -164 kcal/mole,[131] and the most likely value is *ca.* -163 ± 3 kcal/mole. The heat of formation of the liquid is then -167 kcal/mole. For the crystalline polymer, polytetrafluoroethylene, there are two values available, $-199 \cdot 9$[129] and $-193 \cdot 5$ kcal/mole.[132] Taking a mean of these values the calculated heat of polymerization (liquid $\rightarrow$ cryst.) has a value -33 ± 6 kcal/mole.

When direct measurements of polymerization heats are made, care must be taken to estimate the amount of monomer which has been converted to polymer. For methyl methacrylate there is a discrepancy of $0 \cdot 9$ kcal/mole between the two directly measured heats, using isothermal calorimetry. Thus Ekegren *et al.*[127] obtain $-13 \cdot 9 \pm 0 \cdot 3$ kcal/mole, for the heat of polymerization, slightly greater than the value of $-13 \cdot 0 \pm 0 \cdot 2$ kcal/mole found by Tong and Kenyon.[126] These latter authors assumed that there was a 100 per cent conversion of monomer to polymer, whereas Ekegren *et al.* found that there was seldom more than a $93 \cdot 7$ per cent conversion, and these authors have taken this into account. The larger value, of $-13 \cdot 9$, seems the more reliable.

In addition, the degree of polymerization, or mean number of monomer units comprising the polymer molecule must be estimated. The heat of polymerization may vary with the degree of polymerization. For the polymerization of α-methylstyrene, Roberts and Jessup[124] have obtained the heat of polymerization as $(-8 \cdot 424 - 18 \cdot 58/n)$ kcal/mole, for $n = 11$ to 46, at 25 °C, where n is the number of units of α-methylstyrene in the polymer.

For ethylene derivatives, the $-\Delta H$ values vary over a considerable range; from a minimum of $8 \cdot 4$ kcal for α-methylstyrene, through about 13 kcal for the methylacrylic esters, 16 kcal for the ring-substituted styrenes, 18 kcal for vinylidene chloride to a maximum of 33 kcal/mole for tetrafluoroethylene. Variations in the heats of polymerization of these derivatives arise mainly from two causes:

(1) steric strain in the polymer, as a result of bond stretching, bond-angle deformation, or interaction between non-bonded atoms (which tend to make ΔH less negative); and
(2) differences in stabilization energy in monomer and polymer, as a result of conjugation or hyperconjugation.

The first factor, steric hindrance, is presumably the reason for the low heats of polymerization of the 1,1-disubstituted ethylenes, isobutene and the methyl acrylic esters ($-\Delta H = 12{\cdot}6$ to $13{\cdot}9$ kcal/mole). This is because the crowding together of the groups is greater in the polymer than in the monomer. Dainton and Ivin[119] have pointed out that the low heat of polymerization of methyl methacrylate ($-\Delta H = 13{\cdot}9$ kcal) is not likely to be due to stabilization of the monomer because of conjugation. The very similar heats of hydrogenation of isobutene and methyl methacrylate preclude the possibility of stabilization in this latter molecule.

Conjugation to the ethylenic bond makes an appreciable contribution to the stabilization of styrene and its ring-substituted derivatives, which keeps the heat of polymerization fairly low ($-\Delta H = 16{\cdot}0$ to $16{\cdot}5$ kcal/mole). In α-methyl styrene the effect of conjugation is to make the heat of formation of the monomer more negative, whilst the steric effects make the heat of formation of the polymer more positive, so giving a particularly low heat of polymerization of $-8{\cdot}4$ kcal/mole. Most probably the high heat of polymerization of acenaphthylene ($-\Delta H = 24{\cdot}0$ kcal/mole) is due to the release of a large strain energy in the five-membered ring on polymerization.

It is more difficult to account for the particularly high heats of polymerization of those ethylene derivatives in which there is a strongly electronegative group, such as acrylonitrile ($-\Delta H = 17{\cdot}3$ kcal), vinylidene chloride ($-\Delta H = 18{\cdot}0$ kcal), acrylamide ($-\Delta H = 19{\cdot}8$ kcal), vinyl chloride ($-\Delta H = 26{\cdot}0$ kcal and tetrafluoroethylene ($-\Delta H = 33$ kcal/mole). These increased heats of polymerization may be due to a reduction, on polymerization, of repulsion between non-bonding electrons associated with the electronegative groups. Alternatively, they may arise because of stabilization of the polymer caused by a degree of ionic-covalent resonance. Similar effects have already been referred to when the heats of hydrogenation of some substituted acetylenes, and also of the vinyl halides, were considered.

Free Energies and Entropies

The thermodynamics of polymerization reactions have been considered in detail by Dainton and Ivin[119] and in what followos this source has been drawn upon liberally.

The extent to which polymerization occurs depends on the free energy change, ΔG, which is a function of both ΔH, and of the entropy change, ΔS, according to the relationship

$$\Delta G = \Delta H - T \Delta S.$$

Entropies of polymerization have been derived in two ways: from specific heat measurements and also from the *ceiling temperature* of polymerization. The meaning of this term can be seen by looking at the overall reaction which takes place in addition polymerization. This can be represented by the equation $n M_1 \rightarrow M_n$, in which n molecules of monomer M_1 give a polymer M_n, with an accompanying change of $n \Delta a$, in the thermodynamic function a, i.e. H, S, or G.

The first step, in most cases, is the opening of the double bond or ring, involving the conversion of a monomer molecule into an active centre M_1^*, the *initiation* step. This initiation step is followed by *propagation*, in which M_1^* is joined to a second monomer molecule, transferring to the product the capacity for further addition of monomer by the same type of reaction. This repetitive process of the joining of monomer molecules to the reactive chain-centre M_j^* is represented by $M_j^* + M_1 \rightarrow M_{j+1}^*$.

A given polymer sample always contains molecules of differing degrees of polymerization, but if the *mean* degree of polymerization is reasonably large (> 100), then the change in the thermodynamic function for the polymerization process is essentially that for the propagation step. Put another way, if the degree of polymerization is large, contributions to Δa from steps other than propagation will be negligible, and the experimental value of Δa may be equated to that of the propagation step. The other steps, which need not concern us thermodynamically, include the transfer of the capacity of addition to some quite different molecular species, or to its loss in other ways.

When the degree of polymerization is large, the fraction of monomer removed by these other steps is negligible, so that the rate of polymerization, R_p, is given by

$$R_p = K_p[M_1][M^*],$$

where $[M^*]$ is the total concentration of chain centres. Whilst this equation accounts satisfactorily for a number of systems, there are certain others for which it is inadequate. In these cases the observed rate of polymerization can only be accounted for by postulating the significant participation of the reverse of the propagation process, a *depropagation* $M_j^* \rightarrow M_{j-1}^* + M_1$, for which the rate is $K_d[M^*]$. Hence the overall rate of the polymerization reaction is modified to

$$R_p = (K_p[M_1] - K_d)[M^*].$$

The variations in K_p and K_d with temperature, will be given by the Arrhenius expressions

$$K_p = A_p \exp(-E_p/RT) \quad \text{and} \quad K_d = A_d \exp(-E_d/RT).$$

Equating the difference in activation energies to the heat of polymerization, we write $(E_p - E_d) = \Delta H_p$. Now although, at room temperature, K_d may be negligible compared with $K_p[M_1]$, K_d will increase more rapidly with increasing temperature than does $K_p[M_1]$ so that we may predict a temperature Tc, at which $K_p[M_1] = K_d$. At this so-called *ceiling temperature*, the rate of polymerization equals the rate of depolymerization. Equating $K_p[M]$ to K_d then we write

$$Tc = \Delta H_p/R \ln(A_p[M_1]/A_d).$$

The ceiling temperature can also be defined as the temperature, above which the formation of long-chain polymer from monomer, at concentration $[M_1]$, is impossible. At this temperature the free energy of polymerization passes from a negative to a positive value as the temperature is raised, and hence we may write

$$Tc = \Delta H_p/\Delta S_p$$

where ΔH_p and ΔS_p are the heat and entropy changes under the prevailing experimental conditions. Comparing these two equations for Tc, we write

$$\Delta S_p R \ln(A_p/A_d) + R \ln[M_1] = \Delta S_p^0 + R \ln[M_1],$$

where ΔS_p^0 is the entropy change for $[M_1] = 1$ mole/litre, and hence

$$Tc = \Delta H_p/(\Delta S_p^0 + R \ln[M_1]).$$

Values for the entropies of polymerization of some ethylene derivatives, calculated from specific heats and ceiling temperature are shown in Table 2.

TABLE 2
Entropies of self-polymerization (cal/deg mole)

Monomer	$-\Delta S_p^0$	Method
isobutene	28·8	Specific heats at 25 °C [133]
styrene	24·93	Specific heats at 25 °C [134, 135]
methyl methacrylate	28·0	From Tc [136, 137]
tetrafluoroethylene	26·7	Specific heats at − 75·7 °C [138, 139]

[Taken from Dainton and Ivin[119]].

For the change, monomer (liquid) to polymer (crystalline), the ΔS_p^0 values are relatively constant for the ethylene derivatives shown, and the general conclusion drawn from this is that whereas substitution has a considerable effect on ΔH_p it has little effect on ΔS_p.

TABLE 3
Entropies of co-polymerization (cal/deg mole)

Monomer	ΔS_p^0	Monomer	ΔS_p^0
propene + SO_2	− 62·2	*cis*-butene-2 + SO_2	− 69·7
butene-1 + SO_2	− 69·5	*trans*-butene-2 + SO_2	− 66·7
hexene-1 + SO_2	− 69·1	isobutene + SO_2	− 78·5
hexadecene-1 + SO_2	− 66·3	cyclopentene + SO_2	− 64·5

[Taken from Dainton and Ivin[119]].

This same effect is also seen in the entropies of co-polymerization of the olefins with sulphur dioxide, values for which are shown in Table 3. These have been calculated (except for isobutene) from the calorimetric ΔH_p (Table 4) and the Tc values, assuming ΔH_p and ΔS_p to be temperature independent. They are taken from a paper by Cook, Dainton and Ivin.[140]

Co-polymerization

The data considered so far have been for self-polymerization reactions. A few heats of co-polymerization reactions have also been measured for (a) olefins with sulphur dioxide and (b) vinyl acetate with derivatives of maleic and fumaric acids.

The formation of olefin polysulphones from liquid sulphur dioxide and olefins may be represented by the equation

$$SO_2(l) + RCH{=}CHR'(l) \rightarrow -\left[\begin{array}{c} \text{O}\quad\text{R}\quad\text{R}' \\ \| \quad\ | \quad\ | \\ -\text{S}-\text{C}-\text{C}- \\ \| \quad\ | \quad\ | \\ \text{O}\quad\text{H}\quad\text{H} \end{array}\right]- \text{(solid, amorph)} \ldots \Delta H_1.$$

Ivin, Keith and Mackle[141] have determined the heats, ΔH_1, of some polymerization reactions of this type, from measurements of the heats of combustion of liquid olefins and solid polysulphones. These heats of polymerization have also been measured directly, using an isothermal calorimeter. In these cases the heat, ΔH_2, refers to the polymerization of a liquid *mixture* of sulphur dioxide and olefin to polymer dissolved in the reaction mixture. Ivin *et al.*[141] have pointed out that ΔH_2 will differ from ΔH_1 to a small extent depending on (i) the heat of mixing of the monomers, ΔH_3 and (ii) the heat of solution of the polymer, ΔH_4. They show the relationship between these quantities in a cycle, where M denotes olefin and N denotes sulphur dioxide.

$$\begin{array}{ccc} \text{N (liq.)} + \text{M (liq.)} & \xrightarrow{\Delta H_3} & \text{mixture (liq.)} \\ \downarrow \Delta H_1 & & \downarrow \Delta H_2 \\ \text{polymer } (+N+M) & \xrightarrow{\Delta H_4} & \text{polymer} \\ \text{(solid, amorph.)} & & \text{(soln.)} \end{array}$$

These authors have measured the heats of combustion of the polysulphones of the four isomeric butenes, and from these have derived values of ΔH_1 (shown in Table 4). The heats of polymerization, ΔH_2 values, have also been measured directly for seven olefins, including three of the butenes. It was not possible to measure directly the heat of co-polymerization of sulphur dioxide with isobutene, using the fusion calorimeter at 26·9 °C, because the ceiling temperature for this polymerization is at about 5 °C, for a suitable

TABLE 4

Heats of co-polymerization (kcal/mole)

Monomers	Change	$-\Delta H$	Reference
propylene + SO_2	lm→ c	20·2 ± 0·1	(29)
butene-1 + SO_2	lm→ c	21·2 ± 0·1	(29)
	l→ solid	20·1 ± 0·5(ΔH_c)	(141)
hexene-1 + SO_2	lm→c	20·7 ± 0·1	(29)
hexadecene-1 + SO_2	s→ s	19·9 ± 0·1	(29)
cis-butene-2 + SO_2	lm→ c	20·2 ± 0·1	(29)
	l→ solid	17·9 ± 0·4(ΔH_c)	(141)
trans-butene-2 + SO_2	lm→ c	18·7 ± 0·1	(29)
	l→ solid	16·9 ± 0·4(ΔH_c)	(141)
isobutene + SO_2	l→ solid	14·8 ± 0·4(ΔH_c)	(141)
cyclopentene + SO_2	lm→ c	21·7 ± 0·1	(29)
vinyl acetate + diethyl fumarate	lm→ c	18·6 ± 0·3	(142)
vinyl acetate + diethyl maleate	lm→ c	20·2 ± 0·2	(142)
vinyl acetate + maleic anhydride	lm→ c	20·2 ± 0·4	(142)
isopropenyl acetate + maleic anhydride	lm→ c	17·8 ± 0·4	(142)

lm = liquid mixture; c = crystalline; s = solution; l = liquid.

concentration. The values of ΔH_3 and ΔH_4 are not known for the butenes, so that it is not possible to convert ΔH_1 to ΔH_2 values. However, for butene-1 the values are almost identical, and for *cis*- and *trans*-butene the differences are similar (~1 kcal) and in the same direction.

A point not shown by these figures, is that the heats of combustion of the *cis*-butene-2 and *trans*-butene-2 polysulphones are the same, and from this it is assumed that the two polysulphones are identical. This means that there is time for rotation about the opened carbon-carbon bond in the interval between the addition of an olefin molecule to the growing radical and the further addition of a sulphur dioxide molecule.

The main factors which are likely to influence the heat of polymerization are (1) steric hindrance in the polymer, and (2) hyperconjugation and conjugation effects in monomer and polymer. Similar effects to (1) will be involved in any reaction in which the double bond is opened, and we may therefore compare the ΔH values with those of hydrogenation and self-polymerization. Except

TABLE 5
Heats of addition to olefins[a] *(kcal/mole)*

Olefin	$+SO_2$ at 26·9 °C	$+H_2$ at 25 °C[30]		$+Br_2$ at 27 °C[144]		Self-polymerization (calculated)	
	(l)	(g)	(l)	(g)	(CCl_4 soln.)	(g)	(l)
propylene	20·2[b]	29·72	29·8			20·6	20·05
butene-1	21·2	30·12	30·29	28·29	26·9	20·6	20·0
hexene-1	20·7	30·00	30·2			20·5	19·8
hexadecene-1	19·9[c]	30·00					
trans-butene-2	18·7	27·48	27·76			18·1	17·0
cis-butene-2	20·2	28·48	28·91			19·1	17·9
cyclopentene	21·65	26·33	26·44	28·6	25·8		

[a] Taken from Dainton and Ivin.[143]
[b] Polymer insoluble in reaction mixture.
[c] In chloroform solution.

for the heats of self-polymerization, which are calculated values and take no account of steric effects in the polymer, all the values shown in Table 5 were obtained experimentally.

Except in the case of cyclopentene there is good correlation between the values, in so far as there is a similar trend along the series in each case. For cyclopentene, the heat of co-polymerization is 4–5 kcal/mole higher than might have been expected from the heat of hydrogenation. The reason for this high value might be that the presence of the five-membered rings in some way enables the cyclopentene polysulphone to take up energetically more favourable conformations which are denied to other polysulphones, i.e. it is supposed that there exists a considerable amount of interaction between non-bonded atoms in the polysulphones of olefins other than cyclopentene.

It is of interest to compare the relative heat contents of the isomeric solid polysulphones with those of the isomeric liquid heptanes:[30]

```
        C              C  C
        |              |  |
C—C—C—C—C      C—C—C—C—C      C—C—C—C—C—C—C
        |
        C
```

ΔH_f^0(l): $-56{\cdot}07$ $\quad$ $-55{\cdot}81$ $\quad$ $-53{\cdot}71$ kcal/mole.

In these, as in other isomeric paraffins, the isomer containing the quaternary carbon atom has the lowest enthalpy. This is in contrast with the isomeric polysulphones, where it is that of isobutene which has the highest enthalpy, presumably because of steric hindrance between the oxygen atoms and the methyl groups.

```
   ┌ C    O ┐     ┌ C  C  O ┐     ┌                O ┐
   │ |    ‖ │     │ |  |  ‖ │     │                ‖ │
— │—C—C—S—│ —  — │—C—C—S—│ —  — │—C—C—C—C—S—│ —
   │ |    ‖ │     │       ‖ │     │                ‖ │
   └ C    O ┘     └       O ┘     └                O ┘
```

ΔH_f^0(solid, amorph.):
$-101{\cdot}3$ $\quad$ $-100{\cdot}3$ $\quad$ $-101{\cdot}5$ kcal/mole of monomer unit.

Other heats of co-polymerization which are available include those between vinyl acetate and the two isomers diethyl fumarate and diethyl maleate. If the co-polymers derived in these two cases are identical, then the difference between their heats of co-polymerization should be equal to the heat of isomerization of diethyl maleate to diethyl fumarate. Williams[145] has measured the heats of hydrogenation of the two isomers in solution as $-33{\cdot}5 \pm 0{\cdot}1$ and $-29{\cdot}3 \pm 0{\cdot}1$ kcal/mole, respectively, so that the heat of isomerization is $-4{\cdot}2 \pm 0{\cdot}2$ kcal/mole. The observed difference between the heats of co-polymerization is $-1{\cdot}6 \pm 0{\cdot}5$ kcal/mole. The difference of $2{\cdot}6 \pm 0{\cdot}7$ kcal/mole between this value and the heat of isomerization is well outside the combined experimental error. This difference might be accountable in terms of different heats of mixing of the monomers in the two systems, and differences in heats of solution in the hydrogenation reactions. On the other hand it may indicate that the vinyl acetate/diethyl maleate and vinyl acetate/diethyl fumarate polymers are not structurally identical. There are four possible arrangements which can be adopted on co-polymerization:

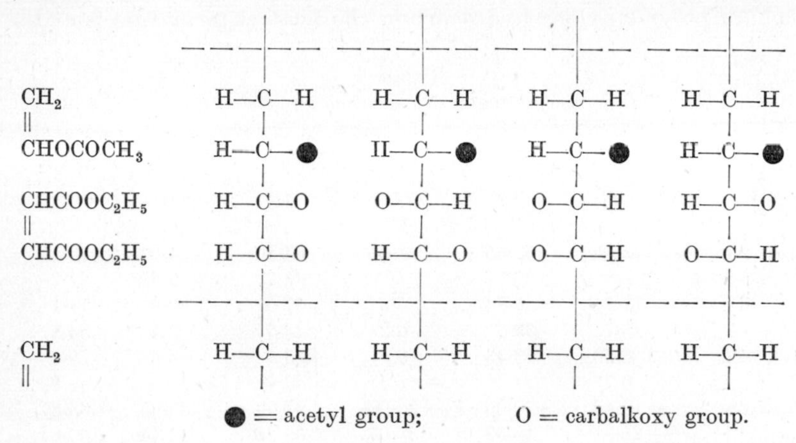

It may be that fumarates and maleates can lead to products where different arrangements predominate, and their interactions may give rise to slight differences in energy content.

Polymerization of Cyclic Compounds

1. Cyclo-alkanes

The cyclic compounds for which most data are available are the cyclo-alkanes. Dainton, Devlin and Small [133] have calculated the change in heat and in free energy for the polymerization to linear polymers of unsubstituted and substituted cyclo-alkanes, viz.,

$$\text{cyclo}(\mathrm{CH_2})_x(\mathrm{l}) \rightarrow 1/n[(\text{—}\mathrm{CH_2}\text{—}\mathrm{CH_2}\ldots\mathrm{CH_2}\text{—})_x]_n(\mathrm{c})$$

$$\text{cyclo}\mathrm{CH_3CH}<[\mathrm{CH_2}]_{x-1}(\mathrm{l}) \rightarrow 1/n[(\text{—}\mathrm{C(CH_3)}\text{—}\mathrm{CH_2}\ldots\mathrm{CH_2}\text{—})_x]_n\ (\mathrm{c})$$

$$\text{cyclo}(\mathrm{CH_3})_2\mathrm{C}<[\mathrm{CH_2}]_{x-1}(\mathrm{l}) \rightarrow 1/n[(\text{—}\mathrm{C(CH_3)_2}\text{—}\mathrm{CH_2}\ldots\mathrm{CH_2}\text{—})_x]_n\,(\mathrm{c})$$

For the straight chain hydrocarbons, C_nH_{2n+2}, the heat of formation in the gaseous state at a given temperature may be represented by a relation of the form [146]

$$\Delta H_f^0 = A + Bn + \Delta,$$

where A and B are constants, and Δ is a 'deviation term' which tends to zero for $n > 6$, and is large for $n = 1$. For these hydrocarbons, we have $A = -15{\cdot}334$, $B = -4{\cdot}926$, and Δ values as follows: $n = 1$, $-2{\cdot}555$; $n = 2$, $+0{\cdot}024$; $n = 3$, $0{\cdot}366$; $n = 4$, $-0{\cdot}038$; $n = 5$, $+0{\cdot}004$; $n = 6$, $0{\cdot}000$. Hence for a long, straight chain polymethylene hydrocarbon the heat of formation per CH_2

TABLE 6

Heats and entropies of formation of cyclo-alkanes[a]

x	$(CH_2)_x$		$(CH_2)_{x-1}CHCH_3$		$(CH_2)_{x-1}C(CH_3)_2$	
	ΔH_f^0	ΔS^0	ΔH_f^0	ΔS^0	ΔH_f^0	ΔS^0
2 g	12·50	52·45	4·88	63·80	−4·04	70·17
1	—	—	*1·2*	*47·2*	*−9·0*	*51·7*
3 g	12·74	56·84	*5·5*	67·6	2·6	74·1
1	8·7	*39·6*	*0·2*	*48·6*	8·4	54·5
4 g	6·26	63·43	*−0·8*	*73·9*	*−8·6*	*79·4*
1	0·7	*44·1*	*−7·1*	*53·4*	*−15·6*	*57·9*
5 g	−18·46	70·00	−25·00	81·24	−33·05	85·87
1	−25·31	48·82	−33·07	59·26	−41·14	63·84
6 g	−29·43	71·28	−36·99	82·06	−43·26	87·24
1	−37·34	48·85	−45·45	59·26	−52·31	63·89
7 g	−28·63	*79·3*				
1	−37·7	*54·8*				
8 g	−29·81	*79·7*				
1	−40·5	*53·0*	Values in italics are estimated			

[a] Taken from Dainton, Devlin and Small.[133]

unit, is $-4{\cdot}926$ kcal. In a similar way, Person and Pimentel[147] have calculated the increment in S^0 per CH_2 group in straight chain hydrocarbons as 9·309 cal/deg.

To estimate the heats of formation and entropies of branched paraffins, "branching factors" may be defined. For the heat of formation, the factor r_H is defined by

$$r_H = \Delta H_f^0 \text{ (branched isomer)} - \Delta H_f^0 \text{ (normal paraffin)}.$$

Using data from the American Petroleum Institute Research Project 44,[30] and extrapolating to the limit of infinitely long chains, values were obtained for the effects of the branching —$CH(CH_3)$— and —$C(CH_3)_2$—, occurring every third, fourth, fifth, or sixth carbon atom. By incorporating heats and entropies of vaporization of long chain hydrocarbons, derived by extrapolation of the known values for the smaller hydrocarbons, it is possible to estimate heats and entropies of formation of the liquid polymers.

The heats of formation and entropies of unsubstituted cycloparaffins up to cyclohexane are known,[30] and the heats of for-

TABLE 7

Heats, entropies and free energies of polymerization[a] *of cyclo-alkanes*[b]

Cyclo-alkane	ΔH^0 (kcal/mole)	ΔS^0 (cal/deg mole)	ΔG^0 (kcal/mole)
$\llcorner CH_2]_x$			
$x = 3$	$-27{\cdot}0$	$-16{\cdot}5$	$-22{\cdot}1$
4	$-25{\cdot}1$	$-13{\cdot}2$	$-21{\cdot}2$
5	$-5{\cdot}2$	$-10{\cdot}2$	$-2{\cdot}2$
6	$0{\cdot}7$	$-2{\cdot}5$	$1{\cdot}4$
7	$-5{\cdot}1$	$-3{\cdot}8$[c]	$-3{\cdot}9$
8	$-8{\cdot}3$	$-0{\cdot}8$[c]	$-8{\cdot}2$
$CH_3{\cdot}CH < [CH_2]_{x-1}$			
$x = 3$	$-25{\cdot}1$	$-20{\cdot}2$	$-19{\cdot}1$
4	$-23{\cdot}9$	$-17{\cdot}2$	$-18{\cdot}8$
5	$-4{\cdot}1$	$-15{\cdot}3$	$0{\cdot}5$
6	$2{\cdot}2$	$-7{\cdot}6$	$4{\cdot}5$
$(CH_3)_2{\cdot}C < [CH_2]_{x-1}$			
$x = 3$	$-23{\cdot}3$	$-22{\cdot}3$	$-16{\cdot}6$
4	$-22{\cdot}3$	$-18{\cdot}0$	$-16{\cdot}0$
5	$-3{\cdot}2$	$-15{\cdot}7$	$1{\cdot}5$
6	$1{\cdot}8$	$-8{\cdot}5$	$4{\cdot}3$

[a] Refers to the process monomer (liquid) → polymer (crystalline).
[b] Taken from Dainton and Ivin.[119]
[c] Finke *et al.*[90]

mation of the seven-, eight- and nine-ring compounds are available.[31] There are no data for the methyl and 1,1-dimethyl substituted cyclopropanes or cyclobutanes, and the entropies of the higher unsubstituted cycloparaffins have not yet been measured. Values of the heats of formation of the substituted three- and four-rings were obtained by interpolation, and entropies of the higher unsubstituted cycloparaffins were obtained by extrapolation. These data for the cyclo-alkanes are summarized in Table 6.

Using these heats of formation of monomer and polymer the heats and entropies of polymerization can be calculated. These ΔH and ΔS values, (Table 7) show that ΔH makes the main contribution to ΔG for three- and four-membered rings, but that for five-, six- and seven-membered rings the heat and entropy contributions are equally important.

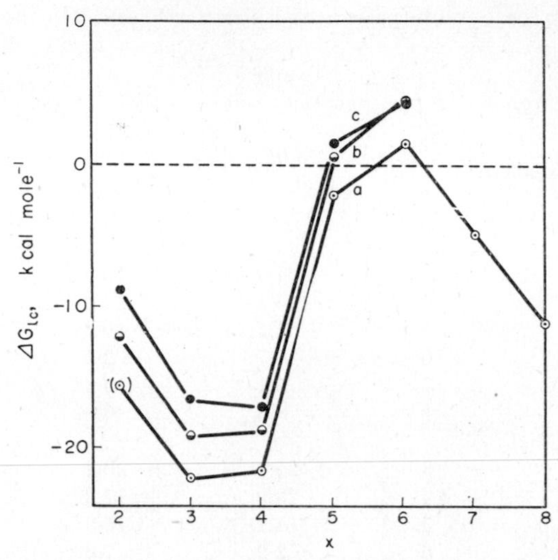

Fig. 1. Polymerization of cyclo-alkanes. Plot of free energies against ring size. (a) unsubstituted; (b) methyl substituted; (c) 1,1-dimethyl substituted (taken from Dainton and Ivin, ref. 119).

From a qualitative point of view, the ring strain in three- and four-membered carbon ring system is large; it is small in five- and six-membered rings, and then increases with further increase in ring size. These changes are mirrored in the ΔH polymerization values. On the other hand, entropy changes do not show this marked dependence on ring strain, but are susceptible to configurational influence.

A plot of the resultant ΔG, against ring size is shown in Fig. 1, and from this it is seen that it is impossible (ΔG is positive) to polymerize cyclohexanes, methylcyclopentane, or 1,1-dimethylcyclopentane, at 25 °C. Although in these cases the ΔS values are less negative than for the three- and four-membered ring polymerizations, the ΔH values are insufficiently negative to produce negative ΔG values.

For the three- and four-membered rings, ΔG values are more negative than for the corresponding "two-membered ring systems" (ethylene, propylene, and isobutene). This is mainly because of the more negative ΔH values for $x = 3$, or 4, due to the strain in the ring system.

No values for ΔG have yet been calculated for $x = 8$, or more. However, stereochemical theory suggests that when x exceeds 5, any strain in the monomer, due to distortion of the carbon valency angles, can be avoided by the molecules adopting one of certain configurations, the number of which increases as x increases. For the values of x between 6 and 11, these configurations usually involve some repulsive interaction between hydrogen atoms, many of which lie within the ring of carbon atoms. Above $x = 12$, this steric effect is absent. It would therefore be expected that above $x = 6$, ΔH would become more negative, pass through a shallow minimum and then increase to a limiting value. In view of the lower structure sensitivity of ΔS, the ΔG values might show a dependence on x which is qualitatively similar to that of ΔH.

2. *Heterocyclic Compounds*

Small [148] has considered the effects of ring size on the heats, free energies and entropies of polymerization of heterocyclic compounds in which the hetero atom is either nitrogen or oxygen. Because of the similar size of carbon, nitrogen and oxygen, and the similar bond angles involved, replacement of a carbon atom by either of these two hetero atoms produces only small changes in the thermodynamic quantities. Although few free energy and entropy data are available for these compounds, a number of heats of polymerization are known, and some of these are shown in Table 8.

The variation in the heat of polymerization of cyclic mono-ethers is similar to that found for the cyclo-alkanes, in that the values become less negative as the ring size increases, $x = 3$, 4, to 5, becoming positive at $x = 6$. The values are shown in Table 9, together with the difference between the heats of polymerization of cyclo-alkanes and cyclo-ethers having the same number of atoms in the ring. The difference is large for the three- and four-membered rings where the effect of introducing an oxygen atom into the ring is to reduce strain considerably. For the five-membered ring the difference is small, and almost zero for the six-membered strainless rings. The heats of polymerization of the cyclic di-ethers, the formals, also follow the same pattern as the cyclo-

TABLE 8

Heats of polymerization of heterocyclic compounds

Compound	No. atoms in ring	ΔH^0 kcal/mole	Ref
Ethers			
$O<(CH_2, CH_2)>(CH_2)_n$			
ethylene oxide, $n = 0$	3	$-22{\cdot}6$ (lc′)[b]	(149)
trimethylene oxide, $n = 1$	4	$-19{\cdot}3$ (ss)	(150)
tetrahydrofuran, $n = 2$	5	$-\ 3{\cdot}5$[a] (lc)	(151)
tetrahydropyran, $n = 3$	6	$+\ 1{\cdot}3$[a] (lc)	(36, 151)
$CH_2<(O—CH_2, O—CH_2)>(CH_2)_n$			
dimethylene formal, $n = 0$ (1,3-dioxolan)	5	$-\ 6{\cdot}2$ (lc)	(151)
trimethylene formal, $n = 1$ (1,3-dioxan)	6	$0{\cdot}0$ (lc)	(151)
tetramethylene formal, $n = 2$	7	$-\ 4{\cdot}7$ (lc)	(151)
pentamethylene formal, $n = 3$	8	$-12{\cdot}8$ (lc)	(151)
$O<(CH_2, CH_2)>CR_2$			
3,3-dimethyl-1-oxacyclobutane, $R = CH_3$	4	$-16{\cdot}1$ (ss)	(150)
3,3-bis(chloromethyl)-1-oxacyclobutane, $R = CH_2Cl$	4	$-15{\cdot}0$ (ss)	(152)
Disulphides			
$S—CH_2$ / $S—CH_2$ $>(CH_2)_n$ (S–S bonded)			
tetramethylene disulphide, $n = 2$	6	$-\ 0{\cdot}5$ (lc)[b]	(122)
pentamethylene disulphide, $n = 3$	7	$-\ 2{\cdot}5$ (lc)	(122)
hexamethylene disulphide, $n = 4$	8	$-\ 3{\cdot}8$ (lc)	(122)
$S—CH_2—CH_2$ / $S—CH_2—CH_2$ $>O$ (S–S bonded)			
1-oxa-4,5-dithiacycloheptane	7	$-\ 1{\cdot}9$ (lc)	(153)

[a] Estimated from heats of combustion of monomer.

[b] Denotes monomer and polymer states: l, liquid; s, solution; c, condensed (liquid or amorphous solid); c′, crystalline.

Table 8 (cont.)

Compound	No. atoms in ring	ΔH^0 kcal/mole	Ref
Amides			
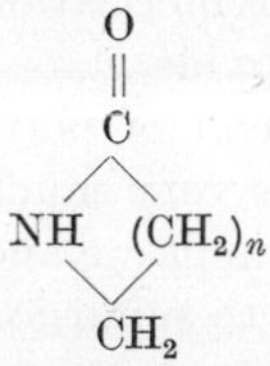 O=C—NH—$(CH_2)_n$—CH_2 (ring)			
pyrrolidone, $n = 2$	5	− 1·1 (lc)	(154)
5-valerolactam, $n = 3$	6	− 2·2 (lc)	(154)
6-hexanolactam, $n = 4$	7	− 3·8 (lc)	(154)
7-heptanolactam, $n = 5$	8	− 5·3 (lc)	(154)
Siloxanes			
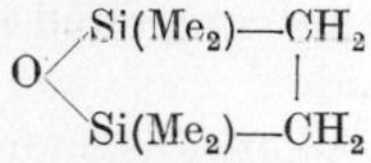 O<$Si(Me_2)$—CH_2, $Si(Me_2)$—CH_2 (ring)			
2,2,5,5-tetramethyl-1-oxa-2,5-disilacyclopentane	5	− 10·0 (lc)	(155)
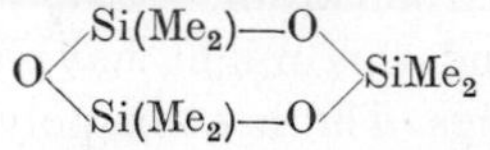 O<$Si(Me_2)$—O, $Si(Me_2)$—O>$SiMe_2$ (ring)			
hexamethyltrisiloxane	6	− 3·5 (lc)	(155)

TABLE 9

Comparison of heats of polymerization cyclo-alkanes and cyclic mono-ethers (kcal/mole)

Ring size, x	3	4	5	6
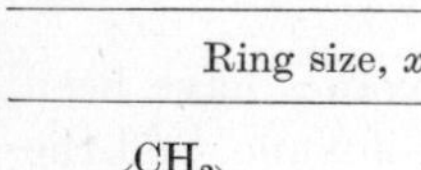 CH_2<(CH_2, CH_2)>$(CH_2)_n$, ΔH	− 27·0	− 25·1	− 5·2	+ 0·7
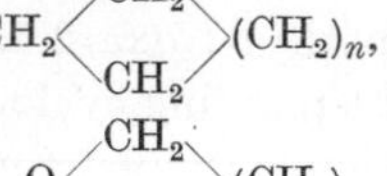 O<(CH_2, CH_2)>$(CH_2)_n$, ΔH	− 22·6	− 19·3[a]	− 3·5	+ 1·3
Difference, $\Delta/\Delta H$	4·4	5·8	1·7	0·6

[a] Monomer, solution → polymer solution.

alkanes, becoming increasingly more negative as the ring size increases, $x = 6$, 7 to 8.

Substitution of extra-annular hydrogen atoms of the cyclic mono-ethers seems to have the same effect on the heat of polymerization as it does in the case of the cyclo-alkanes. Thus, for the 3,3-disubstituted-1-oxacyclobutanes the heats of polymerization are less than for the parent compound, trimethylene oxide.

For the cyclic disulphides, the variation in the heat of polymerization, in passing from $x = 6$, through 7, to 8, is very much less than for the corresponding cyclo-alkanes. In cycloheptane and cyclo-octane, there is a certain amount of strain due to repulsion between hydrogen atoms inside the ring. With the replacement of two carbon atoms by larger sulphur atoms, the ring size is expanded, and repulsion between non-bonded atoms is reduced. The introduction of a third hetero atom into the seven-membered ring, to give 1-oxa-4,5-dithiacycloheptane, reduces the strain energy even more, so that the heat of polymerization of this compound is less negative than that of pentamethylene disulphide.

A comparison of the lactams with the cyclo-alkanes is more difficult, since here there is not only a substitution by a nitrogen atom, but also replacement of an sp^3 hybrid carbon atom, —CH_2—, by an sp^2 hybrid carbon atom, —CO—, and this might have a considerable effect on the strain in some rings. The heat of polymerization of the lactams becomes steadily more negative as the ring size increases from five-, through six- and seven-, to eight-membered rings. The change is much less than for the corresponding cyclo-alkane series. The pattern is more like that for the cyclic disulphides. Again, it seems reasonable to suppose that the strain in these lactams is very much less than in the corresponding cyclo-alkanes.

The heats of polymerization of two cyclic siloxanes have been measured: the six-membered ring, hexamethyltrisiloxane, and the five-membered "paraffin-siloxane", 2,2,5,5-tetramethyl-1-oxa-2,5-disilacyclopentane (shown in Table 8.) For the corresponding cyclopentane the heat of polymerization is $-5{\cdot}2$ kcal/mole, whilst for the "paraffin-siloxane" it is $-10{\cdot}0$ kcal/mole. Thus, the effect of replacement of —$(CH_2)_3$— by —$Si(Me_2)$—O—$Si(Me_2)$— in the cyclopentane molecule appears to either increase the ring strain in the monomer, or to stabilize the polymer, to the extent of some

5 kcal/mole of monomer. Replacement of —CH_2— by —O— in the cyclopentane molecule reduces the heat of polymerization from $-5{\cdot}2$ to $-3{\cdot}5$ kcal/mole, and the replacement of —CH_2— by —$C(Me_2)$— in cyclopentane also reduces the heat of polymerization to $-3{\cdot}2$ kcal/mole. These figures suggest that strain in the five-membered ring is reduced either by the introduction of an oxygen atom or by methyl substitution of the hydrogen atoms. Whilst this is not necessarily the case for the paraffin-siloxane molecule, it appears that the increased heat of polymerization of this molecule is due rather to stabilization of the polymer.

A similar effect is seen in the larger heat of polymerization of hexamethyltrisiloxane ($-3{\cdot}5$ kcal) compared with that of cyclohexane ($+0{\cdot}7$ kcal). Again this might be interpreted as due to stabilization of the polymer due to increased possibility of electron delocalization involving $d_\pi - p_\pi$ bonding. This idea will be considered in some greater detail in a later chapter.

CHAPTER 6

MOLECULAR ADDITION COMPOUNDS

Introduction

The heats of two different types of addition reactions have been presented in the preceding chapters; hydrogenation and polymerization. A considerable amount of thermochemical data is also available for another type of addition reaction, in which molecular addition compounds are formed.

Before examining the results of some of these investigations, it would be well to consider briefly the nature of the co-ordinate link in different types of donor-acceptor compounds. This has been discussed in terms of the molecular orbital theory by Mulliken.[156] In the simplest case, the $D \rightarrow A$ linkage is regarded as a resonance hybrid built up from a 'no-bond' structure, (D, A), and an electron transfer structure, $(\overset{+}{D} - \overset{-}{A})$. Thus, for the compound DA, the wave function ψ_N of the ground state is described by

$$\psi_N = a\psi_0(D, A) + b\psi_1(\overset{+}{D} - \overset{-}{A}).$$

In this equation ψ_0 is the no-bond wave function and ψ_1 is the donor wave function corresponding to complete transfer of an electron from D to A. In the more stable addition compounds, the second term, involving ψ_1, predominates.

Two important classes of neutral molecule donors are the weak π-donors (unsaturated or aromatic hydrocarbons, etc.) and the often strong n- (or 'onium) donors, NR_3, OR_2, etc. For π-donors, the donated electrons in the structure $\overset{+}{D} - \overset{-}{A}$ derive from a bonding molecular orbital; for n-donors, from a non-bonding molecular orbital, occupied in the original donor by a lone pair of electrons. Neutral molecule acceptors include π-acceptors, such as nitroaromatic compounds, maleic anhydride, etc., which combine especially with π-donors to form loose complexes. Much more stable complexes are formed between v-(vacant orbital) acceptors, such as BX_3, BR_3, AlX_3, InX_3, etc., and the n-donors NR_3, SR_2, etc.

The relative stability of molecular addition compounds of the donor-acceptor type has been widely studied. H. C. Brown[157] and his co-workers have carried out a great deal of work on boron addition compounds, with a view to establishing the magnitude of steric interaction energies. Other workers[158,159] have investigated gallium, indium, and thallium addition compounds to elucidate additional factors which affect relative acceptor, and donor properties.

Two main experimental methods have been used for these investigations:

(a) Dissociation pressures are measured, over a suitable temperature range, of the equilibrium, $DA = D + A$, in the gas phase, where D and A are the donor and acceptor molecules. From the variation of $\log K_p$ with $1/T$, heats of dissociation are derived.

(b) Direct calorimetric measurements of the heats of reaction $D + A = DA$, or alternatively, the heat of decomposition of DA into specified products, are made.

Since many of the Group III addition compounds are volatile, easily dissociated compounds, the "high-temperature bulb" vapour pressure apparatus of Burg and Schlesinger[160] has proved well suited to studies of dissociation equilibria. Direct calorimetric measurements have generally been made in simple Dewar-vessel calorimeters.

Since the electron transfer structure $\overset{+}{D} - \overset{-}{A}$ is of such importance in bonding donor and acceptor molecules, one might conclude that two of the most important factors influencing the strength of $D \rightarrow A$ bonds are ionization potential of the donor molecule and electron affinity of the acceptor molecule. These quantities might also be considered as an absolute measure of donor and acceptor strength, in the sense that donor power is aided by low ionization potential and acceptor power by high electron affinity.

Steric and Inductive Effects

In Table 1, the heats of addition reactions are shown for four series of compounds. The first series (*a*) is for the reactions between boron trimethyl and either ammonia or the methylamines, and shows the steady rise in $-\Delta H$ values, along the series ammonia, methylamine, dimethylamine with a fall on passing from dimethylamine to trimethylamine.

TABLE 1

Heats of addition reactions. Boron compounds with amines and ethers

Compound	$-\Delta H$ kcal/mole	Compound	$-\Delta H$ kcal/mole
(*a*)		(*b*)	
$H_3N \cdot BMe_3$	13·75	$H_3N \cdot BMe_3$	13·75
$MeNH_2 \cdot BMe_3$	17·64	$EtNH_2 \cdot BMe_3$	18·00
$Me_2NH \cdot BMe_3$	19·26	$Et_2NH \cdot BMe_3$	16·31
$Me_3N \cdot BMe_3$	17·62	$Et_3N \cdot BMe_3$	10
		(Quinuclidine)·BMe_3	19·94
(*c*)		(*d*)	
$Me_2O \cdot BF_3$	13·3[161 162]	$Me_3N \cdot BMe_3$	17·6
$Et_2O \cdot BF_3$	10·9[161]	$Me_3N \cdot BHMe_2$	23·6
(Tetrahydrofuran)·BF_3	13·4	$Me_3N \cdot BH_2Me$	Not known
		$Me_3N \cdot BH_3$[a]	31·5

Data from ref. 157 except where otherwise indicated.

[a] The heat actually measured was for the reaction $Me_3N + \frac{1}{2}(B_2H_6)$. The figure quoted is calculated from this by inclusion of 14·2 kcal/mole for the dissociation process $\frac{1}{2}(B_2H_6) = BH_3$.

The increase in $-\Delta H$ values can be ascribed to the inductive, electron-releasing tendency of the methyl group. Fig. 1, taken from a paper by McCoy and Bauer[163] shows a plot of these heats against the degree of methyl substitution, and also of the ionization potentials of ammonia and the amines. It is seen that replacement of a hydrogen atom in ammonia by a methyl group causes a *decrease* in ionization potential. Substitution of a second hydrogen atom produces about half the effect, and thereafter the change becomes linear. As far as dimethylamine there is a striking parallel between the ionization potential and the heat of addition to boron trimethyl, due to the inductive effect. The decrease in $-\Delta H$ on passing from dimethylamine to trimethylamine is presumably caused by steric effects, due to the bulky trimethylamine molecule. Much the same trends are shown for the addition compounds of diborane with ammonia and the amines.

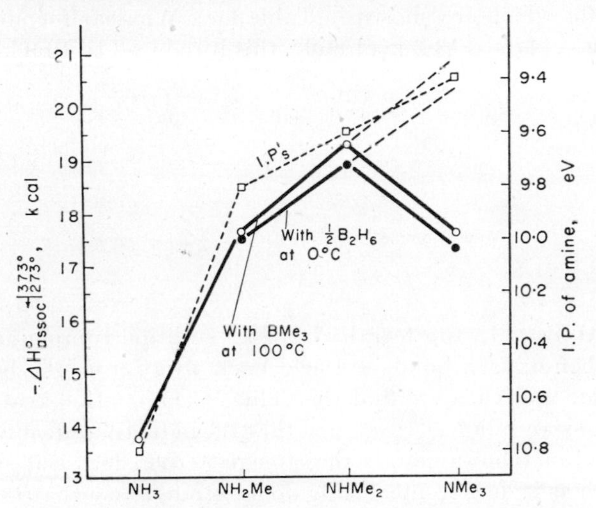

FIG. 1. Ionization potentials and heats of addition reactions of substituted amines. (taken from McCoy and Bauer, ref. 163).

In the addition compounds formed between boron trimethyl and the ethylamines (*b*), the steric effect is more marked. The heat of addition of boron trimethyl to diethylamine ($-\Delta H = 16{\cdot}31$ kcal) is less then the heat of addition to ethylamine ($-\Delta H = 18{\cdot}0$ kcal). The heat of addition to triethylamine ($-\Delta H = 10$ kcal) is very much less, presumably because the steric requirements of three ethyl groups are much larger than those of three methyl groups, resulting in much greater strain in the triethylamine compound. An examination of molecular models, Fig. 2, shows that it is possible to rotate only two of three ethyl groups out of the way of the boron trimethyl molecule, so that some interference from one ethyl group must occur on forming the addition compound.

On the other hand, for the addition of quinuclidine to boron trimethyl we have $-\Delta H = 19{\cdot}94$ kcal/mole, which is the highest heat observed for any tertiary amine. In the quinuclidine compound there is no steric hindrance to the approach of the acceptor molecule, because the carbon-nitrogen bonds are "pinned back", away from the boron trimethyl molecule. Consequently, steric strains are much reduced.

The same effect is seen in the boron trifluoride etherates, ΔH values for which are shown in Table 1 (*c*). Whereas for $Me_2O \cdot BF_3$ we have $-\Delta H = 13{\cdot}3$ kcal/mole, this is reduced to 10·9 kcal/mole

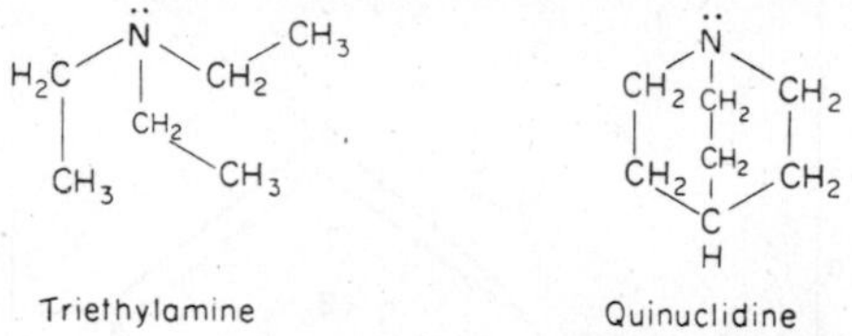

Triethylamine Quinuclidine

FIG. 2.

for $Et_2O \cdot BF_3$. In the tetrahydrofuran addition compound, where the carbon-oxygen bonds are held back, away from the boron trifluoridine molecule, we find the value $-\Delta H = 13{\cdot}6$ kcal/mole.

McCoy and Bauer[163] suggest that the inductive effect in methyl substitution follows exactly the same pattern in decreasing acceptor strength as it does in increasing donor strength, so that the acceptor strength should decrease in the order $BH_3 > BH_2Me > BHMe_2 > BMe_3$. $-\Delta H$ values for the reaction between these compounds and trimethylamine, are shown in Table 1 (*d*). In the absence of steric strain in the compound $Me_3N \cdot BMe_3$ the $-\Delta H$ value would probably be increased from 17·6 to about 25·4 kcal/mole.[164] There is less strain in the compound $Me_3N \cdot BHMe_2$, and the "correction" to be applied for strain energy would probably be some 4 kcal in this case, so that the $-\Delta H$ value would be about 28·0 kcal/mole for the unstrained compound. The values for both of these methyl substituted borines are less than for the borine group itself in the compound $Me_3N \cdot BH_3$, for which we have $-\Delta H = 31{\cdot}5$ kcal/mole. From these figures it appears that BH_3 is a better acceptor than BMe_3.

Another example of the effects of steric strain is seen in the heats of reaction (in nitrobenzene solution) of pyridines with various boron acceptors. The data are shown in Table 2. Although it is preferable to have heats of addition for gas phase reactions, we are interested here only on *differences* of heats, and in other cases, where both gas phase and nitrobenzene solution heats have been measured, the differences have been found much the same.

The effect of introducing a methyl group into pyridine to give 2-picoline, and a second to give 2,6-lutidine is to increase the pk_a value by a regular increment. The increase is attributed to the inductive effect of the methyl group. Likewise the heat of reaction with methane sulphonic acid shows a regular increase. In both cases a proton is added, the steric requirements of which are small, and the increased basic strength results from the presence of one, or two methyl groups. The heat of addition to diborane shows a slight decrease along the series, due to steric interaction between BH_3 and Me groups. With the increasing steric requirements of BF_3 and BMe_3, the strains become larger and the observed heats drop sharply. Trimethylboron fails to add to 2,6-lutidine, despite its being a stronger base than pyridine.

TABLE 2

Heats of addition reactions. Boron compounds with pyridines[a]

		Pyridine (N)	CH_3-substituted (2-picoline)	CH_3, CH_3 (2,6-lutidine)
	pk_a	5·17	5·97	6·75
$-\Delta H$	$MeSO_3H$	17·1	18·3	19·5
	$\frac{1}{2}(B_2H_6)$	17·9	17·2	16·3
	BF_3	25·0	23·2	17·5
	BMe_3	15·3	9·95	—

[a] At 22°C in nitrobenzene solution: donor (soln.) + acceptor (soln.) → product (soln.). Taken from Brown.[157]

Acceptor Molecules: π-Bonding

It has been suggested that the decreasing acceptor strength along the series $BH_3 > BH_2Me > BHMe_2 > BMe_3$ is due to the inductive or electron-releasing effect of the methyl group. Perhaps it is more revealing to say that in the boron trimethyl molecule there is a certain amount of π-bonding, due to delocalization of the bonding electrons of the methyl group to the vacant $2p$-orbital of the boron atom. This strengthens the bonding in boron trimethyl in a way not possible in the borine group, BH_3. For co-ordination to occur, the molecule must be in an sp^3 state of hybridization and less energy will be required for the reorganization $Bsp^2 \rightarrow Bsp^3$ in BH_3 than in BMe_3, since in this latter molecule the π-bonding must be destroyed.

TABLE 3

Heats of addition reactions. Boron and aluminium halides

Compound	$-\Delta H$ kcal/mole	Compound	$-\Delta H$ kcal/mole
(*a*) $C_5H_5N \cdot BF_3$	34·2[a] (91)[b]	(c) $C_5H_5N \cdot AlCl_3$	68·3[c] (99·9)[b]
$\cdot BCl_3$	45·2 (84)	$\cdot AlBr_3$	63·4 (91·7)
$\cdot BBr_3$	51·8 (86·5)	$\cdot AlI_3$	63·4 (82·6)
(*b*) $C_5H_5N \cdot BCl_3$	40·7[d]	$Me_3N \cdot AlCl_3$	64·5
$\cdot BBr_3$	52·9	$\cdot AlBr_3$	61·7
		$\cdot AlI_3$	62·2
$C_5H_{10}NH \cdot BCl_3$	84·0	$H_3N \cdot AlCl_3$	60·0
$\cdot BBr_3$	121·3	$\cdot AlBr_3$	62·0
		$\cdot AlI_3$	55·4

[a] $C_5H_5N(soln) + BX_3(g) = C_5H_5N \cdot BX_3(soln)$, in nitrobenzene.
[b] Refers to "intrinsic" heats of addition.
[c] $RN(g) + AlX_3(g) = RN \cdot AlX_3(c)$.
[d] $RN(l) + BX_3(g) = RN \cdot BX_3(c)$.

Such an approach has been made, in detail, by Cotton and Leto[(165)] to explain relative acceptor strengths of the boron and aluminium halides, BF_3, BCl_3, BBr_3; and $AlCl_3$, $AlBr_3$ and AlI_3. Stone[(166)] has summarized the available thermochemical data for boron halide addition compounds, and this suggests that the order of relative acceptor power is $BBr_3 > BCl_3 > BF_3$, which is the *reverse* of that expected from electronegativity and steric considerations. The more electronegative fluorine should enable a greater charge transfer to take place in $\overset{+}{D} \rightarrow \overset{-}{B}F_3$ than in $\overset{+}{D} \rightarrow \overset{-}{B}Br_3$ and so produce stronger bonding in the boron trifluoride compound. Moreover, the bulky bromine atoms would produce more steric strain, in the addition compounds, than the small fluorine atoms.

The results of some of the calorimetric work which has been carried out to determine the relative order of acceptor strength are shown in Table 3. The order of acceptor strength for the boron halides is confirmed by the work of Brown and Holmes[167] who report the heats of reaction of pyridine with the three boron halides in nitrobenzene solution (*a*), and also by Greenwood[168] who measured heats of addition of boron trichloride, and boron tribromide to both pyridine and piperidine (*b*). The order of acceptor strength of the aluminium halides was established by Eley and Watts,[169] from measurements of the heats of addition of these halides to ammonia, trimethylamine and pyridine, (*c*). Although the data given in Table 3 do not refer to gas phase reactions, it is unlikely that the order of acceptor strength would be altered by correction to the gas phase.

The $-\Delta H$ values suggest that BF_3 is a much weaker acceptor than BCl_3, which, in turn, is considerably weaker than BBr_3 as an acceptor. In contrast to this trend, all the aluminium halides appear to be equally good acceptors, in that the $-\Delta H$ values differ by not more than 5 kcal/mole. However, from these figures it is not possible to show that BBr_3 is *intrinsically* a better acceptor than BF_3, since it may be that the reorganization energy of BBr_3 is very much lower than that of the chloride. Likewise the apparently equal acceptor strength of $AlBr_3$ and AlI_3 may be fortuitous, for it is possible that an *intrinsically* greater acceptor strength in $AlBr_3$ is offset by a larger reorganization energy, in comparison with AlI_3. Cotton and Leto[165] suggest that two factors are likely to predominate in the reorganization process. These are (i) the energy of breaking the π-bonds and (ii) the change in strength of the M—X bonds, when the hybrid state of the boron or aluminium atom changes. To establish the importance of these they first calculate the intrinsic dissociation energies, corresponding to the dissociation processes

$$BX_3(g) = B^*(g) + 3X^*(g),$$

and

$$AlX_3(g) = Al^*(g) + 3X^*(g).$$

The starred atoms refer to the boron and aluminium atoms in their valence state, the $sxy\ V_3$ state. It is unlikely that the halogen atoms will use pure p-bonding, i.e. be in the $s^2x^2y^2z$, V_1 state, but rather that a stronger bond, involving some sp hybridization will be used. The valence state $sx^2y^2z^2, V_1$ lies well above the state $s^2x^2y^2z, V_1$, in energy, and the amount of s character it is sensible to include is thus sharply limited by the rapid increase in promotion energy required, despite the generally superior overlaps obtained by using halogen hybrid orbitals with a limited admixture

TABLE 4[a]

Dissociation energies of boron halides to atoms in valence states

Process	BF_3	BCl_3	BBr_3
	(ΔH, kcal/mole)		
(*a*) $BX_3(g) = B(c) + \frac{3}{2}X_2(\text{g or l})$	265	98	45
(*b*) $B(c) = B(g)$	141	141	141
(*c*) $B(g) = B^*(g)$	127	127	127
(*d*) $\frac{3}{2}X_2(\text{g or l}) = 3X(g)$	55	87	80
(*e*) $3X(g) = 3X^*(g)$	85·9	42·2	39·1
Hence we obtain the relation, (*a*) +(*b*) + (*c*) + (*d*) + (*e*): $BX_3(g) = B^*(g) + 3X^*(g)$	674	495	432

[a] Taken from Cotton and Leto[(165)]:

(*a*) $\Delta H_f^0(BX_3, g)$ values from ref. 170, except $\Delta H_f^0(BCl_3, g) = 97{\cdot}5$ kcal/mole, recommended by Skinner and Smith[(171)].

(*b*) Ref. 172.

(*c*) B* denotes boron in valence state $sxy\ V_3$ state. Promotional energy from ref. 173.

(*d*) Ref. 170.

(*e*) X* denotes an *sp* hybrid state. Promotional energy from ref. 165.

of s-character. Allowance for s-character was made, therefore, using a simple minimum energy principle. The values used to calculate these *intrinsic* bond dissociation energies are shown in Tables 4 and 5.

The *intrinsic* dissociation energy, derived in this way, is then divided into a σ-bond energy and a π-bond energy (from the σ- and π-overlaps). The contribution to the reorganization energy, caused by the alteration in M—X σ-bond energy with change of the hybridization of the boron or aluminium atom, is relatively small in each case, being about 0·3 kcal/mole. It is estimated roughly by using the relative values of the σ-overlap in the two hybrid states of the atom. The final reorganization energies are listed in Table 6.

TABLE 5[a]

Dissociation energies of aluminium halides to atoms in valence states

	Process	$AlCl_3$	$AlBr_3$	AlI_3
		(ΔH, kcal/mole)		
(*a*)	$AlX_3(g) = \frac{1}{2}Al_2X_6(g)$	−14·5	−13·3	−11·3
	$\frac{1}{2}Al_2X_6(g) = \frac{1}{2}Al_2X_6(c)$	−13·5	−9·7	−12·1
(*b*)	$\frac{1}{2}Al_2X_6(c) = Al(c) + \frac{3}{2}X_2$(g or l)	+168·6	+125·8	+31·1
(*c*)	$Al(c) = Al(g)$	77·5	77·5	77·5
(*d*)	$\frac{3}{2}X_2$(g or l) $= 3X(g)$	87·0	80·1	76·4
(*e*)	$Al(g) = Al^*(g)$	107·2	107·2	107·2
(*f*)	$3X(g) = 3X^*(g)$	61·0	51·4	44·7
	Hence we obtain the relationship, (*a*) + (*b*) + (*c*) + (*d*) + (*e*) + (*f*): $AlX_3(g) = Al^*(g) + 3X^*(g)$	473	409	314

[a] Taken from Cotton and Letto [165].
(*a*) Ref. 174.
(*b*) $\Delta H_f^0(AlX_3, c)$; X = Cl, ref. 175; X = Br, ref. 170; X = I, ref. 172.
(*c*) Ref. 172.
(*d*) Ref. 170.
(*e*) Al* denotes $s^2x^2y^2z\ V_1$. Promotional energy from ref. 173.
(*f*) X* denotes an *sp* hybrid state. Promotional energy from ref. 165.

TABLE 6

Bond and reorganization energies in MX_3, kcal/mole

	BF_3	BCl_3	BBr_3	$AlCl_3$	$AlBr_3$	AlI_3
Total intrinsic bond dissociation energy	674	495	432	473	409	314
Total σ-bond energy	626	465	406	442	381	295
Total π-bond energy	48	30	26	31	28	19
Reorganization energy	48·3	30·3	26·2	31·6	28·3	19·2

These reorganization energies are the *sum* of the π-bond energies and the energy changes in the σ-bonds when the metal atom changes its hybridization from sp^2 to sp^3. The reorganization energy of BF_3 is some 18 kcal/mole greater than that of BCl_3. Unless the strength of a co-ordinate bond, of say an amine, is greater by this amount to BF_3 than to BCl_3, then BF_3 will be a weaker acceptor, at least as measured by the heat change accompanying the complex formation. The same type of argument applies to the series of aluminium halide complexes.

Confirmation of the relative amount of π-bonding in the boron halides is found in two other ways, (a) force constants and (b) bond lengths. According to Herzberg,[176] the force constants for the out-of-plane bending of the boron halides are in the ratio 0·87 for BF_3, 0·42 for BCl_3, and 0·29 for BBr_3. Certainly an important factor in determining the restoring force for such a distortion must be the B—X π-bonding, which is maximal in the planar equilibrium state. These constants are in the same order as the π-bond energies, $BF_3 > BCl_3 > BBr_3$.

If appreciable metal-halogen π-bonding is assumed to exist in the free, planar halide molecules, and to be eliminated in the complex halide, a corresponding increase in the metal-halogen bond distances should occur. In the case of BF_3, in which the greatest π-bonding has been calculated by Cotton and Leto, experimental results demonstrate a considerable lengthening of the B—F bonds in the complex molecules. In free boron trifluoride the B—F distance is $1·30 \pm 0·02$ Å whilst in several complexes of boron trifluoride with alkyl amines Hoard *et al.*[177] have reported B—F distances of 1·38 to 1·40 Å.

A somewhat similar situation is found in the donor molecules Me_3N and SiH_3Me_2N. Although there are no thermochemical data available, it has been shown qualitatively[178] that the complex $Me_3N \cdot BMe_3$ is much more stable than $SiH_3Me_2N \cdot BMe_3$. This can be ascribed to the greater reorganization energy required to quench the π-bonding in the silyldimethylamine, where there is the possibility of d_π-p_π-bonding between the silicon and nitrogen atoms.

With values for these reorganization energies for the boron and aluminium halides, it is now possible to calculate the intrinsic heats of addition reactions, that is the heat change if *no* energy were required to break the π-bonding in the acceptor molecule. These values are shown in Table 3, in parentheses, for the two series (*a*) and (*b*). They refer to the reactions $RN(g) + MX_3(g) = RN \cdot MX_3(c)$ To obtain the values for the series (*a*) it was assumed that the heats of solution of pyridine and the complex are the same, and the heat of vaporization of pyridine was taken as 8·5 kcal/mole. These intrinsic heats of addition show a decrease in acceptor strength along the series $BF_3 > BBr_3 \simeq BCl_3$, and also along the series $AlCl_3 > AlBr_3 > AlI_3$. Also, these intrinsic heats of addition show that aluminium trichloride is a better acceptor than boron trichloride. A similar order is found for the heats of addition of trimethylamine to the trialkyls of the Group III elements. The $-\Delta H$ values are as follows $Me_3N \cdot AlMe_3$, > 30 kcal;[158,179] $Me_3N \cdot BMe_3$, 17·62 kcal, or 26·6 kcal if compensation for strain is made;[157] $Me_3N \cdot GaMe_3$, 21·0 kcal; and $Me_3N \cdot InMe_3$, 19·9 kcal/mole.[158,179] Since there is likely to be much less reorganization energy for the trialkyl than for the trihalide compounds of these Group III elements the order of acceptor strength will probably be unchanged, i.e. Al > B > Ga > In.

Donor Molecules: Donor Strength and Reorganization Energy

Stone[166] has suggested that the reorganization energy of the *donor* molecule may be an important factor which affects the heats of addition reactions. Thus, for example, the heat of addition of boron trimethyl to trimethylamine ($-\Delta H = 17{\cdot}62$ kcal/mole) is only slightly greater than the heat of addition of boron trimethyl to trimethylphosphine ($-\Delta H = 16{\cdot}47$ kcal/mole).[157] Now it is likely that the steric strain in the compound $Me_3P \cdot BMe_3$ will be very much less than that in the corresponding $Me_3N \cdot BMe_3$, because of the longer phosphorus-boron bond length as compared with the length of the nitrogen-boron bond. The strain energy in the addition compound $Me_3N \cdot BMe_3$ has been estimated[164] as *ca.* 9 kcal/mole, so that if strainless addition compounds were formed in each case, the $-\Delta H$ value for the trimethylamine addition would be at least 10 kcal/mole greater than for the trimethylphosphine addition. Where steric requirements are less, as in the case of the compounds $Me_3N \cdot BF_3$ and $Me_3P \cdot BF_3$, the measured values[167] for $-\Delta H$ (~30·9 and 18·9 kcal/mole, respectively) differ by about 12 kcal/mole.

In these two cases, phosphorus is a weaker donor than nitrogen, to the extent of about 10–12 kcal/mole. The reason for this may lie in the larger reorganization energy which is required to prepare the phosphorus atom to enable it to form a co-ordinate link. In trimethylamine the nitrogen atom already has nearly sp^3 hybridization—the CNC angle is 109°—and little reorganization energy is required to prepare this molecule for addition to boron trimethyl.

By comparison, the CPC angle in trimethylphosphine is 100° which is consistent with much less *s* character in the bonding orbitals, and consequently greater reorganization energy.

The difference in these reorganization energies cannot wholly account for the variation of ~12 kcal in the heats of addition reactions. This variation must be, in part, due to a weaker σ-bond between phosphorus and boron atoms than between nitrogen and boron atoms. This can be shown from the heats of addition reactions between gallium trimethyl and either trimethylamine or trimethylphosphine. These heats are shown in Table 7, together with similar data for indium trimethyl.

TABLE 7

Heats of addition reactions. Boron, gallium and indium trimethyl

Compound	$-\Delta H$, kcal/mole	Compound	$-\Delta H$, kcal/mole
$Me_3N \cdot BMe_3$	17·62[157]	$Me_3N \cdot BF_3$	~30·9[167]
$Me_3P \cdot BMe_3$	16·47	$Me_3P \cdot BF_3$	18·9
$Me_3N \cdot GaMe_3$	21[a]	$Me_3N \cdot InMe_3$	19·9[158, 179]
$Me_3P \cdot GaMe_3$	18[158, 179]	$Me_3P \cdot InMe_3$	17·1
$Me_3As \cdot GaMe_3$	10		

[a] Coates and Hayter, unpublished results, quoted by Stone.[166]

Although there will be a certain amount of steric strain in the compound $Me_3N \cdot GaMe_3$, it should be very much less than in the corresponding $Me_3N \cdot BMe_3$. This is because the gallium atom is so much larger than the boron atom, so that there will be much less interaction between the methyl groups in the gallium addition compound. If we estimate this strain energy as *ca.* 3 kcal/mole (as compared with 9 kcal/mole for the boron addition compound $Me_3N \cdot BMe_3$), then the heat of the addition reaction in which an *unstrained* molecule $Me_3N \cdot GaMe_3$ was formed would be *ca.* 24 kcal/mole. This is only 6 kcal/mole greater than the heat of the addition reaction in which the phosphorus compound, $Me_3P \cdot GaMe_3$, is formed—where it is unlikely that there will be any steric strain. There can be very little strain in either of the two compounds $Me_3N \cdot InMe_3$ or $Me_3P \cdot InMe_3$, and here the difference between the two heats of addition is only 3 kcal/mole. To summarize: for the unstrained compounds the *difference* between the heats of addition of trimethylamine and trimethylphosphine to (a) boron trimethyl, (b) gallium trimethyl and (c) indium trimethyl are about 12, 6 and 3 kcal/mole, respectively. If the only factor affecting these heats was the reorganization energy of the donor molecule, these differences ought to be the same. The figures suggest that variations are partly due to nitrogen being intrinsically a better donor than phosphorus, and that the boron atom, as acceptor, is more able to exploit this tendency than either the gallium or indium atoms.

TABLE 8

Heats of addition reactions. Gallium trichloride[a]

Compound	$-\Delta H$, kcal/mole	Compound	$-\Delta H$, kcal/mole
$C_5H_5N \cdot GaCl_3$	29·7	$Et_2O \cdot GaCl_3 (l)$	9·3
$(C_5H_5N)_2 \cdot GaCl_3$	41·4		(Δ6·2)
$C_5H_{10}NH \cdot GaCl_3$	32·8	$(Et_2O)_2 \cdot GaCl_3 (l)$	15·5
$(C_5H_{10}NH)_2 \cdot GaCl_3$	54·3	$Cl_3PO \cdot GaCl_3$	10·2
$Cl_3P \cdot GaCl_3$	3·4	$Me_2CO \cdot GaCl_3$	15·3
$Cl_3As \cdot GaCl_3$	1·4	$MeC(Cl)O \cdot GaCl_3$	4·1

[a] Refers to reaction: donor (l) + $GaCl_3$(c) → complex (c), except where shown otherwise.

Greenwood [159, 168, 180, 181] has made a study of the heats of addition of a number of donors to gallium trichloride. The results are shown in Table 8. For the 1 : 1 complexes there is the expected decrease in donor strength along the series pyridine, phosphorus trichloride, arsenic trichloride, although it is uncertain to what extent this trend is influenced by reorganization energies of the donor molecules. The larger heat of co-ordination of piperidine to gallium trichloride, as compared with that for pyridine is in keeping with the greater availability of the lone electron pair on the nitrogen atom in the saturated heterocyclic system.

Only two values are available for these reactions in the gas phase: $Et_2O \cdot GaCl_3$, $-\Delta H = 22·3$, and $Cl_3PO \cdot GaCl_3$, $-\Delta H = 22·6$ kcal/mole. These imply that the oxygen atom in ether, or in phosphorus oxychloride, is a better donor by about 12 kcal/mole, than is the chlorine atom in dimeric gallium chloride itself. The heat of dimerization of gallium trichloride, which refers to two $Cl \rightarrow Ga$ bonds is $\sim$21 kcal/mole.

In three cases, with pyridine, piperidine, and with ether, heats of addition of a second donor molecule were measured, although for these there are no gas phase heats. However, the difference between the heats of addition of the first and second mole of ether, $\Delta H = -6{\cdot}2$kcal/mole, refers to the reaction:

$$Et_2O \cdot GaCl_3(c) + Et_2O(l) \rightarrow (Et_2O)_2 \cdot GaCl_3(c),$$

and if we make the simplifying assumption that the heats of sublimation of the two complexes are approximately equal then we may write

$$Et_2O \cdot GaCl_3(g) + Et_2O(g) \rightarrow (Et_2O)_2 \cdot GaCl_3(g), \quad \Delta H = -12{\cdot}6 \text{ kcal/mole},$$

by incorporating the heat of vaporization of diethylether, 6·4 kcal/mole. This value is some 10 kcal/mole less than the heat evolved on addition of the first mole of ether in the gas phase, to monomeric gallium trichloride, which is calculated as $\Delta H = -22{\cdot}3$ kcal/mole. Thus the formation of 5-co-ordinate gallium (the dietherate) appears to weaken the bonding of the molecule.

Addition Compounds: π-Bonding

1. Acceptor Atoms with Available d-*Orbitals*

In the addition compounds in which boron is the acceptor atom, it is most unlikely that there will be any additional π-bonding, because there are no vacant orbitals of sufficiently low energy. The same is probably true for addition compounds in which aluminium is the acceptor atom, where the vacant $3d$-orbitals are of a somewhat higher energy than the sp^3 hybrids, used in the σ-bonding. Where there are d-orbitals available, for example when the acceptor atom is gallium, tin, or a transition metal, π-bonding may occur. In an addition compound of the type $R_3A \cdot MX_3$, where the molecule MX_3 might be gallium trimethyl, and R_3A might be one of the series Me_3N, Me_3P, Me_3As, the bonding could be composite. It would consist of a σ-component and a π-component, a d_π—d_π bond. The contribution of this Δ-bond would be nil where the donor atom was nitrogen, but would become important for the later atoms of the series, phosphorus, arsenic, etc. Kabesh and Nyholm[182] have suggested that the contribution of this π-component to the total strength of the bond would depend mainly on two factors. These are (a) the relative availability of d-electron pairs and (b) the relative overlap of the two d-orbitals, of donor and acceptor atoms, which will depend on their relative sizes. With increase in atomic weight of the donor atom the relative availability increases, but the extent

TABLE 9

Heats of addition reactions. Aluminium and gallium trimethyl

Compound	$-\Delta H$, kcal/mole	Compound	$-\Delta H$, kcal/mole
$Me_2O \cdot AlMe_3$	>19[a]	$Me_2O \cdot GaMe_3$	9·5
$Me_2S \cdot$	19	$Me_2S \cdot$	~ 8
$Me_2Se \cdot$	16	$Me_2Se \cdot$	10
$Me_2Te \cdot$	<16	$Me_2Te \cdot$	8

[a] The heats actually measured are for the dissociation $Me_2A \cdot AlMe_3 \rightarrow Me_2A + \frac{1}{2} Al_2Me_6$. The figure is calculated from this by inclusion of 10·1 kcal/mole for the dissociation process $\frac{1}{2} Al_2Me_6 \rightarrow AlMe_3$.[183]

of the overlap decreases, so that the π-component will tend to remain fairly constant. In contrast, the strength of the σ-component will decrease as the donor atom alters along the series: nitrogen, phosphorus, arsenic, etc.

Although there are values for the heats of addition reactions in which the compounds $Me_3N \cdot GaMe_3$, $Me_3P \cdot GaMe_3$ and $Me_3As \cdot GaMe_3$ are formed (Table 7), there appear to be no values available for the corresponding compounds involving aluminium trimethyl. A comparison between the gallium addition compounds, where Δ-bonding is possible and the aluminium compounds, where Δ-bonding is unlikely, cannot be made. However, some data have been obtained for the compounds $R_2A \cdot MX_3$, where MX_3 is either aluminium trimethyl or gallium trimethyl and the $R_2A \cdot$ molecules are Me_2O, Me_2S, Me_2Se and Me_2Te. These values are shown in Table 9.

For the aluminium addition compounds, where there will be little Δ-bonding, the order of decreasing donor strength of the Group VI ligands is $O > S > Se > Te$. This is the order which is expected if only σ-bonds are involved. For the gallium trimethyl compounds the order is changed to $O \gtrless Se > S \gtrless Te$. This reversal of sulphur and selenium is probably due to the possibility of Δ-bonding involving the $3d$-orbitals of the selenium and gallium atoms. Thus, in addition to the structure $Me_2Se \cdot GaMe_3$, the two others which will have a significant contribution are (a) $Me_2\overset{+}{Se}$—$\overset{-}{Ga}Me_3$ and (b) $Me_2Se = GaMe_3$. The electronic configurations of the atoms in the second structure are shown in Fig. 3. The π-bonding can occur between the penultimate, $3d$-orbital of the gallium and the ultimate, $4d$-orbital of the selenium.

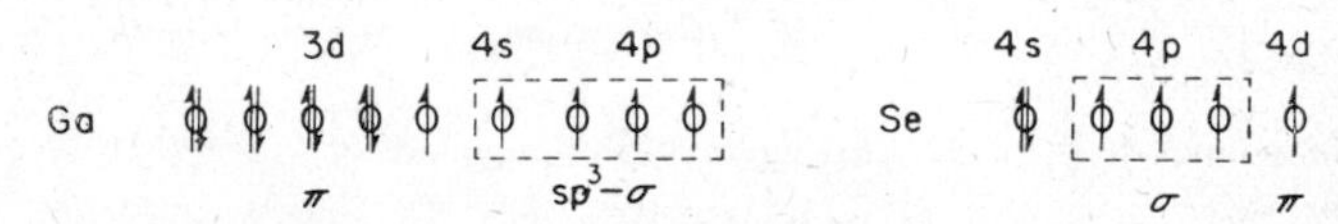

FIG. 3. Electronic structure of the compound $Me_2Se \cdot GaMe_3$.

2. Acceptor Molecules with pseudo p_π*-Orbitals*

A rather more special case of addition π-bonding between donor and acceptor probably exists in complexes between borine and a donor molecule involving a second row element, such as $Me_2S \cdot BH_3$.

Towards the first row element nitrogen, boron trifluoride and borine appear to be equally good acceptors and for the addition reactions, in the gas phase, we have the heats, $Me_3N \cdot BH_3$, $-\Delta H = 31{\cdot}3$; $Me_3N \cdot BF_3$, $-\Delta H = 30{\cdot}9$ kcal/mole. Towards oxygen, boron trifluoride is a much stronger acceptor than is borine, for whilst the heat of addition, $Me_2O \cdot BF_3$, $-\Delta H = 13{\cdot}3$ kcal/mole is comparatively large, the compound $Me_2O \cdot BH_3$ is very unstable, is completely dissociated in the gas phase, and the heat of addition must be very small.

Towards the corresponding second row element sulphur, the situation is reversed and the compound $Me_2S \cdot BF_3$ is much less stable than $Me_2O \cdot BF_3$, whilst for $Me_2S \cdot BH_3$ we have $-\Delta H = 20{\cdot}1$ kcal/mole. Values for other thioethers are similar: $Et_2S \cdot BH_3$, $-\Delta H = 20{\cdot}0$; and $(CH_2)_4S \cdot BH_3$, $-\Delta H = 18{\cdot}0$ kcal/mole.[184]

The unusual order of co-ordination towards borine suggests that the classical description of donor-acceptor bonding in terms of a σ-bond alone may be inadequate when applied to some borine adducts. It has been suggested[185] that the three $1s$ atomic orbitals of the three hydrogen atoms in borine combine to form a *pseudo* p-orbital having π-symmetry. This *pseudo* p_π-orbital could then overlap with a vacant orbital of the ligand. Thus, whereas the donor-acceptor bonds in $Me_3N \cdot BH_3$ and $Me_2O \cdot BH_3$ are adequately described by only a σ-bond, in $Me_2S \cdot BH_3$ and $Me_3P \cdot BH_3$ there may be both σ- and π-bond character. This would account for their being unexpectedly strong.

This treatment of borine is similar to that given by Coulson [186] for the methyl group, in which the three hydrogens are regarded as a *pseudo*-atom giving rise to a π-type orbital. There is, however, an important, difference between the effects postulated for the borine and the "hyperconjugation" considered previously. A charge separation occurs in $Me_2\overset{+}{S}—\overset{-}{B}H_3$ of a magnitude probably not encountered in the olefins. Electron drift from the BH_3 group would lower the energy of the molecule not only by delocalization effects, but also by partial neutralization of the charge separation set up by the lone-pair σ-bond.

It is necessary to postulate that a similar drift of electron density does not occur from the BF_3 group, or that if it does its magnitude is too small to influence the bonding appreciably. This postulate is reasonable when the high electronegativity of fluorine is considered.

Graham and Stone[185] have also suggested that weak supplementary π-bonding, with partial electron transfer from the B—H bonds to the vacant $2p_\pi$-orbital of carbon, may account for the stability of $OC \cdot BH_3$, and the apparent non-existence of $OC \cdot BF_3$, as opposed to Burg's thesis that it is the large reorganization energy of the boron trifluoride molecule which prevents formation of the boron trifluoride carbonyl.

Similarly, the existence of $F_3P \cdot BH_3$ as a stable compound [187] may be due to additional π-bonding involving overlap of a vacant $3d$-orbital of phosphorus with the *pseudo* π-orbital provided by the BH_3 group.

Conclusion

We have been considering the formation of molecular addition compounds from acceptor molecules containing a Group III atom, (boron, aluminium, gallium, indium, or thallium) and a donor molecule containing either a Group V atom, (nitrogen, phosphorus, or arsenic) or a Group VI atom (oxygen, sulphur, selenium or tellurium). The heats of these addition reactions are influenced mainly by the intrinsic acceptor and donor strength of the atoms, but this is modified by three factors. The first, and most clearly seen, is that of steric interference between non-bonded atoms. The second factor is the energy which is required to "reorganize" the acceptor or donor molecule, in preparation for the formation of a co-ordinate bond. This means the energy required to alter the hybrid state of the atom, and also, in the case of the acceptor molecule, the energy necessary to break the π-bonding. The third factor is the possibility of additional π-bonding in the molecular addition compound. This may be either d_π-d_π-bonding or possibly d_π-(*pseudo*) p_π-bonding, where borine is involved.

There are very few thermochemical data for molecular addition compounds in which the acceptor atom is a transition metal, and information about such compounds would be most useful. For example, the heats of addition of triphenylphosphine oxide to transition-metal halides, to give compounds of the type $Ph_3PO \cdot MX_2$, where MX_2 is CdI_2 ZnI_2, $CoCl_2$, $CoBr_2$, etc. would be valuable. From the P—O stretching frequency it would be possible to estimate the relative difference in the d_π-d_π-bonding in the addition compounds, and estimate the contribution to the total bond strength of the σ- and π-bond components.[188]

CHAPTER 7

BOND DISSOCIATION ENERGIES AND HEATS OF FORMATION OF FREE RADICALS

Introduction

Some of the heats of addition reactions mentioned in the last chapter were obtained directly, by measuring the heat change when the donor and acceptor molecules were allowed to react. However, a large number have been found by measurement of the heat of the reverse process, the dissociation of the molecular addition compound into the two molecular components. In these cases the dissociating species are stable molecules and, except in a few instances, either experimental method is suitable to measure the overall change in bond strength.

Generally, it is not possible to measure, by direct calorimetric methods, the strength of a bond formed when two radicals or atoms are joined together. It is more convenient to measure the bond dissociation energy. Experimental methods for determining bond dissociation energies in diatomic and polyatomic molecules have been described in detail elsewhere.[4, 189, 190] The two methods which have been most widely used for polyatomic molecules are those based on kinetic studies of pyrolysis in the presence of excess toluene as carrier gas, and the electron impact method, in which measurements are made of the appearance potentials of the ionic fragments produced by electron collision.

The measurement of bond dissociation energies provides the only practical means of determining the heat of formation of free radicals. Thus if the dissociation energy of the process $RX \rightarrow R + X$ be known, then the heat of formation of the free radical R is related to the bond dissociation energy, $D(R—X)$ by the equation

$$D(\mathrm{R—X}) = \Delta H_f^0(\mathrm{R,g}) + \Delta H_f^0(\mathrm{X,g}) - \Delta H_f^0(\mathrm{RX,g}).$$

This relationship may be used to determine an unknown bond dissociation energy $D(R—X')$, in another molecule RX', provided that the heats of formation $\Delta H_f^0(RX',g)$ and $\Delta H_f^0(X',g)$ are known. Thus, from $D(CH_3—H)$, $\Delta H_f^0(H,g)$ and $\Delta H_f^0(CH_4,g)$ a value for $\Delta H_f^0(CH_3,g)$ can be obtained. Used in conjunction with $\Delta H_f^0(CH_3Cl,g)$ and $\Delta H_f^0(Cl,g)$ this can give a value for $D(CH_3—Cl)$. An experimental determination of this dissociation energy would serve as a cross-check on the reliability of the thermochemical data used.

There are, therefore, two different methods of approach for bond dissociation energies. The first, direct method involves measuring the heats of reactions in which radicals are formed, this being essential to the measurement of the heats of formation of the radicals. The second, indirect method is to determine heats of formation of the compounds and from the known heats of formation of radicals to calculate bond dissociation energies.

In the following pages we shall review the available data from which the heats of formation of radicals can be calculated and then use these values to determine other bond dissociation energies. In this way it is possible to build up a set of bond dissociation energies and to observe the trends in these energies, within homologous series. These dissociation energies reflect differences in strain and stabilization energies between the dissociating molecule and the dissociation products, in much the same way as do heats of hydrogenation, polymerization or molecular addition reactions.

Heats of Formation of Free Radicals

1. Alkyl Radicals

Dissociation energies for C—H bonds have been obtained from electron impact measurements both by the "direct" and "indirect" method. The dissociation energy $D(CH_3—H)$ in methane was determined[191] by measuring the appearance potential of the CH_3^+ ion when methane was fed into the ionization chamber. This is taken to be the energy of the process

$$CH_4 \rightarrow CH_3^+ + e^-; \qquad \Delta H = 333{\cdot}0 \pm 2{\cdot}3 \text{ kcal/mole.}$$

Here the potential, measured in electron volts, is expressed in kcal. In order to determine the dissociation energy to an uncharged methyl radical, a second measurement was made, the ionization potential of the methyl radical, or the appearance potential of the CH_3^+ ion derived from methyl radicals. This is the energy of the process

$$CH_3 \rightarrow CH_3^+ + e^-; \quad \Delta H = 230{\cdot}6 \pm 2{\cdot}3 \text{ kcal/mole.}$$

Hence by difference:

$$CH_4 \rightarrow CH_3 + H; \quad \Delta H = 102{\cdot}4 \pm 4{\cdot}6 \text{ kcal/mole,}$$

and from the heats of formation of methane and atomic hydrogen we derive $\Delta H_f^0(CH_3, g) = 32$ kcal/mole. This is the direct method of electron impact measurement.

TABLE 1

Heats of formation of alkyl radicals, at 25°C, in kcal/mole

Bond	D(R—H)	$-\Delta H_f^0$(RH,g)	ΔH_f^0(R,g)
CH_3—H	102	17·889	32 ± 1
C_2H_5—H	97	20·236	25 ± 2
n-C_3H_7—H	99	24·820	22 ± 3
s-C_3H_7—H	94	24·820	17 ± 2
n-C_4H_9—H	101	30·15	18·5 ± 3
t-C_4H_9—H	89·5	32·15	5 ± 2

Using the indirect method it is not necessary to make the difficult measurement of the ionization potential of the radical, and also the heat of formation of the radical is found more directly. Under the impact of electron bombardment, propane can dissociate into ethyl ions and methyl radicals. Ethane can dissociate to produce ethyl ions and hydrogen atoms, so that the *difference* between the energies of these two processes corresponds to that for the reaction between propane and a hydrogen atom to give ethane and a methyl radical. The heats of these processes are[192]

$$C_3H_8 \rightarrow C_2H_5^+ + CH_3 + e^-; \quad \Delta H = 334{\cdot}4 \text{ kcal/mole}$$
$$C_2H_6 \rightarrow C_2H_5^+ + H + e^-; \quad \Delta H = 350{\cdot}6 \text{ kcal/mole}$$
$$\text{hence } C_3H_8 + H \rightarrow C_2H_6 + CH_3; \quad \Delta H = -16{\cdot}2 \text{ kcal/mole.}$$

Incorporating the heats of formation of gaseous propane, $-24{\cdot}8$; ethane, $-20{\cdot}24$; and hydrogen atoms, 52·09 kcal/mole leads to $\Delta H_f^0(CH_3, g) = 32$ kcal/mole.

The bond dissociation energies for C—H bonds, and the heats of formation of the alkyl radicals which have been obtained from electron impact measurements[193] are shown in Table 1, together with the heats of formation of the hydrocarbons on which they are based.

2. *Vinyl Radical*

From the appearance potential of the vinyl ion from ethylene, $CH_2{=}CH_2 \rightarrow CH_2{=}CH^+ + H + e^-$, and the ionization potential of the vinyl radical, Harrison and Lossing[194] obtained $D(C_2H_3—H) = 105 \pm 3$ kcal/mole. Combination of the heat of formation of gaseous ethylene (12·5 kcal/mole) and of the hydrogen atom (52·09 kcal/mole) gives $\Delta H_f^0(C_2H_3, g) = 65 \pm 3$ kcal/mole.

3. *Benzyl Radical*

Two determinations of the heats of formation of the benzyl radical, $C_6H_5CH_2$, have been made through the dissociation energies $D(C_6H_5CH_2—H)$ in toluene, and $D(C_6H_5CH_2—Br)$ in benzyl bromide. The earlier value of $D(C_6H_5CH_2—H) = 77{\cdot}5 \pm 1{\cdot}3$ kcal/mole was obtained by Szwarc[195] from kinetic measurements of the pyrolysis of toluene. This was confirmed by Schissler and Stevenson,[196] who obtained 77 ± 3 kcal/mole from their measurements of the appearance potential of the $C_7H_7^+$ ion, which was assumed to be the benzyl ion, by the indirect electron impact method. Farmer *et al.*[197] criticized these conclusions because the ionization potential of the benzyl radical, when determined directly, was about 16 kcal lower than that based on the data of Schissler and Stevenson. It may be that in the electron impact work it was the tropylium ion and not the benzyl ion which was formed, since it has been shown recently[198] that the tropylium ion is produced from toluene. The value $D(C_6H_5CH_2—H) = 77$ kcal/mole gives a heat of formation

$$\Delta H_f^0(C_6H_5CH_2, g) = 37 \text{ kcal/mole.}$$

The alternative approach is through the dissociation energy $D(C_6H_5CH_2—Br) = 50{\cdot}5$ kcal/mole, measured by Szwarc *et al.*[199] These authors consider that the error associated with this value is likely to be very small. Unfortunately, however, the heat of formation of benzyl bromide is not well established and the value $\Delta H_f^0(C_6H_5CH_2Br, g) = 17{\cdot}0 \pm 3{\cdot}0$ kcal/mole obtained by Gellner and Skinner[200] is open to question. Using this value gives $\Delta H_f^0(C_6H_5CH_2, g) = 41$ kcal/mole.

4. Phenyl Radical

No value of $D(C_6H_5—H)$ in benzene has been measured; however the heat of the dissociation process $C_6H_5—CH_3 \rightarrow C_6H_5 + CH_3$ has been obtained, $D(C_6H_5—CH_3) = 91$ kcal/mole.[201] Taking the heat of formation of gaseous toluene as 11·95 kcal/mole, and that of the methyl radical as 32 kcal/mole, this leads to $\Delta H_f^0(C_6H_5, g) = 71 \pm 3$ kcal/mole.

The heats of formation of these radicals can be used to calculate bond dissociation energies D(R—X) in other compounds, provided ΔH_f^0(RX, g) and ΔH_f^0(X, g) are known. In Table 2 values are given for dissociation energies of the C—C, C—halogen, and C—N bonds which have been calculated in this way, and also some directly measured values with which they may be compared. In

TABLE 2

Calculated and observed bond dissociation energies, in kcal/mole

Bond	ΔH^0_f(g)	D(R—X) calc.	D(R—X) obs.
$CH_3—CH_3$	$-20·24 \pm 0·02$[30]	84	85–89 (P),[208] 89 (E)[201]
$CH_3—CH_2CH_3$	$-24·82 \pm 0·02$	82	85 (E)[201]
$CH_3CH_2—CH_2CH_3$	$-30·15 \pm 0·02$	80	78 (E)[192]
$CH_3—Cl$	$-20·6 \pm 0·2$[14]	81	80 (E)[209]
$CH_3CH_2—Cl$	$-26·2 \pm 0·5$	80	83 ± 7 (E)[210]
$CH_3—Br$	$-9·6 \pm 0·5$	68	67 (E[209] and P[190])
$CH_3CH_2—Br$	$-15·3 \pm 0·5$	67	65 (E)[210]
$CH_3—I$	$3·0 \pm 1·5$	54	53 (E)[211]
$CH_3CH_2—I$	$-2·5 \pm 1·5$	53	51 (P)[190] 54 ± 10 (E)[212]
$C_6H_5—Br$	$+25·4 \pm 2·0$	71	71 (P)[213]
$CH_3—NO_2$	$-13·1 \pm 0·3$[204]	53	53·6 (P),[214] 59 (E)[201]
$CH_3—NH_2$	$-5·1 \pm 0·1$[205]	81	91 (E)[215]
$C_2H_3—H$	$12·5 \pm 0·1$[30]	105	—
$C_2H_3—CH_3$	$4·88 \pm 0·1$	92·5	—
$C_2H_3—C_2H_3$	$26·33 \pm 0·1$	104	—
$C_2H_3—Cl$	$8·89 \pm 0·5$[206]	85·5	—
$C_2H_3—Br$	$18·68 \pm 0·5$[207]	73·4	—
$C_6H_5—H$	$19·82 \pm 0·02$[30]	103·0	—

E, electron compact; P, pyrolysis.

effect this is a comparison between the accuracy of the measurement of the C—H bond dissociation energies, from which the heats of formation of the alkyl radicals are derived, and of the dissociation energies of other bonds. The calculated dissociation energies are based on the following additional data: ΔH_f^0(g); Cl, 28·94; Br, 26·71; I, 25·48;[4] NO_2, 8·09;[170] and NH_2, 44·0 kcal/mole.[202,203]

In most cases the experimentally observed D(R—X) values are close to those calculated from ΔH_f^0(R, g) and ΔH_f^0(RX, g) to within ± 2 kcal/mole, which is the accuracy associated with most measurements of dissociation energies derived from pyrolysis or electron impact data. In some cases better correlation may be found when the heats of formation of the RX molecules are more accurately known. The calculated and observed dissociation energies for these R—X bonds show a consistent trend, which is that as R changes from CH_3 to CH_3CH_2 the bond dissociation energy decreases. Thus, the carbon-carbon bond dissociation energy in propane is less than in ethane; and the carbon-bromine bond dissociation energy is less in ethyl bromide than in methyl bromide, etc. However, it may be that $D(C_3H_7$—Br) is greater than $D(C_2H_5$—Br) and it should not be assumed that increase in the number of carbon atoms in the R group necessarily always reduces D(R—X).

Although there are no experimentally measured values for bond dissociation energies of vinyl—X bonds, it is interesting to compare the calculated values with the corresponding ethyl—X bond dissociation energies. In every case the value D(vinyl—X) is greater than D(ethyl—X) by some 5 to 10 kcal/mole. Thus, we have $D(C_2H_3$—H) = 105) and $D(C_2H_5$—H) = 97 kcal/mole and also the pair $D(C_2H_3$—Br) = 73 kcal/mole and D (C_2H_5—Br) = 67 kcal/mole. These lower values of D(ethyl—X) compared with the corresponding D(vinyl—X) are possibly due to "resonance stabilization" of the ethyl radical being greater than that of the vinyl radical. This difference is increased to 24 kcal/mole when the carbon-carbon bond dissociation energies are compared in butane and 1,3-butadiene, i.e. $D(CH_3CH_2$—$CH_2CH_3)$ = 80; and $D(C_2H_3$—$C_2H_3)$ = 104 kcal/mole. The stronger bond in 1,3-butadiene is probably due to the operation of two factors; firstly the fact that the vinyl radicals to which it dissociates are less resonance stabilized than the ethyl radicals into which butane dissociates; and secondly that the central carbon-carbon bond is stronger in butadiene than in butane (either by delocalization of double bonds or by virtue of a stronger Csp^2—Csp^2 central bond). In this connection, it should be noted that $D(C_2H_3—H)$ and $D(C_6H_5—H)$ values are very similar, as are the values for $D(C_2H_3—Br)$ and $D(C_6H_5—Br)$.

Another special case of a carbon-carbon bond dissociation energy is that in cyanogen, NC—CN. A value for this bond dissociation energy may be calculated from a knowledge of the heat of formation of the cyanide radical.

5. Cyanide Radical

One method of deriving $\Delta H_f^0(CN, g)$ is based on values for $D(CH_3—CN)$ and $\Delta H_f^0(CH_3CN, g)$. The dissociation energy $D(CH_3—CN)$ has been calculated by Long[216] from spectroscopic data as 105·0 kcal/mole, at 0 °K. This is likely to be an upper limit since the excitation energy of the dissociating CN radical is uncertain, and allowance must be made for this in calculating the dissociation energy. Using the electron impact method, McDowell and Warren[217] measured the appearance potential of the CH_3^+ ion in the dissociation $CH_3CN \rightarrow CH_3^+ + CN$. From the known ionization potential of the methyl radical the dissociation energy $D(CH_3—CN)$ for the process $CH_3CN \rightarrow CH_3 + CN$, was calculated as 104·2 kcal/mole at 25 °C. The heat of formation of methyl cyanide is based on early work, and using modern physical constants Long calculates from these data the value $\Delta H_f^0(CH_3CN, g) = 19{\cdot}8$ kcal/mole. These quantities give a value $\Delta H_f^0(CN, g) = 92 \pm 2$ kcal/mole.

The heat of formation of the cyanide radical has also been obtained more directly by Brewer *et al.*[218] who measured the concentration of CN ions in the equilibrium $2C(\text{graphite}) + N_2(g) \rightleftharpoons 2CN(g)$. They obtained $\Delta H_f^0(CN, g) = 94 \pm 6$ kcal/mole, in agreement with the value obtained indirectly.

Perhaps the most valuable application of these determinations of the heat of formation of the cyanide radical is to calculate $D(NC—CN)$ from the relationship

$$D(NC—CN) = 2\Delta H_f^0(CN, g) - \Delta H_f^0(C_2N_2, g).$$

A recently obtained heat of formation of cyanogen, $\Delta H_f^0(C_2N_2, g) = 73{\cdot}84 \pm 0{\cdot}43$ kcal/mole,[210] gives $D(NC—CN) = 112$ kcal/mole, and establishes the value for a dissociation energy over which there has been much controversy.

The heat of formation of the cyanide radical may be combined with the heats of formation of the propyl, isopropyl and phenyl radicals, and the heats of formation of the corresponding cyanides to give D(C—CN) values, shown in Table 3. These calculated bond dissociation energies have not yet been verified by direct measurement.

TABLE 3

Calculated bond dissociation energies, in kcal/mole

Bond	ΔH_f^0(g)[220]	D(C—CN)
C_3H_7—CN	7·45	107·1
s-C_3H_7—CN	5·6	103·5
C_6H_5—CN	52·3	108·7

6. *Halogen-substituted Alkyl Radicals*

From electron impact measurements, Lossing and co-workers[221] obtained bond dissociation energies $D(CCl_3$—Cl), $D(CCl_3$—Br), $D(CF_3$—H) and $D(CF_3$—F). Values for only one of these dissociation energies has been established from pyrolysis experiments—for $D(CCl_3$—Br). For this dissociation energy the figures varied from 45 to 57 kcal/mole, but Szwarc[222] selected a value 49·0 as the best. Combined with the relevant heats of formation, these dissociation energies lead to values for the heats of formation of the radicals CCl_3 and CF_3, shown in Table 4. With the heats of formation of the compounds CCl_3H, CCl_3F, CF_3Cl and CF_3CF_3, these data can be used to derive values for the dissociation energies $D(CCl_3$—H), $D(CCl_3$—F) and $D(CF_3$—Cl). These are shown in the lower part of Table 4. It is worth noting that the derived value for $D(CCl_3$—H) is the same as that deduced by Szwarc[222] from the experiments of Braunwarth and Schumaker[223] on the photobromination of chloroform. With these series of bond dissociation energies, it is possible to observe the effects of replacing the hydrogen atoms, in an alkyl compound, by either fluorine or chlorine atoms.

The effect on dissociation energies of bonding chlorine atoms to carbon, as compared with hydrogen atoms can be seen in the following set of dissociation energies:

$$D(CCl_3\text{—H}) = 89 \pm 2; \quad D(CCl_3\text{—F}) = 102 \pm 7;$$
$$D(CH_3\text{—H}) = 102 \pm 2; \quad D(CH_3\text{—F}) = 108 \pm 5 \text{ kcal/mole.}$$[223a]

TABLE 4

Heats of formation of halogen-substituted alkyl radicals, and derived bond dissociation energies, at 25°C, in kcal/mole

Bond (R—X)	D(R—X) (measured)[221]	ΔH_f^0(RX, g)	ΔH_f^0(X, g)[4]	ΔH_f^0(R, g)	
CCl_3—Cl	67·9 ± 3	− 25·5[170]	28·94	13·5 ± 3	Mean value *13·4 ± 3*
CCl_3—Br	49·5 ± 3 (49·0)[222]	− 9·4[224]	26·71	13·4 ± 3	
CF_3—H	103 ± 4	− 169 ± 2[221]	52·09	− 118 ± 4	Mean value *− 117 ± 4*
CF_3—F	121 ± 4	− 218·3[132]	18·5	− 115 ± 4	
	D(R—X) (derived)				
CCl_3—H	89 ± 3·5 (89 ± 2)[222]	− 24 ± 0·5[170]	52·09	13·4	
CCl_3—F	102 ± 7	− 70 ± 4[130]	18·5	13·4	
CF_3—Cl	83 ± 3	− 171 ± 1[130]	28·94	117	
CF_3—CF_3	69 ± [illegible]	− 303 ± 2[130]	117	117	

Replacement of hydrogen atoms, bonded to the carbon, by chlorine atoms causes a lowering of the dissociation energy by 6 to 13 kcal/mole. This might be due to the greater repulsion caused by the introduction of the bulky chlorine atoms. One can argue that in the tetrahedral CCl_3X molecule there is considerable chlorine–chlorine repulsion which is greatly reduced in the CCl_3 radical, which even if not planar will be very much "flattened". This type of repulsion is less between non-bonded hydrogen atoms in the CH_3X molecule so that "flattening" of the CH_3 radical has much less effect in reducing strain.

The effect on dissociation energies of bonding fluorine atoms to carbon is shown in the sequence:

$$D(CF_3—H) = 103 \pm 4; \quad D(CF_3—Cl) = 83 \pm 3;$$
$$D(CH_3—H) = 102 \pm 2; \quad D(CH_3—Cl) = 80 \pm 2;$$

$$D(CF_3—Br) = 64{\cdot}5 \pm 2;^{(222)} \quad D(CF_3—I) = 57 \pm 4;^{(222)}$$
$$D(CH_3—Br) = 68 \pm 2; \quad D(CH_3—I) = 54 \pm 2;$$

$$D(CF_3—F) = 121 \pm 4;$$
$$D(CH_3—F) = 108 \pm 5 \text{ kcal/mole.}$$

This shows that D(C—H), D(C—Cl), D(C—Br) and D(C—I) are almost the same whether hydrogen or fluorine is bonded to the carbon. By contrast D(C—F) is considerably stronger ($\sim$15 kcal) in CF_4 than in CH_3F. This is consistent with a shortening of the C—F bond in CF_4, attributed by Pauling[225] to resonance of the double-bond-ionic type.

Using $\Delta H_f^0(CF_3, g) = -117$, and $\Delta H_f^0(C_2F_6, g) = -303$ kcal/mole gives $D(CF_3—CF_3) = 69$ kcal/mole, which seems very low when compared with $D(CH_3—CH_3) = 84$ kcal/mole. This low value may be due to considerable repulsion between the non-bonded fluorine atoms, or it may be that $\Delta H_f^0(C_2F_6, g)$ is in error by 10–20 kcal/mole.

7. *Alkoxy Radicals*

The heats of formation of alkoxy radicals, RO, have been derived from bond dissociation energies, measured by kinetic methods, in nitrites, nitrates and peroxides, i.e. D(RO—NO), $D(RO—NO_2)$ and D(RO—OR). These bond dissociation energies, taken from Gray's paper[226] are shown in Table 5. The heats of formation of the radicals, RO, are calculated from the heats of formation of the dissociating compounds, and the values $\Delta H_f^0(\mathrm{NO, g}) = 21{\cdot}6$; $\Delta H_f^0(\mathrm{NO_2, g}) = 8{\cdot}0$;(170) and $\Delta H_f^0(\mathrm{OH, g}) = 9{\cdot}1$ kcal/mole.

TABLE 5

Heats of formation of alkoxy radicals, at 25°C, in kcal/mole

Bond	D(RO—A)	ΔH_f^0(ROA, g)	ΔH_f^0(RO, g)
Nitrites			
CH_3O—NO	36·4	− 14·9	− 0·1
C_2H_5O—NO	37·7	− 24·2	− 8·1
n-C_3H_7O—NO	37·7	− 31·7	− 15·6
Nitrates			
CH_3O—NO_2	38·4	− 29·0	+ 0·6
C_2H_5O—NO_2	36·4	− 37·0	− 8·6
n-C_3H_7O—NO_2	37·4	− 41·6	− 12·0
Hydroperoxides			
t-C_4H_9O—OH	39·1	− 52·3	− 22·1
Peroxides			
C_2H_5O—OC_2H_5	31·6	− 47·3	− 7·9
t-(C_4H_9O—OC_4H_9)	37	− 84·7	− 23·9

From these data Gray selected a set of "best values" for the heats of formation of alkoxy radicals, which are shown in Table 6. These heats of formation, when combined with the heats of formation of the alkyl radicals may be used to calculate the carbon–oxygen bond dissociation in the alkoxy radicals. Values are shown in Table 6. In addition, these heats of formation of alkoxy radicals may be combined with similar data for the alcohols and ethers to obtain bond dissociation energies D(R—OH), D(RO—H) and D(R—OR′). These derived energies are given in Table 7.

It is apparent that the energy required to break the oxygen–hydrogen bond in alcohols, D(RO—H), lies close to 100 kcal/mole, varying little from one alcohol to another. This value is markedly less than D(HO—H) = 119 kcal/mole in water, to the extent of some 19 kcal/mole.

TABLE 6

Heats of formation of alkoxy radicals ('best values') and derived dissociation energies, D(R—O), at 25°C, in kcal/mole

Bond	$-\Delta H_f^0$(RO, g)	D(R—O)
CH_3—O	0·5 ± 3	91
C_2H_5—O	8·5 ± 3	92
n-C_3H_7—O	13 ± 3	94
s-C_3H_7—O	18 ± 4	94
n-C_4H_9—O	17 ± 4	95
t-C_4H_9—O	23 ± 4	89

TABLE 7

Calculated bond dissociation energies; D(R—OH), D(R—OR′) and D(RO—H) at 25°C, in kcal/mole

Bond	$-\Delta H_f^0$ (ROH, g)	D(RO—H)	Bond	D(R—OH)
(*a*) *Alcohols*				
HO—H	57·80	119	H—OH	119
CH_3O—H	48·1	100	CH_3—OH	89 (90 P.D.)
C_2H_5O—H	56·3	100	C_2H_5—OH	90 (90 P.D.)
n-C_3H_7O—H	62·2	101	n-C_3H_7—OH	93
s-C_3H_7O—H	65·9	100	s-C_3H_7—OH	92
n-C_4H_9O—H	67·8	103	n-C_4H_9—OH	95
t-C_4H_9O—H	77·0	106	t-C_4H_9—OH	91

P.D., obtained experimentally by photo-dissociation.

Bond	$-\Delta H_f^0$(ROR′,g)	D(R—OR′)
(*b*) *Ethers*		
CH_3—OCH_3	45·3	77
CH_3—OC_2H_5	53·2	76
C_2H_5—OCH_3	53·2	77
C_2H_5—OC_2H_5	61·2	77

The values $D(CH_3—OH) = 89$ and $D(C_2H_5—OH) = 90$ kcal/mole are close to the values shown in parentheses in Table 7 (a), obtained from photo-dissociation data by Terenin and Neujmin.[227]

These authors measured the dissociation energies for the processes $ROH \rightarrow R + OH^*$, in which excited OH radicals were produced. By allowing for the excitation energy of the OH radical the energy for the processes $ROH \rightarrow R + OH$ were calculated.

Whereas in the alcohols and alkoxy radicals $D(R—O)$ values vary from 90 to 95 kcal/mole, in the ethers $D(R—O)$ lies close to 77 kcal/mole (Table 7(b)), a reduction of about 15 kcal/mole as compared with the energy required to break this bond in the alcohols.

8. *Thioalkoxy Radicals*

Franklin and Lumpkin[228] have used the "indirect" electron impact method to determine heats of formation of the radicals CH_3S, C_2H_5S, and SH. To determine $\Delta H_f^0(RS, g)$ they measured the appearance potential of the RS^+ ion by the bombardment firstly of the dialkyl sulphide, and secondly of the dialkyl disulphide, which dissociate according to the equations

$$RSR \rightarrow RS^+ + R,$$
$$RS\cdot SR \rightarrow RS^+ + RS.$$

The corresponding thermochemical equations, with the appearance potentials converted to ΔH values are

$$\Delta H_f^0(RSR, g) = \Delta H_f^0(RS^+, g) + \Delta H_f^0(R, g) - \Delta H_1,$$
$$\Delta H_f^0(RS\cdot SR, g) = \Delta H_f^0(RS^+, g) + \Delta H_f^0(RS, g) - \Delta H_2.$$

Taking the difference between these two equations gives a relationship for which all the ΔH terms are known, except $\Delta H_f^0(RS, g)$. These terms are shown in kcal/mole for $R = CH_3$ and $R = C_2H_5$ beneath the thermochemical relationship.

$$\Delta H_f^0(RS, g) = \Delta H_f^0(R, g) - \Delta H_f^0(RSR, g) + \Delta H_f^0(RS\cdot SR, g)$$

$[R = CH_3]$	$+32$	$-9{\cdot}0$	$-5{\cdot}8$
$[R = C_2H_5]$	$+25$	$-19{\cdot}8$	$-17{\cdot}4$

$$+ (\Delta H_2 - \Delta H_1)$$
$$(262{\cdot}5 - 262{\cdot}5)$$
$$(257{\cdot}8 - 257{\cdot}2).$$

From this we derive $\Delta H_f^0(CH_3S, g) = 35$; and $\Delta H_f^0(C_2H_5S, g) =$ 28 kcal/mole.

To establish $\Delta H_f^0(\text{SH, g})$ the appearance potentials for the carbonium ions, R^+, were measured in the electron bombardment of the alkyl thiols, which dissociate according to the process $RSH \rightarrow R^+ + SH$, whence we obtain the relationship,

$$\Delta H_f^0(\text{SH, g}) = \Delta H_f^0(\text{RSH, g}) - \Delta H_f^0(\text{R}^+\text{, g}) + \Delta H.$$

TABLE 8

Heat of formation of the SH *radical, at 25°C, in kcal/mole*

Compound	R^+	$\Delta H_f^0(\text{R}^+\text{, g})$	$\Delta H_f^0(\text{RSH, g})$	$\Delta H_f^0(\text{SH, g})$
C_2H_5SH	$C_2H_5^+$	223[229]	− 11·03[230]	35·6
n-C_3H_7SH	n-$C_3H_7^+$	197[229]	− 16·04[231]	43·4
t-C_4H_9SH	t-$C_4H_9^+$	168[228]	− 26·0[232]	35·7
			Mean 38·2 kcal/mole	

For a particular thiol, only this one measurement is required, because the heats of formation of the carbonium ions are known, for example from the energy of the process $CH_4 \rightarrow CH_3^+ + H$. The relevant data necessary to calculate $\Delta H_f^0(\text{SH, g})$ are shown in Table 8.

The heat of formation of the SH radical may be combined with $\Delta H_f^0(\text{RSH, g})$ to give $D(\text{R—SH})$ values, whilst $\Delta H_f^0(\text{CH}_3\text{S, g})$ can be used in conjunction with $\Delta H_f^0(\text{RSCH}_3\text{, g})$ to give $D(\text{R—SCH}_3)$. Values for $D(\text{RS—H})$ can be derived from heats of formation of the RS radicals, as may the dissociation energies $D(\text{RS—SR})$. These are shown in Table 9.

Values for $D(\text{CH}_3\text{—SH}) = 76$, and $D(\text{C}_2\text{H}_5\text{—SH}) = 74$ kcal/mole may be compared with those of 67 and 63·5 kcal/mole, respectively, obtained by Sehon and Darwent [233] for studies on the pyrolysis of methane and ethanethiol. The agreement is not good. These authors also obtained $D(\text{C}_6\text{H}_5\text{CH}_2\text{—SH}) = 53$ kcal/mole, but in the absence of a heat of formation of the compound it is not possible to derive $\Delta H_f^0(\text{SH, g})$.

Three points emerge from these figures. These are, (*a*) that the $D(\text{RS—H})$ values, at 90–96 kcal/mole are much the same as $D(\text{HS—H})$ at 95 kcal/mole; this is in contrast to the difference between $D(\text{RO—H})$ and $D(\text{HO—H})$, some 19 kcal/mole. Sec-

TABLE 9

Calculated bond dissociation energies; D(R—SH), D(RS—H), D(R—SCH_3) and D(RS—SR), at 25°C, in kcal/mole

Bond	$-\Delta H_f^0$(RSH, g)	D(R—SH)	Bond	D(RS—H)
H—SH	4·82[170]	95	HS—H	95
CH_3—SH	5·47[230a]	76	CH_3S—H	90
C_2H_5—SH	11·03[231]	74	C_2H_5S—H	96
n-C_3H_7—SH	16·04[231]	76		
s-C_3H_7—SH	18·04[231]	73		
t-C_4H_9—SH	26·0[232]	69		
C_6H_5—SH	26·66[234]	81		

Bond	$-\Delta H_f^0$($RSCH_3$, g)	D(R—SCH_3)	Bond	ΔH_f^0(RSSR, g)	D(RS—SR)
CH_3—SCH_3	8·98[230]	76	HS—SH	− 2·9[170]	73
C_2H_5—SCH_3	14·07[231]	74	CH_3S—SCH_3	5·8[236]	76
n-C_3H_7—SCH_3	19·36[235]	76	C_2H_5S—SC_2H_5	17·4[236]	73
s-C_3H_7—SCH_3	21·43[232]	73			

ondly (*b*), the values for $D(R—SH)$ and $D(R—SCH_3)$ are the same, where R is an alkyl radical, once more in contrast to the corresponding oxygen compounds, where $D(R—OR)$ are less than $D(R—OH)$ by about 15 kcal/mole. Finally (*c*), the dissociation energies $D(RS—SR)$ ~75 kcal/mole are considerably less than $D(S—S)$ in the diatomic molecule, S_2. This is not surprising since this latter bond will have some double bond character, and it is reasonable to expect dissociation energy to be greater. The value $D(C_2H_5S—SC_2H_5) = 73$ kcal/mole is only 23 kcal/mole less than $D(C_2H_5S—H) = 96$ kcal/mole, whereas we have $D(C_2H_5O—OC_2H_5) = 32$ kcal/mole against $D(C_2H_5O—H) = 100$ kcal/mole, a difference of 68 kcal/mole. It is not surprising that the thiols are readily oxidized to disulphides, whereas alcohols are not oxidized to peroxides; and also that the disulphides are so much more thermally stable than the corresponding peroxides.

9. *Alkyl Amino Radicals*

The heats of formation of the radicals NH_2, CH_3NH and $(CH_3)_2N$ have been determined by Dibeler, Franklin and Reese[203] from electron impact measurements on hydrazine, and the methyl-substituted hydrazines. The values they obtained are $\Delta H_f^0(NH_2, g) = 44 \pm 2$; $\Delta H_f^0(CH_3NH, g) = 48 \pm 2$; and $\Delta H_f^0[(CH_3)_2N, g] = 51 \pm 2$ kcal/mole. The value for the NH_2 radical is close to that calculated from Szwarc's pyrolysis measurements of hydrazine. The value $D(H_2N—NH_2) = 60 \pm 4$ kcal/mole, when combined with $\Delta H_f^0(N_2H_4, g) = 22{\cdot}1$ kcal/mole,[170] leads to $\Delta H_f^0(NH_2, g) = 41 \pm 2$ kcal/mole, from the relationship

$$D(H_2N—NH_2) = 2\,\Delta H_f^0(NH_2, g) - \Delta H_f^0(N_2H_4, g).$$

With the heats of formation of the amino, and alkyl amino radicals, it is possible to calculate the dissociation energies for a number of carbon–nitrogen, nitrogen–nitrogen and nitrogen–hydrogen bonds. These are shown in Table 10, together with the relevant heats of formation of the parent compounds, in which the bonds occur.

Within the limits of error for these dissociation energies, which are probably about ± 3 kcal/mole, two trends can be noticed. Firstly, it appears as if values for $D(N—H)$ are almost unaffected by methyl substitution of hydrogen atoms bonded to the nitrogen.

TABLE 10

Calculated bond dissociation energies; D(RN—C), D(RN—H) and D(RN—NR), at 25°C, in kcal/mole

Bond	ΔH_f^0 (RNCH$_3$, g)	D(RN—CH$_3$)	Bond	ΔH_f^0 (RNH, g)	D(RN—H)
$H_2N—CH_3$	-5.1[205]	81	$H_2N—H$	-11.09[170]	107
$CH_3(H)N—CH_3$	-4.2[205]	84	$CH_3(H)N—H$	-5.1[205]	105
$(CH_3)_2N—CH_3$	-5.2[205]	88	$(CH_3)_2N—H$	-4.2[205]	107

Bond	ΔH_f^0 (RNNH$_2$, g)	D(RN—NH$_2$)	Bond	ΔH_f^0 (RN—NR, g)	D(RN—NR)
$H_2N—NH_2$	22.1[170]	66	$H_2N—NH_2$	22.1[170]	66
$CH_3(H)N—NH_2$	22.3[237]	70	$CH_3(H)N—N(H)CH_3$	22.8[229][a]	73
$(CH_3)_2N—NH_2$	21.9[238]	73	$(CH_3)_2N—N(CH_3)_2$	—	—

[a] Assuming ΔH vap. = 10 kcal/mole.

This is in marked contrast to the corresponding oxygen compounds where we find $D(HO—H) = 119$ and $D(CH_3O—H) = 100$ kcal/mole, a sharp decrease in dissociation energy with methyl substitution. The same trend is found in the hydrocarbon series where we have the following $D(C—H)$ values: $D(CH_3—H) = 102$, $D(CH_3CH_2—H) = 97$, $D(Me_2CH—H) = 94$, and $D(Me_3C—H) = 89{\cdot}5$ kcal/mole. Secondly, the dissociation energies $D(N—N)$ show increasing values with methyl substitution. It should be borne in mind that these N—N dissociation energies refer to nitrogen in the oxidation state of $+3$, although similar variations are found where the oxidation state of one of the nitrogen atoms is increased to $+5$, as in the nitramine series, where we have $D(NH_2—NO_2) = 57$ kcal/mole[240] but $D(Me_2N—NO_2) = 59$ kcal/mole. The reasons for this variation with methyl substitution are not clear.

TABLE 11

Heats of formation of the radicals RCOO, *at 25°C, in kcal/mole*

Bond	D(O—O)	ΔH_f^0(RCO·O—OCO·R, g)	ΔH_f^0 (RCOO, g)
$CH_3CO \cdot O—O \cdot CO \cdot CH_3$	29·5	− 119	− 45 ± 2
$C_2H_5CO \cdot O—O \cdot CO \cdot C_2H_5$	30·0	− 138	− 54 ± 2
n-$C_3H_7CO \cdot O—O \cdot CO \cdot$n-$C_3H_7$	30·0	− 150	− 60 ± 2
$C_6H_5CO \cdot O—O \cdot CO \cdot C_6H_5$	31·0	− 73·8	− 21 ± 2

10. Radicals RCOO

The heats of formation of the radicals RCOO, where $R = CH_3$, C_2H_5, n-C_3H_7 and C_6H_5, have been determined from dissociation energies $D(RCO \cdot O—O \cdot CO \cdot R)$, obtained from pyrolysis measurements[241, 242] on the respective peroxides. These dissociation energies are combined with the heats of formation of the gaseous peroxides[243] to give the values of $\Delta H_f^0(RCOO, g)$ shown in Table 11.

The heat of dissociation of an acid into an acid radical and a hydrogen atom, i.e. $RCO \cdot OH(g) \rightarrow RCO \cdot O(g) + H(g)$, is given by the thermochemical equation

$$D(RCO \cdot O—H, g) = \Delta H_f^0(RCO \cdot O, g) + \Delta H_f^0(H, g) - \Delta H_f^0(RCO \cdot OH, g).$$

The heat of formation of gaseous acetic acid is $-109{\cdot}9$ [244] kcal/mole, which refers to one half of the heat of formation of the dimer, so that one half of the heat of dimerization must be subtracted from this heat of formation to give that of gaseous, monomeric acetic acid. The heat of dimerization has been measured as $-14{\cdot}5$ kcal/mole,[245] so that we arrive at a value of $-102{\cdot}8$ kcal/mole for the heat of formation of the gaseous monomer. Using the value for the heat of formation of the radical CH_3COO of -45 ± 2 kcal/mole we obtain the value $D(CH_3COO{-}H) = 110 \pm 2$ kcal/mole from the relationship

$$D(CH_3CO \cdot O{-}H) = \Delta H_f^0(CH_3CO \cdot O, g) + \Delta H_f^0(H, g) - \Delta H_f^0(CH_3CO \cdot OH, g).$$

This value of 110 ± 2 kcal/mole for the oxygen-hydrogen bond dissociation energy in acetic acid is slightly higher than the dissociation energy for the oxygen-hydrogen bond in methyl alcohol (100 kcal/mole).

It is, of course, much easier to abstract a proton (as distinct from a hydrogen atom in the calculations above) from acetic acid in aqueous solution than from methyl alcohol and this is probably due to (*a*) the greater electron affinity of the radical CH_3COO, and/or (*b*) the greater heat of solvation of the CH_3COO^- ion formed. Some idea of the magnitude of these quantities, at least as a combined value, can be obtained in the following way. The heat of the combined effect of (*a*) and (*b*) is that of the equation $CH_3COO(g) + e^- \rightarrow CH_3COO^-(aq)$. This may be derived from the following set of thermochemical equations:

$$CH_3COOH(g, mon) \rightarrow CH_3COO(g) + H(g), \quad \Delta H_1 = +110 \text{ kcal/mole}$$

$$CH_3COOH(g, mon) \rightarrow CH_3COOH(aq), \quad \Delta H_2 = \sim -7 \text{ kcal/mole}$$ [170]

$$CH_3COOH(aq) \rightarrow CH_3COO^-(aq) + H^+(aq), \quad \Delta H_3 = -0{\cdot}07 \text{ kcal/mole}$$ [246]

$$H(g) \rightarrow H^+(aq) + e^-, \quad \Delta H_4 = +54 \text{ kcal/mole}$$ [247]

$$\text{Hence, } CH_3COO(g) + e^- \rightarrow CH_3COO^-(aq), (\Delta H_2 - \Delta H_1 + \Delta H_3 - \Delta H_4) = -171 \text{ kcal/mole}.$$

Stepwise Dissociation Energies

Although a considerable number of bond dissociation energies in polyatomic molecules have been measured, little is known of the bond dissociation energies in free radicals themselves.

In a few favourable cases these dissociation energies are known quite accurately. The two dissociation energies in the stepwise dissociation of the water molecule, $D(\text{HO—H})$ and $D(\text{H—O})$ are an example. The most accurate result for $D(\text{O—H})$ is probably the spectroscopic evaluation of a dissociation limit for an excited state of OH, leading to $D(\text{O—H}) = 102{\cdot}37$ kcal/mole, at 25 °C.[248] From the relationship

$$D(\text{HO—H}) + D(\text{H—O}) = 2\,\Delta H_f^0(\text{H, g}) + \Delta H_f^0(\text{O, g}) - \Delta H_f^0(\text{H}_2\text{O, g})$$

we obtain $D(\text{HO—H}) + D(\text{H—O}) = 221{\cdot}5$ kcal/mole, at 25 °C, so that if $D(\text{O—H}) = 102{\cdot}37$, then $D(\text{HO—H}) = 119{\cdot}1$ kcal/mole. This leads to a value $\Delta H_f^0(\text{OH, g}) = 9{\cdot}1$ kcal/mole. Another approach is to determine $\Delta H_f^0(\text{OH, g})$ from the dissociation energy of the process $H_2O_2(g) \rightarrow 2OH(g)$, for which $D(\text{HO—OH}) \sim 48$ kcal/mole.[249] Combined with $\Delta H_f^0(\text{H}_2\text{O}_2\text{, g}) = -32{\cdot}53 \pm 0{\cdot}04$ kcal/mole[250 251] this leads to $\Delta H_f^0(\text{OH, g}) = 7{\cdot}8$ kcal/mole.

A similar approach has also been made already to $D(\text{HS—H})$ and $D(\text{H—S})$. In this case the value $\Delta H_f^0(\text{HS, g}) = 38{\cdot}2$ kcal/mole gives $D(\text{H—S}) = 80$ kcal/mole, and from $\Delta H_f^0(\text{H}_2\text{S, g}) = -4{\cdot}8$ kcal/mole, the value $D(\text{HS—H}) = 95$ kcal/mole was derived.

The case of ammonia is slightly more complex since here there are three stepwise dissociation energies $D(\text{H}_2\text{N—H})$, $D(\text{HN—H})$, and $D(\text{N—H})$. Determination of the heat of formation of the NH_2 radical, $\Delta H_f^0(\text{NH}_2\text{, g}) = 44 \pm 2$ kcal/mole, referred to previously, and $\Delta H_f^0(\text{NH}_3\text{, g}) = -11{\cdot}09$ lead to $D(\text{H}_2\text{N—H}) = 107$ kcal/mole. Gaydon[189] gives $D(\text{N—H}) = 85 \pm 11$ kcal/mole from spectroscopic data, so that since the sum of the three dissociation energies is 280 kcal/mole, then $D(\text{HN—H}) = 88$ kcal/mole.

For the amines the stepwise dissociation energies are known less reliably than those of ammonia itself. A method of deriving $\Delta H_f^0(\text{CH}_3\text{N, g})$ and $\Delta H_f^0(\text{C}_2\text{H}_5\text{N, g})$ suggested by Gowenlock,[252] is based on a dissociation energy of methyl and ethyl azides, for the processes, $RN_3 \rightarrow RN + N_2$, for which the values have been given

$D(CH_3N—N_2) = 43{\cdot}15$ and $D(C_2H_5N—N_2) = 39{\cdot}7$ kcal/mole.[253] Unfortunately, the heats of formation of methyl and ethyl azides are unknown. However, Gray[254] has suggested that for the azides the dissociation energy $D(R—N_3)$ has a mean value of about 72 kcal/mole. From the relationship

$$\Delta H_f^0(RN_3, g) = \Delta H_f^0(R, g) + \Delta H_f^0(N_3, g) - D(R—N_3),$$

taking the $\Delta H_f^0(g)$ values: CH_3, $+32{\cdot}0$; C_2H_5, $+25{\cdot}0$; and N_3, 105 kcal/mole;[254] we obtain $\Delta H_f^0(CH_3N_3, g) = 65$, and $\Delta H_f^0(C_2H_5N_3, g) = 58$ kcal/mole. From these we then derive

$$\Delta H_f^0(CH_3N, g) = 108{\cdot}5, \text{ and } \Delta H_f^0(C_2H_5N, g) = 97{\cdot}5 \text{ kcal/mole.}$$

From $\Delta H_f^0(CH_3NH, g) = 48$ kcal/mole, referred to previously, and the relationship

$D(CH_3N—H) = \Delta H_f^0(CH_3N, g) + \Delta H_f^0(H, g) - \Delta H_f^0(CH_3NH, g)$

it follows that $D(CH_3N—H) = 113$ kcal/mole. This may be compared with $D(CH_3NH—H) = 105$ kcal/mole.

A yet more complicated situation is presented by the stepwise dissociation energies of methane, for although $D(CH_3—H)$ is well established, the same cannot be said for the dissociation energies $D(CH_2—H)$ and $D(C—H)$. Representing the successive dissociation energies by D_1, D_2, D_3, and D_4, one can equate the sum of the dissociation energies to the heat of formation of CH_4 from the atoms, at 25 °C,

$$(D_1 + D_2 + D_3 + D_4) = \Delta H_f^0(C, g) + 4\Delta H_f^0(H, g) - \Delta H_f^0(CH_4, g) = 397 \text{ kcal/mole.}$$

Of the individual D values, we have $D_1 = 102{\cdot}5$ kcal/mole, and $D_4 \sim 81$ kcal/mole,[189] so that we calculate $(D_2 + D_3) \sim 214$ kcal/mole. Electron impact studies on methane and methyl radicals have been made by Waldron,[255] and by Langer, Hipple and Stevenson[256] from which D_2 and D_3 values were obtained, but the investigators differed in their conclusions. Waldron obtained $D_2 = 78 \pm 5$, and $D_3 = 128 \pm 9$ kcal/mole, conforming (within the limits of error quoted) with the probable requirement that $(D_3 + D_4) \sim 214$ kcal/mole. On the other hand, Langer *et al.* gave $D_2 = 87 \pm 7$, and $D_3 = 92 \pm 7$ kcal/mole.

CHAPTER 8

METAL-CARBON AND METAL-HALOGEN BONDS

Introduction

The non-transition metals of the *b*-groups of the Periodic Table form a number of simple, covalent alkyls and halides, and since they are comparatively easy to investigate thermochemically, a fair amount of data is available for them. One of the ways in which this has been used is to gain information about covalent bonding in which these metal atoms are involved. Although, in general, the transition metals do not form stable alkyl compounds, metal–carbon bonds are found in the carbonyls which are neutral co-ordination compounds, and also in the cyclopentadienyl compounds, and the bonding in these compounds is of particular interest. In the transition metal halides the bonding is simpler, and here thermochemical data can be of help in establishing the factors which influence the stability of different valence states.

Mean Bond Dissociation Energies

1. Representative and b*-Group Elements*

The heats of formation of a number of simple organic compounds of *b*-Group metals of Groups II, III, IV and V have been determined by reaction and combustion calorimetry. Some of these are listed in Table 1, together with $\varDelta H_f^0$ values for organic compounds of some "representative" elements. The values have been used, in conjunction with the heats of formation of organic radicals, listed previously, and heats of atomization of metals,[4] to calculate mean dissociation energies from the relationship,

$$\bar{D}(\text{M—R}) = \frac{1}{n}\,\varDelta H_f^0(\text{M, g}) + \varDelta H_f^0(\text{R, g}) - \frac{1}{n}\,\varDelta H_f^0(\text{MR}_n\text{, g}).$$

TABLE 1

Heats of formation of organo-metallic compounds[a]

Compound	ΔH_f^0 (liq) (kcal/mole)	ΔH_f^0 (g) (kcal/mole)	Compound	ΔH_f^0 (liq) (kcal/mole)	ΔH_f^0 (g) (kcal/mole)
Group I			*Group IV*		
LiBu	−33·5 ± 1	−0·5[257]	CMe_4	−44·98	−39·67[30]
			$SiMe_4$	−75·0 ± 2	−69·0[262]
Group II			$SnMe_4$	−21·4 ± 10	−13·6
$ZnMe_2$	+ 6·3 ± 1	+13·0	$PbMe_4$	+23·5 ± 0·3	+32·6[263]
$ZnEt_2$	+ 4·3 ± 1	+13·1	$PbEt_4$	+12·8 ± 0·6	+23·0
$ZnPr_2$	−13·6 ± 5	− 3·9[258]			
$ZnBu_2$	−24·9 ± 6	−14·6[258]	*Group V*		
$CdMe_2$	+16·7 ± 0·5	+25·2	NMe_3	−11·0	− 5·2[205]
$CdEt_2$	+14·5 ± 0·5	+ 24·5[259]	PMe_3	−30·1 ± 0·5	−23·2
$HgMe_2$	+12·3 ± 2	+20·4	PPh_3	+54·3 ± 2	+72·4[114]
$HgEt_2$	+ 5·2 ± 2	+15·9	$AsMe_3$	− 3·5 ± 1·5	+ 3·7
$HgPr_2$	− 8·6 ± 3	+ 4·2[260]	$SbMe_3$	− 1·4 ± 3	+ 6·4
Hg^iPr_2	− 3·8 ± 3	+ 8·7[260]	$BiMe_3$	−37·5 ± 2	−29·2
$HgPh_2$(c)	+65·4 ± 2	+88·0			
Group III					
BMe_3	−34·8 ± 3	−30·1			
BEt_3	−46·8	−38·0			
B^nBu_3	−83·9	−70·8			
B^sBu_3	−75·0 ± 6	−60·0			
$AlMe_3$	−26·9 ± 3	−12·0			
$GaMe_3$	−14·5 ± 8	− 6·7[8, 261]			

[a] Values taken from Skinner's compilation,[14] except where other references are given.

These data are shown in Table 2. There are two notable trends in the dissociation energies. The first is that for a given metal, e.g. mercury, there is a decrease in dissociation energy along the series methyl, ethyl and isopropyl, following the same pattern as the decrease in dissociation energies D(R—H), where R is the alkyl group, already noted. The exception to this is that when R is phenyl, for both mercury and phosphorus, the $\bar{D}$ values in MR_n are greater than would be predicted from the corresponding D(R—H), possibly because of conjugation of the mercury $2p$ or phosphorus $3d$-orbitals with the π-orbitals of the benzene ring, thus strengthening the bond. The second trend is that within a Group the mean dissociation energy decreases with increasing atomic weight of the metal.

TABLE 2

Mean dissociation energies, $\bar{D}$, in organo-metallic compounds MR_n

	ΔH_f^0 (M, g)[4]	$\bar{D}$(M—R) in kcal/mole					
		Me	Et	Pr	^iPr	Bu	Ph
Group I							
Li	38					57±4	
Group II							
Zn	31·2	41±1·5	34±2·5	40±5·5		41±6	
Cd	27	33±1	26±2·5				
Hg	14·65	29±2	24±3	27±4·5	20±3·5		33±5
Group III							
B	141	89±2	85±3			89±4	
Al	75	61±2					
Ga	66	56±3					
Group IV							
C	170·9	85±1					
Si	110[309]	77±3					
Sn	72	53±3·5					
Pb	46	35±1	31±3				
Group V							
N	112·9	71±1					
P	75·3	65±1					71±4
As	60	53±1·6					
Sb	61	50±2					
Bi	50	38±2					

2. *Transition Metals, Carbonyls*

In contrast to the stable *b*-Group metal alkyls, with their comparatively strong metal-carbon bonds the transition metals do not form stable alkyl compounds; Jaffé and Doak[265, 266] have discussed the instability of these compounds in terms of molecular orbital theory. They find that the overlap integrals between the d^ns-hybrids of the transition metals and the sp^3-carbon orbitals are relatively small, by comparison with, say, the overlap integral between zinc sp-hybrids and carbon sp^3-orbitals. This means that in the highest valence state of the metal, the metal-carbon bonds would be weak due to the relatively weak bond forming power of $d^n s$-hybrids. The bonds cannot be stabilized by a large ionic-covalent resonance energy, as the electronegativity difference[264] between the metal and carbon is not great enough. Nor can they be stabilized by adopting a low co-ordination number, whilst retaining the high valence, since the alkyl groups are unable to form π-bonds to the metal.

TABLE 3

Heats of formation[a] *and mean dissociation energies, metal carbonyls*

Compound	ΔH_f^0 (l) kcal/mole	ΔH_f^0 (g)[b] kcal/mole	ΔH_f^0 (M, g)[4] kcal/g atom	$\bar{D}$(M—CO) kcal/mole
$Ni(CO)_4$	$-151{\cdot}6 \pm 0{\cdot}5$	$-145{\cdot}1$	101	35
$Fe(CO)_5$	$-187{\cdot}8 \pm 1{\cdot}0$	$[-172{\cdot}8]$	99	28
$Cr(CO)_6$	$-257{\cdot}6 \pm 0{\cdot}5$	$[-242{\cdot}6]$	94·0	30
$Mo(CO)_6$	$-234{\cdot}8 \pm 0{\cdot}3$	$[-219{\cdot}8]$	155·5	36
$W(CO)_6$	$-227{\cdot}3 \pm 0{\cdot}3$	$[-212{\cdot}3]$	202·0	42
$Mn_2(CO)_{10}$	$-400{\cdot}9 \pm 1{\cdot}5$[267]	$-385{\cdot}9$[268]	68	

[a] Values taken from Skinner's compilation,[14] except where other reference given.

[b] Bracketed values calculated using assumed latent heat of evaporation of 15 kcal/mole.

Where such π-bonds can be formed, as in the carbonyl compounds of the transition metals, stable molecules result. Moreover, high co-ordination numbers are achieved in these neutral co-ordination compounds, examples of which are $Cr(CO)_6$, $Mn_2(CO)_{10}$, $Fe(CO)_5$ and $Ni(CO)_4$.

In Table 3, the heats of formation of these compounds are given, together with those for the carbonyls of two other metals of the chromium group, molybdenum and tungsten. The mean dissociation energies refer to the processes,

$$M(CO)_n(g) \rightarrow M(g) + nCO(g).$$

Two trends are revealed in the mean dissociation energies; (i) a regular increase along the series $Cr(CO)_6$, $Mo(CO)_6$, $W(CO)_6$; and (ii) an increase from $Fe(CO)_5$ to $Ni(CO)_4$.

This suggests that the trend in their ordinary chemical and physical stability, which runs in the opposite direction, is due to kinetic factors.

The C—O bond in the carbonyls is quite different from that in the carbon monoxide molecule, and Cotton *et al.*[9] have endeavoured to calculate the "reorganization energy" of the CO group when the carbonyl compound dissociates to give a metal atom and a CO molecule. Their calculation was based on three parameters of the C—O bond: (*a*) the increase in bond length in the carbonyls, 1·15 to 1·16 Å, as compared with 1·13 Å in the carbon monoxide molecule; (*b*) the altered stretching force constants; and (*c*) the change in the infrared C—O stretching frequency. These authors estimate that of the mean dissociation energy, some 32 kcal/mole is required to strengthen the C—O bond on dissociation.

The bonding in these carbonyl compounds is composite, consisting of a σ-component and also a π-component, involving the π-orbitals of the CO radical and the $3d$-orbitals of the metal atom. This is favoured in $Ni(CO)_4$, where, in the tetrahedral configuration the nickel atom has $3d$-electrons available in all four positions. In $Fe(CO)_5$, the iron, in the trigonal bipyramid configuration has $3d$-electrons available in only four of the five positions. One would therefore expect a greater degree of double bonding in nickel carbonyl than in iron pentacarbonyl. This is in good agreement with the dissociation energies of the metal-carbon bond in the nickel compound and in iron pentacarbonyl, as shown in Table 3. The same reasoning would also explain the lack of bond shortening (Table 4)

TABLE 4

Bond distances in metal carbonyls[a]

Carbonyl	R_{M-C} Å	R_{C-O} Å	R_{M-C} Å (calculated)[b]
$Ni(CO)_4$	1·84 ± 0·03	1·15 ± 0·03	1·92
$Fe(CO)_5$	1·84 ± 0·03	1·15 ± 0·04	1·94
$Cr(CO)_6$	1·92 ± 0·04	1·16 ± 0·05	1·94
$Mo(CO)_6$	2·08 ± 0·04	1·15 ± 0·05	2·06
$W(CO)_6$	2·06 ± 0·04	1·13 ± 0·05	2·07

[a] Taken from the Review by Cable and Sheline.[270]

[b] Calculated from covalent radii given by Moeller.[269]

in the octahedral metal carbonyls $Cr(CO)_6$, $Mo(CO)_6$ and $W(CO)_6$, in which π-bonds can be formed in only three of the six positions.

The polynuclear carbonyl $Mn_2(CO)_{10}$ involves a manganese-manganese bond and five carbon-metal bonds to each of the manganese atoms, so that dissociation of the molecule into manganese atoms and carbon monoxide molecules involves breaking two different types of bonds. Only if D(Mn—Mn) were known would it be possible to calculate $\bar{D}$(Mn—CO).

3. *Cyclopentadienyl and Benzene Compounds*

The situation in the biscyclopentadienyl compounds is quite different. In these compounds, of general formula $(C_5H_5)_2M$, where M is a transition metal, the cyclopentadienyl groups are bonded to the metal atom in a different way from that encountered in either the simple metal alkyls or in the carbonyl compounds. In

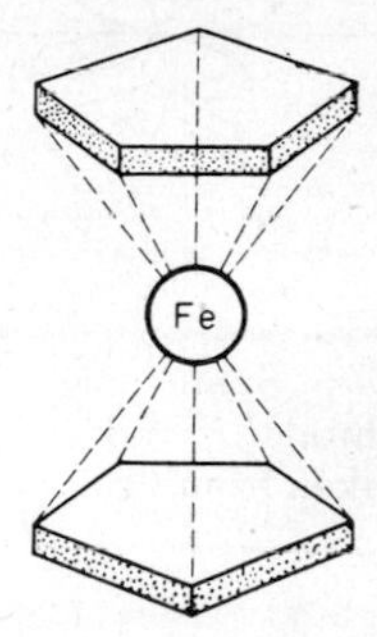

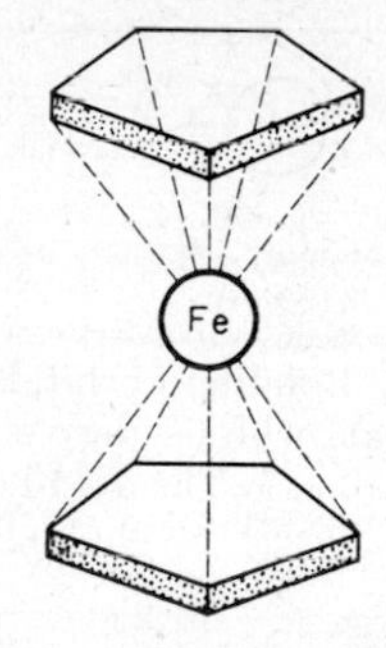

FIG. 1. Ferrocene

ferrocene, $(C_5H_5)_2Fe$, the iron atom is sandwiched between the two cyclopentadienyl radicals, as shown in Fig. 1.

The fundamental points about the electronic structure of these compounds are (1) the high symmetry of the C_5H_5 radical, which allows low energy orbitals extending round the ring, and (2) the possibility of forming bonds between some of these orbitals and those atomic orbitals of the metals which have suitable symmetry to combine with the cyclopentadienyl molecular orbitals, without greatly disturbing the latter.[271] Atomic orbitals of suitable symmetry involve d orbitals either alone or hybridized with s orbitals, and for this reason these compounds are formed by transition metals.

The state of the cyclopentadienyl radical may be described in terms of five molecular orbitals, which are formed from the π-type orbitals of the five carbon atoms. These molecular orbitals, which are shown in Fig. 2, are: one of Σ-type (*a*), containing two electrons; two of Π-type (*b* & *c*), containing one and two electrons,

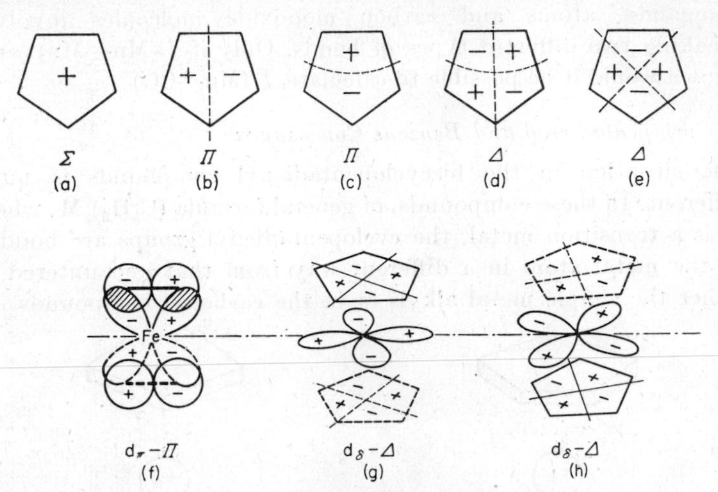

FIG. 2. Bonding orbitals in ferrocene. *a–e*, Symmetries of the molecular orbitals derived from atomic π orbitals. *F*, A d_{π}-π-bond in ferrocene. *g*, *h*, The d_{δ}-Δ-bonds in ferrocene (taken from Craig, Maccoll, Nyholm, Orgel and Sutton, ref. 272).

respectively; and two of the Δ-type (*d* & *e*) which are unoccupied. The symmetries of these Σ, Π and Δ orbitals are analogous to the atomic orbitals, *s*, *p* and *d*.

Only the $3d$- and $4s$-orbitals of the iron atom need be considered, and there are eight electrons to dispose. Taking the iron atom as origin and the xy plane as parallel to the rings and going through the iron nucleus, there are two $3d$-orbitals in the xy plane, *viz.* $3d_{x^2-y^2}$ and $3d_{xy}$, and each of these will contain two electrons. The orbitals $3d_{yz}$ and $3d_{xz}$ will be singly occupied and have suitable symmetry to combine with the Π-cyclopentadienyl orbitals. The remaining two electrons of the iron atom could go into either the $3d_{z^2}$ orbital, or into a hybrid orbital formed from a mixture of the $3d_{z^2}$ and $4s$-orbitals. The electron pair may have a lower energy in this hybrid orbital.

The valence state is shown schematically in Fig. 3. The singly occupied $3d_{yz}$-orbital forms a d_π–Π bond with the Π_x-orbital of one radical, and the $3d_{xz}$-orbital with the Π_y-orbital of the other radical. These two bonds are identical, and at right angles, as represented in Fig. 2, (*f*). It is possible that there may also be some electron transfer from the doubly occupied $3d_{xy}$-orbital of the iron atom to a vacant Δ-orbital of one radical, and from the $3d_{x^2-y^2}$-orbital to a Δ-orbital of the other radical, to form two d_δ-Δ bonds, as shown in Fig. 2, (*g*) and (*h*).

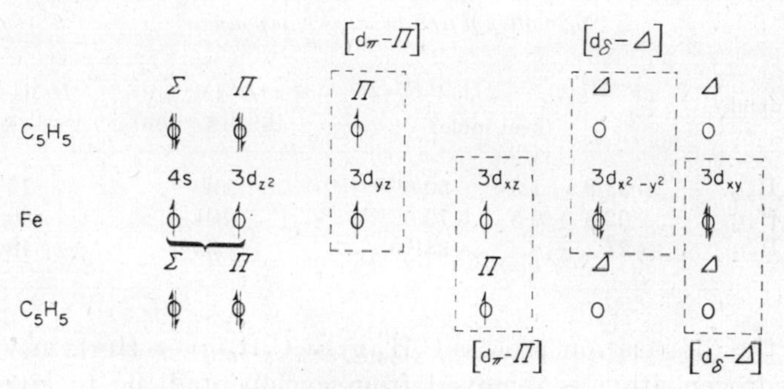

FIG. 3. Electronic structure of ferrocene.

For the corresponding nickel compound, $Ni(C_5H_5)_2$, the hypothetical valence state of the nickel atom is taken as arising from the configuration $3d^84s^2$. The lower promotional energy is due to the ground state having the same multiplicity as the greater part of the valence state and contributing heavily to it. The two electrons, additional to the configuration of iron, are assumed to occupy the $3d_{z^2}-4s$ hybrid orbital, which is antibonding, and this is likely to lead to a considerable weakening of the metal-ring bonding.

An attempt has been made to calculate the metal-ring bond dissociation energy in ferrocene, and in the biscyclopentadienyl compounds of nickel, ruthenium and osmium, for which heat of formation data are available. Some of these heats of formation are shown in Table 5.

The mean dissociation energies for the processes

$$(C_5H_5)_2M(g) \rightarrow M(g) + 2C_5H_5(g)$$

have been derived using a calculated value of $\Delta H_f^0(C_5H_5, g)$ ~ 50 kcal/mole. Cotton and Wilkinson[(273)] obtained this value in the following way. The heat of formation of gaseous cyclopentadiene may be calculated as $+32{\cdot}4$ kcal/mole from the heat of formation of gaseous cyclopentane ($-18{\cdot}5$ kcal/mole),[30] and the heat of gas phase hydrogenation of cyclopentadiene to cyclopentane, $\Delta H = -50{\cdot}9$ kcal/mole.[68] These are related by the equation

$$\Delta H_f^0(\text{cyclopentadiene, g}) = \Delta H_f^0(\text{cyclopentane, g}) - \Delta H.$$

TABLE 5

Heats of formation, mean and intrinsic dissociation energies, metal cyclopentadienyl and benzene compounds

Compound	ΔH_f^0 (c) (kcal/mole)	ΔH_f^0 (g) (kcal/mole)	ΔH_f^0 (M, g)[4] (kcal/g atom)	$\bar{D}$(M—R) (kcal/mole)
$Fe(C_5H_5)_2$	$+33{\cdot}8 \pm 1{\cdot}5$	$+50{\cdot}6$[273, 274]	99	75
$Ni(C_5H_5)_2$	$+62{\cdot}8 \pm 0{\cdot}5$	$+79{\cdot}6$[275]	101	60
$Cr(C_6H_6)_2$	$+21 \pm 8$	$+38$[276]	94·0	48

For the dissociation process $C_5H_6(g) \rightarrow C_5H_5(g) + H(g)$, in which a hydrogen atom is removed from cyclopentadiene to give the cyclopentadienyl radical, it is assumed that D(C—H) ~ 100 kcal/mole, which is the value found in the normal alkanes. Using the following thermochemical relationship

$$\bar{D}(\text{C—H}) = \Delta H_f^0(C_5H_5, g) + \Delta H_f^0(H, g) - \Delta H_f^0(C_5H_6, g)$$

and the value $\Delta H_f^0(H, g) = 52{\cdot}09$ kcal/g atom, we calculate $\Delta H_f^0(C_5H_5, g) = 80$ kcal/mole. However, it is suggested that the cyclopentadienyl radical will have ~ 30 kcal/mole more resonance energy than the cyclopentadiene molecule, and on this basis $\Delta H_f^0(C_5H_5, g) \sim 50$ kcal/mole. Mean dissociation energies for the metal-ring bonds, can now be calculated from the relationship

$$2\bar{D}(\text{M—R}) = \Delta H_f^0(\text{M,g}) + \Delta H_f^0(C_5H_5,\text{g}) - \Delta H_f^0[\text{M}(C_5H_5)_2,\text{g}].$$

These values are shown in Table 5.

The mean dissociation energies, derived in this way, show the bonding in ferrocene to be some 15 kcal/mole stronger than in the corresponding nickel compound. This is in keeping with the conclusion that the antibonding orbitals are occupied in the nickel compound, an idea which is also supported by structural studies.

In ferrocene the Fe—C bond distances are about 2·05 Å, whilst in the nickel compound the Ni—C bond distance is about 0·15 Å greater. Infra-red spectral data provide further evidence.[275] The sharp peak at 817 cm^{-1} in the ferrocene spectrum is likely to arise from Fe—C stretching; in the nickel compound the corresponding peak has moved to 775 cm^{-1}. In addition, the peak 1420 cm^{-1} attributed to C—C stretching in ferrocene[277] is moved to a slightly higher wave number of ~1440 in biscyclopentadienyl nickel, indicating slightly stronger C—C bonds in the nickel compound, which would be expected from at least partial occupancy of an anti-bonding orbital.

The other compound of this type for which thermochemical data are available is chromium bisbenzene, $Cr(C_6H_6)_2$. The mean dissociation energy for the bond between the metal and the benzene ring may be calculated using the value $\Delta H_f^0(C_6H_6, g) = +19{\cdot}82$ kcal/mole, and the value obtained is $\bar{D}(Cr—C_6H_6) = 48$ kcal/mole.

Stepwise Dissociation Energies

1. b-*Group Metal Alkyls*

So far we have considered mean dissociation energies, or the *average* energy required to remove an X group from a compound MX_n. This is generally not the same as the separate or stepwise dissociation energies required to remove the X groups in turn. Various compounds of the type MX_2 have been studied to determine the stepwise dissociation energies $D_1 = D(X—MX)$ and $D_2 = D(X—M)$. These compounds are of particular interest because it should be possible to measure $(D_1 + D_2)$ from heats of formation, and D_1 by kinetic or other studies. Hence, D_2 is obtainable by difference, or in favourable cases measured directly, as a check on the derived value.

An early and successful investigation of this type was made by Wieland[278] on $HgCl_2$. He measured $D_1(Cl—HgCl)$ by a photochemical method, and $D_2(Cl—Hg)$ by analysis of the HgCl spectrum. The sum of these values agrees satisfactorily with $(D_1 + D_2)$ from thermochemical studies. More recently, Warhurst *et al.*[279] have investigated the pyrolysis of organo-mercury compounds, HgR_2, and found that these fall into two classes according to the type of decomposition. The first group contains those alkyls which dissociate to lose one R group, i.e. $HgR_2 \rightarrow HgR + R$. The activation energy of this process is taken as the dissociation energy, D_1, of the first mercury-carbon bond. On the other hand, there are those compounds in which it is supposed that the activation energy is not localized in one bond, but in both the metal-carbon bonds, so that the first step is assumed to be $HgR_2 \rightarrow Hg + 2R$. In these cases the activation energies of the first order decompositions are approximately equal to the sum $(D_1 + D_2)$. In the case of $ZnMe_2$, Price and Trotmann–Dickenson[280] were able to measure both D(Me—ZnMe) and D(Me—Zn), obtaining values, the sum of which checks satisfactorily with the thermochemical $(D_1 + D_2)$. These results, together with others are listed in Table 6.

In each of the examples, $D_1 > D_2$, but the differences $(D_1 - D_2)$ are very variable. Some of the factors leading to unequal D values have been discussed previously.[281, 282] Skinner[283] has suggested the following type of approach to this problem. Let us consider the molecule MR (for example Hg—CH_3). There are three "ideal states" which may be formulated:

(i)	M:	·R	(no bond),
(ii)	·M:R		(a covalent bond),
(iii)	$\cdot\overset{+}{M}$	$:\overset{-}{R}$	(an ionic bond).

The covalent bond (ii) is probably a hybrid bond, because generally hybrid orbitals form stronger bonds. As a first approximation we may describe the bond by the wave-function

$$\psi(MR) = a\,\psi(M^0\text{—}R) + b\,\psi(M^{II}\text{—}R) + c\,\psi\left(\overset{+}{M}\,\overset{-}{R}\right),$$

where a, b, and c are unknown mixing coefficients.

Suppose, for a moment, we neglect the no-bond term (i) and also the ionic-bond term (iii) and consider only the covalent-bond term (ii). In order to deal with this term we must first identify the valence-state of the metal atom M, and then calculate the energy required to excite the atom to this state. For a metat atom in Group II the simplest assumption is that the M—R bond is an sp-hybrid bond. Very generally, the M atom in M^{II}—R could be represented by M, h_1, h_2, the two valence electrons being hybridized. In the molecule R—M^{II}—R, these hybrid bonds h_1 and h_2 would be equivalent and probably sp in type, but in M^{II}—R we have only one bond, so that h_1 no longer needs to be the same as h_2.

TABLE 6

Bond dissociation energies in MX_2 molecules, in kcal/mole[a]

Molecule	$(D_1 + D_2)$	D_1	D_2	$(D_1 - D_2)$
$HgMe_2$	59 ± 4	51 ± 2	*ca.* 8	43
$HgEt_2$	50 ± 6	42 ± 2	*ca.* 8	34
$HgCl_2$	106 ± 2	81 ± 1	24	57
$HgBr_2$	89 ± 2	72	17	55
HgI_2	69 ± 2	61	8 ± 1	53
$CdMe_2$	67 ± 3	45 ± 2	*ca.* 22	23
$ZnMe_2$	83 ± 3	47 ± 2	*ca.* 35	12

[a] Taken from Skinner's compilation.[14]

Actually the hybrid h_1, used to form the M^{II}—R bond will be the particular admixture of s and p which gives the strongest bond relative to the excitation energy required. The other orbital, h_2, does not have to form a bond in M^{II}—R, so that it could be a weaker bonding orbital. The important point here is that h_1 and h_2 are *not necessarily equivalent.*

Now the "valence state energy" of M, $h_1 h_2$ depends on what the particular hybrid orbitals, h_1 and h_2 are. If they are simply s, p (i.e. no hybridization) the valence-state excitation will require a certain energy; if they are both sp hybrids, another energy; and if they are non-equivalent hybrids, yet a different energy value. In order to calculate the valence state energy of the M atom in M^{II}—R it is essential to know, therefore, what particular hybrid orbitals, h_1 and h_2, are used.

However it is certainly inadequate to represent the bonding in the molecule MR simply by the term $\psi(M^{II}—R)$, which we have considered so far, and we must at least include the no-bond term $\psi(M^0—R)$.

For the sake of argument, the situation can be illustrated in a much simplified way, by supposing that $\psi(MR)$ can be expressed adequately by

$$\psi(MR) = 0{\cdot}5\ \psi(M^0—R) + 0{\cdot}5\ \psi(M^{II}—R).$$

We can say that it is not necessary to excite the metal atom, as far as the no-bond (M^0—R) part is concerned, but that excitation of the metal atom is required before the covalent-bond (M^{II}—R) can be formed. Let the energy to excite the free atom $M^0 \rightarrow M^{II}$ (having defined M^{II} as M, V_2, $h_1 h_2$) be x. Then to form a bond consisting of 50 per cent (M^0—R) and 50 per cent (M^{II}—R), we would require an excitation energy of $x/2$. This term we might call the "effective valence state energy".

We can think of the process of bond formation taking place hypothetically in two stages; (*a*) the metal atom is excited by supplying a certain amount of energy, which generally will be less than the valence state excitation energy for the state M, V_2, $h_1 h_2$; (*b*) the bond is formed and energy is liberated. Conversely, in the dissociation process $MR \rightarrow M^0 + R$, a certain amount of energy will be required to break the bond, but as the metal atom falls from the excited to the ground state energy will be liberated. The dissociation energy D_2 is a measure of the overall energy change. This is shown diagrammatically on the left side of Fig. 4.

Turning now to the molecule MR_2, (for example $HgMe_2$) some of the ideal states which may be formulated are

(i)	$R^{\cdot}$	M:	$R^{\cdot}$	(no-bond),
(ii)		R:M:R		(covalent bonds),
(iii)	$\overset{-}{R}$:	$\overset{++}{M}$	:$\overset{-}{R}$	(ionic bonds),
(iv)		R:$\overset{+}{M}$	:$\overset{-}{R}$	(a covalent and an ionic bond).

so that we would write

$$\psi(MR_2) = a\,\psi(RM^0R) + b\,\psi(R—M^{II}—R) + c\,\psi\left(\overset{-}{R}\,\overset{++}{M}\,\overset{-}{R}\right) + \cdots$$

In this case the valence state excitation energy, for the state M, V_2, $h_1 h_2$ (where $h_1 = h_2 = sp$) will not necessarily be the same as for the molecule MR, and also the mixing coefficients $a, b, \ldots$ will certainly not be the same as in MR. Hence the "effective valence state excitation energy" will probably be quite different for the metal atom in the two molecules MR and MR_2. The dissociation process $MR_2 \rightarrow M^0 + 2R$ is shown on the right side of Fig. 4, and the two parts of the diagram are connected by the dissociation energy D_1, the difference between $(D_1 + D_2)$ and D_2.

It can be seen that these dissociation energies will depend, in part, on the effective valence state excitation energies, which in turn depend on the particular hybrid orbitals used in the two molecules MR and MR_2, and also on the contribution of no-bond and ionic-bond structures. Since these factors have not yet been calculated in these particular cases, it is not possible to carry out a quantitative analysis of the dissociation energies. Nevertheless, it is apparent that the relationship connecting D_1 and D_2 is not a simple one to unravel.

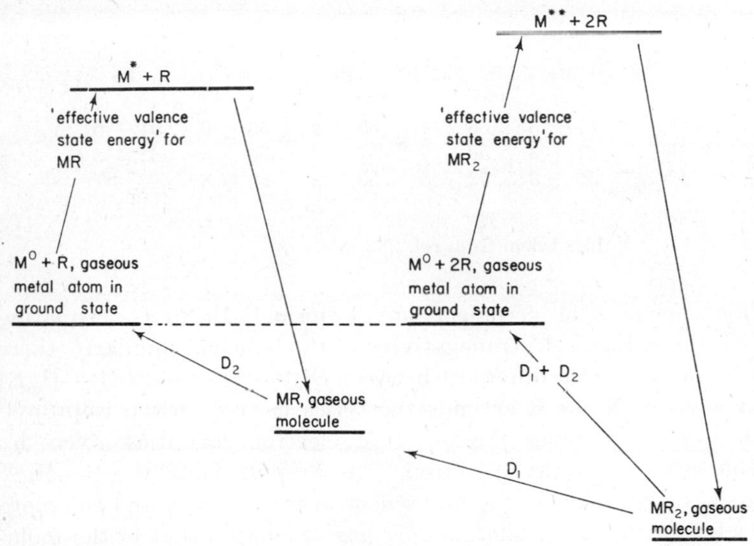

FIG. 4. Energy diagram for the dissociation of an organo-metallic compound, MR_2.

In the molecules considered so far, the bonds to the metal atom have all been of the same type. Some information is available about how the metal-carbon is affected by attaching other atoms to the metal, e.g. in molecules of the type RHgX, where R is an alkyl or aryl group and X is a halogen. The bond dissociation energy D(R—HgX) has been measured directly by pyrolysis for a number of compounds. It can also be calculated from ΔH_f^0(RHgX, g) using the thermochemical equation:

$$D(\text{R—HgX}) = \Delta H_f^0(\text{HgX, g}) + \Delta H_f^0(\text{R, g}) - \Delta H_f^0(\text{RHgX, g}).$$

In this way D(R—HgX) values have been calculated where R = methyl, ethyl, propyl, isopropyl, and phenyl, and where X = Cl, Br, and I, and these are shown in Table 7.

Comparison of D(Me—HgX) ~ 60 kcal/mole with D(Me—HgMe) = 50 kcal/mole, shows a marked strengthening of the Hg—C bond in the mixed compounds, to the extent of some 10 kcal/mole.

TABLE 7

Bond dissociation energies, D(R—HgX), in RHgX compounds[a], *in kcal/mole*

	Me	Et	Pr	iPr	Ph
Cl	64 ± 3	58 ± 4	60 ± 4	56 ± 6	64 ± 6
Br	61 ± 3	56 ± 4	57 ± 4	55 ± 5	62 ± 2
I	59 ± 3	52 ± 5	53 ± 5	50 ± 6	

[a] Values taken from ref. 282.

This decreases in passing from Cl through Br to I, correlating with the reduced electronegativity of the halogen. Similarly, there is an increase in the difference between D(R—HgX) and D(R—HgR) for a given X, as R ascends the series methyl, ethyl, isopropyl. This trend matches the order of electronegativities given by Kharasch,[(284)] methyl > ethyl > isopropyl. Thus the R—HgX bond is strengthened the more electronegative is X and the more electropositive is R. Sheridan[(285)] has calculated that in the molecules RHgX, the Hg—Cl bond has 62 per cent ionic character, compared with 53 per cent for the Hg—Br bond, so that the bonding in RHgX is considerably influenced by resonance between the covalent R—Hg—X and the ionic R—$\overset{+}{\text{Hg}}$ $\overset{-}{\text{X}}$ structures. These ionic-covalent resonance energies will be sensitive to changes in electronegativity, particularly of X, and to a lesser extent of R.[(286)]

It has also been found[(287)] that whereas in trimethyl arsine D(Me—$AsMe_2$) = 54·5 kcal/mole in the molecule $As(CF_3)_3$, $D[F_3C—As(CF_3)_2]$ = 57·4 kcal/mole. Thus replacement of the methyl groups by the more electronegative trifluoromethyl groups causes a strengthening of the As—C bond by ~3 kcal/mole.

A simpler expression of the bond strengthening in mixed compounds is in terms of the heat of the gas phase redistribution reaction

$$\tfrac{1}{2}\,HgR_2 + \tfrac{1}{2}\,HgX_2 \rightarrow RHgX.$$

Thus, for R=Me, and X=Cl, $\Delta H = -6{\cdot}6$ kcal/mole. The negative value of ΔH implies a bond strengthening in the mixed compound, which is taken to arise from ionicity changes in the bonds, although it offers no indication which of the bonds are strengthened. Similarly, for the tin alkyls, there appears to be considerable bond strengthening in the mixed compounds,[(26)] e.g.

$$\tfrac{3}{4}SnMe_4 + \tfrac{1}{4}SnBr_4 \rightarrow Me_3SnBr, \quad \Delta H = -10{\cdot}8 + 3 \text{ kcal/mole.}$$

2. Transition Metal Halides

For want of a value for the valence-state excitation energy of the mercury atom in the compounds HgR_2, it was difficult to calculate to what extent the dissociation energies were affected by these excitation energies. For the series of compounds $TiCl_4$, $TiCl_3$ and $TiCl_2$ both heats of formation and excitation energies are available, and from these it is possible to show the effect of excitation energy and also of electronegativity changes on the Ti—Cl dissociation energies.

TABLE 8[a]

Heats of formation and mean dissociation energies, titanium halides

Compound	ΔH_f^0 (g), kcal/mole	$\bar{D}$(Ti—Cl), kcal/mole
$TiCl_4$	− 181·6	102·5
$TiCl_3$	− 128·7	109·4
$TiCl_2$	− 69·4	120·0

[a] Taken from ref. 288.

The thermochemical data are summarized in Table 8, which shows the heats of formation of the gaseous chlorides, and the mean dissociation energies for the Ti—Cl bonds in $TiCl_4$, $TiCl_3$ and $TiCl_2$, It is seen that the mean dissociation energy increases along the series $TiCl_4$, $TiCl_3$, $TiCl_2$. The question arises, to what extent are these mean dissociation energies influenced by the valence state excitation energies in the different molecules? These valence-state excitation energies have been calculated by Pilcher and Skinner[(288)] in the following way.

Of the eight alternative valence-states available to the titanium atom, in its compounds, (namely those derived from d^4, d^3s,

d^3p, d^2sp, d^2p^2, sdp^2, dp^3 and sp^3), the state d^3s has almost the lowest excitation energy, with negligible steric repulsion and relatively high bonding power. The square planar dsp^2 and d^2p^2 are comparatively unfavourable, as is the tetrahedral sp^3. However, it would appear most profitable to adopt a little isovalent hybridization, and form a hybrid obtained by mixing d^3s and sp^3; thus the bonding power, S, increases very rapidly from 2·44 for pure

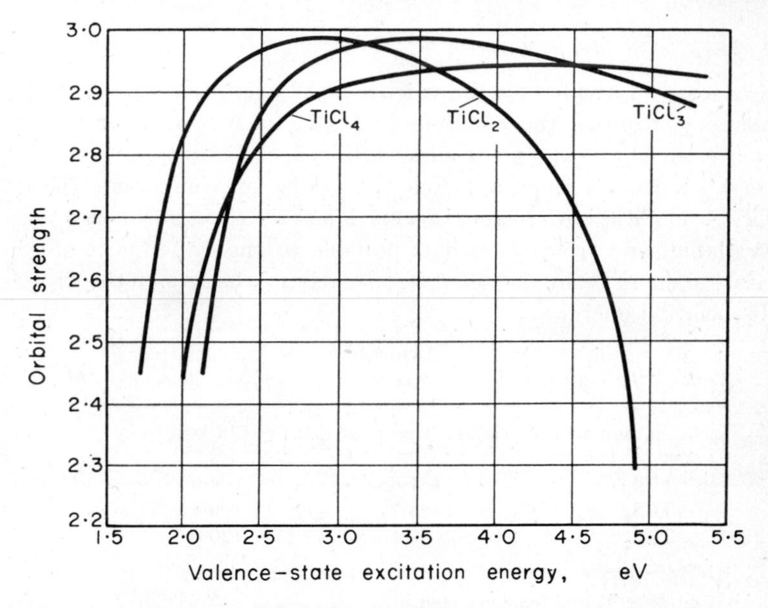

FIG. 5. Orbital strength and valence-state excitation energy of titanium chlorides (taken from Pilcher and Skinner, ref. 288).

d^3s to $> 2{\cdot}9$ on admixture of a little sp^3, for the additional cost of about 20 kcal/g atom. For $TiCl_4$ the *maximum* orbital strength derives from a configuration $sp^{9/8}d^{15/8}$.

The geometrical structures of TiCl and $TiCl_2$ are not known, and calculations were made by assuming $TiCl_3$ to have a trigonal planar structure and the $TiCl_2$ molecule to be angular, with the Cl—Ti—Cl angle 120°. The bonding orbitals in both $TiCl_2$ and the diatomic molecule TiCl are taken to be of the trigonal type.

Figure 5, taken from Pilcher and Skinner's paper, shows a plot of the bonding power or orbital strength of the hybridized orbitals, S, against the excitation energy required to achieve it, for $TiCl_4$, $TiCl_3$ and $TiCl_2$. The figure shows that in the region $S > 2{\cdot}9$, greater bonding power can be achieved for less expenditure of valence-state energy for the angular $TiCl_2$ than for the trigonal $TiCl_3$, which, in turn, requires less expenditure of energy than for the tetrahedral $TiCl_4$ molecule. This same conclusion is expressed in a slightly different way in Table 9, which lists the valence-state excitation energies, *V.E.*, required to form bonding orbitals of *maximum* strength in $TiCl_4$, $TiCl_3$, $TiCl_2$ and TiCl. Also given are the calculated ionization potentials, *I.P.*, of a bonding electron of Ti in these configurations, which are very approximate measures of the electronegativity of the atom in the particular valence state.

TABLE 9[a]

Valence-state excitation energies of titanium halides

Compound	Isovalent confign.	Bond Strength S	*V.E.* (kcal/mole)	*I.P.* (kcal/mole)
$TiCl_4$	$sp^{9/8}d^{15/8}$	2·945	96·2	213·5
$TiCl_3$	$sp^{8/9}d^{19/9}$	2·987	80·0	194·2
$TiCl_2$ (singlet)	$s^{38/27}p^{16/27}d^2$	2·987	67·3	185·6
TiCl (quartet)	$s^{19/27}p^{8/27}d^3$	2·987	61·3	111·4

[a] Taken from ref. 288

Energetically it might be more profitable for the titanium atom to adopt orbitals of less than maximum strength, with correspondingly less expenditure in valence-state energies, and furthermore assumptions have been made about the structural models of $TiCl_3$ and $TiCl_2$ which may be unrealistic. However, a qualitative significance can be attached to the values in the table, the important features of which are:

(i) valence-state excitation energies *decrease* in the sense $TiCl_4 > TiCl_3 > TiCl_2 > TiCl$; and

(ii) the electronegativity of the titanium atom (as reflected by the valence-state ionization potentials) decreases in a similar manner, i.e. a greater electronegativity *difference* appears between titanium and chlorine along the series $TiCl_4$, $TiCl_3$, $TiCl_2$, TiCl. The reason for these variations is that the degree of p-character in the isovalent configuration to produce four, three, two and finally one *strong* bonding orbital, decreases with the decrease in number of bonding orbitals; thus in $TiCl_4$ it is $p^{9/8}$, whilst in TiCl only $p^{8/27}$. Both diminishing valence-state energy and also increasing ionic character (and hence ionic-covalent resonance) operate in influencing the observed bond strengths which increase in passing from $TiCl_4$ through $TiCl_3$ and $TiCl_2$ to TiCl.

The explanation for this increase probably lies in an increase in ionic-covalent resonance stabilization in the sequence $TiCl_4 \rightarrow TiCl_3 \rightarrow TiCl_2$. The electronegativity of the titanium atom (as reflected by the valence-state ionization potentials) falls along the series $TiCl_4$, $TiCl_3$, $TiCl_2$, which makes for a *greater* electronegativity difference between the titanium and chlorine atoms along this series, and consequently greater stabilization, due to this cause.

Summary

In this chapter we have been concerned with the dissociation energies of M—R bonds in compounds of the type MR_n. In the group of compounds investigated, M is either a transition metal, a representative metal (e.g. Li, Al) or a *b*-Group metal (e.g. Zn, Ga). The group R is either an organic radical (e.g. methyl, cyclopentadienyl) or a halogen atom.

The bond strengths in these compounds are influenced by a number of factors which include the following. (i) Valence state excitation energies. (ii) Ionic-covalent resonance stabilization, seen for example in compounds RHgX, and $TiCl_x$. (iii) The possibility of additional π-bonding, for example π-bonding is probably more marked in $Ni(CO)_4$ than in $Fe(CO)_5$. (iv) The effect of anti-bonding electrons, a factor which may account for stronger metal-ring bonding in the compound $Fe(C_5H_5)_2$ than in $Ni(C_5H_5)_2$.

CHAPTER 9

IONIZATION ENERGIES IN AQUEOUS SOLUTION

Introduction

So far we have considered only those dissociation processes which take place in the gas phase. This chapter is concerned with dissociation processes, or more strictly with ionization processes in aqueous solution. This introduces a number of additional variable factors. For example, the ionization process $CH_3COOH(aq) \rightarrow CH_3COO^-(aq) + H^+(aq)$, can be thought of as occurring in a number of separate stages:

(*a*) $CH_3COOH(aq) \rightarrow CH_3COOH(g)$;
(*b*) $CH_3COOH(g) \rightarrow CH_3COO(g) + H(g)$;
(*c*) $CH_3COO(g) + e^- \rightarrow CH_3COO^-(g)$;
(*d*) $CH_3COO^-(g) \rightarrow CH_3COO^-(aq)$;
(*e*) $H(g) \rightarrow H^+(aq) + e^-$.

For a homologous series of acids, RCOOH, the ionization heat will, therefore, be affected by the dissociation energy of the oxygen-hydrogen bond (*b*), the electron affinity of the radical RCOO (*c*), and the hydration energy of the ion $RCOO^-$(d). From a study of the variations of ionization heats, within a homologous series, it may be possible to suggest which of these factors is important.

Hitherto, the many studies of ionization processes in solution have been confined mainly to determination of dissociation constants, from which free energies of ionization can be calculated. Relatively few investigations have been concerned with heats and entropies of ionization. Some heats and entropies of ionization have been calculated from electrochemical data by Everett and Wynne-Jones[(289)] and by Harned and Owen.[(290)] There have been few data available for members of homologous series of compounds.

In a recent series of papers, Laidler[(291)] and his co-workers have measured the heats of neutralization of a number of such series, including the aliphatic acids;[246] methyl-substituted pyridines,[292] phenols,[293] and anilines;[294] and some methyl- and methoxy-substituted benzoic acids.[295] Other workers have investigated substituted phenols,[295,297] and a number of halo-acetic acids.[298] These studies have been made in an endeavour to establish to what extent variations in acid strength (the free energy of ionization) are dependent on entropy effects or on heat effects, and in the latter case whether these are due to changes in bond strengths or in hydration heats.

Heats of Neutralization of Strong Acids and Strong Bases

The heats of neutralization of strong acids by strong bases have been measured on a number of occasions. The early calorimetric studies, prior to 1930, are those of Richards and Rowe[299] and of Richards and Hall,[300] who worked with a variety of strong acids and bases at concentrations, after mixing, of 1 M and higher. A number of workers, including Rossini[301] and Pitzer[302] have used Richards' data, together with heats of dilution, to calculate the heat, at infinite dilution and at 25 °C, of the process
$H_3O^+ + OH^- \rightarrow 2H_2O$ $\Delta H = -13{\cdot}32$ to $-13{\cdot}27$ kcal/g equivalent. Later work of Bender and Bierman[303] and of Bierman and Weber,[304] in 1954, has provided support for this value of $-13{\cdot}32$ kcal/g equivalent.

The heat of this process, at infinite dilution, can also be calculated from the temperature dependence of various cells, and values of 13·49 and 13·51 kcal have been obtained by Everett and Wynne–Jones[289] and by Harned and Owen,[290] respectively.

The calorimetric values are lower than the electrochemical ones by 0·15 to 0·2 kcal, which is outside the range of errors of the electrochemical values of $\pm$ 0·05 kcal, although the errors of the thermochemical values are difficult to assess.

Because of the lack of sensitivity of the calorimeters used, the determinations had to be made at fairly high concentrations, ($\sim$1 M) so that a sufficiently large heat was evolved to be measured accurately. The weakness of this early calorimetric work lies in the large heat corrections involved in extrapolating to infinite dilution.

Recently, Papée, Canady and Laidler[305] have used a very sensitive calorimeter, a microcalorimeter of the Tian-Calvet type, which is capable of making accurate ($\pm 0{\cdot}5$ per cent) measurements of heats as small as 5×10^{-2} calories. With samples of 10 ml, this means that accurate measurements can be made of heats of neutralization down to concentrations of about $5 \times 10^{-4} M$.

Using this technique, the heats of neutralization of sulphuric acid and sodium hydroxide and of hydrochloric acid and sodium hydroxide have been measured at concentrations $5 \times 10^{-4} N$ to $3 \times 10^{-2} N$, and this has permitted the value at infinite dilution to be obtained by a short extrapolation.

The following values, at infinite dilution and at 25 °C, were obtained:

$$H_2SO_4\text{—}NaOH, \quad \Delta H^0 = -13{\cdot}52 \pm 0{\cdot}06 \text{ kcal/g equivalent,}$$

and $$HCl\text{—}NaOH, \quad \Delta H^0 = -13{\cdot}48 \pm 0{\cdot}05 \text{ kcal/g equivalent.}$$

Thus they arrive at an average value of ΔH^0 for the process, $H_3O^+ + OH^- \rightarrow 2H_2O$, $\Delta H^0 = -13{\cdot}50 \pm 0{\cdot}05$ kcal/g equivalent, which is close to that obtained from electrochemical data.

Aliphatic Acids

The heats of neutralization, ΔH_n, for some aliphatic acids, which are shown in Table 1, are those of the process

$$RCOOH + OH^- \rightarrow RCOO^- + H_2O,$$

occurring at infinite dilution. By combining the value $\Delta H = -13{\cdot}50$ kcal/g equivalent for the neutralization

$$H_3O^+ + OH^- \rightarrow 2H_2O,$$

we obtain the heats of ionization, ΔH, for the process

$$RCOOH + H_2O \rightarrow RCOO^- + H_3O^+.$$

From the pk values for these acids, the free energies, ΔG, may be calculated, and using the relationship $\Delta G = \Delta H - T\Delta S$, the entropies of ionization, ΔS, may be derived. Such data for some aliphatic acids are shown in Table 1.

It is seen that the ΔG values become more positive along the series formic, acetic, propionic acid, corresponding to the decrease in acidic character. Thus the difference in ΔG between formic and acetic is 1·35 kcal and between acetic and propionic acids, 0·16 kcal. There is, however, no particular relationship between ΔH and ΔG, and, in fact, the ΔH values remain practically constant, the change between formic and acetic acids being only 0·07 kcal.

TABLE 1

Heats and entropies of ionization

Acid	*pk*	ΔH_n (kcal/mole)	ΔH (kcal/mole)	ΔG (kcal/mole)	ΔS (cal/mole deg)
Formic	3·77	$-13{\cdot}63 \pm 0{\cdot}04$	$-0{\cdot}13$	5·14	$-17{\cdot}7$
Acetic	4·76	$-13{\cdot}57 \pm 0{\cdot}02$	$-0{\cdot}07$	6·49	$-22{\cdot}0$
Propionic	4·88	$-13{\cdot}58 \pm 0{\cdot}02$	$-0{\cdot}08$	6·65	$-22{\cdot}6$

The entropy of ionization decreases as the acid becomes more complex, and there is some relationship between ΔS and ΔG. The rather surprising fact emerges that the decrease in acid strength is an *entropy effect*. The explanation may be that since the acid is weakened by the addition of methyl groups, the conjugate base, the $RCOO^-$ ion, becomes progressively stronger, i.e. the negative charge is intensified. This will cause more electrorestriction of water molecules, and lowering of the entropy of the ion. The larger entropy losses are associated, therefore, with the weaker acids, acetic and propionic.

Methyl-substituted Compounds

We turn now to the ionization process of a series of methyl monosubstituted ring systems: pyridines, anilines, phenols, and substituted benzoic acids. Table 2 shows the free energies, ΔG, the heats, ΔH, and entropies of ionization, ΔS, for a number of these compounds. The compounds fall into two classes, according to the different ionic nature of the ionization process. The pyridine and aniline ionizations are of the type

$$BH^+ + H_2O \rightarrow B + H_3O^+,$$

and the heats of ionization are simply the heats of neutralization,

TABLE 2

Free energies, heats, and entropies of ionization, methyl mono-substituted compounds

	ΔG (kcal/mole)	ΔH (kcal/mole)	ΔS (cal/mole deg)		ΔG (kcal/mole)	ΔH (kcal/mole)	ΔS (cal/mole deg)
Ionization process: $BH^+ + H_2O \rightarrow B + H_3O^+$							
Pyridine	7·12	5·70	− 4·76	Aniline	6·24	6·74	1·66
2-Picoline	8·13	6·95	− 3·95	*o*-Toluidine	5·98	8·25	7·60
3-Picoline	7·68	6·70	− 3·28	*m*-Toluidine	6·35	8·00	5·53
4-Picoline	8·15	7·03	− 3·77	*p*-Toluidine	6·91	4·98	− 6·48
Ionization process: $BH + H_2O \rightarrow B^- + H_3O^+$							
Benzoic acid	5·74	0·09	− 18·9	Phenol	13·63	5·60	− 27·0
o-Toluic acid	5·33	− 1·50	− 22·9	*o*-Cresol	14·03	7·13	− 23·2
m-Toluic acid	5·78	0·07	− 19·2	*m*-Cresol	13·76	4·90	− 29·8
p-Toluic acid	5·92	0·24	− 19·0	*p*-Cresol	14·00	4·23	− 32·8
Phenol	13·61	5·65	− 27·0	Phenol	13·61	5·65	− 27·0
o-Chlorophenol	11·64	4·63	− 23·5	*o*-Nitrophenol	9·85	4·66	− 17·4
m-Chlorophenol	—	—	—	*m*-Nitrophenol	11·42	4·71	− 22·5
p-Chlorophenol	12·81	5·80	− 23·5	*p*-Nitrophenol	9·74	4·70	− 16·9

with a reversal sign. The phenol and benzoic acid ionizations are of the type

$$BH + H_2O \rightarrow B^- + H_3O^+.$$

Here the heats of ionization are calculated from a measured value of the heat of neutralization $BH + OH^- \rightarrow B^- + H_2O$, together with the known heat of neutralization $H_3O^+ + OH^- \rightarrow 2\,H_2O$.

The ΔG values are the easiest to interpret. Amongst these mono-methyl derivatives, the introduction of a methyl group into any position of pyridine, aniline or benzoic acid causes, in general, an *increase* in ΔG. (The exceptions to this generalization are (i) *o*-toluidine and (ii) *o*-toluic acid.) This effect is usually attributed, in a somewhat sweeping way, to the inductive effect of the methyl group, which decreases the ease with which the proton is lost by the acid.

1. Picolines

This simple explanation would seem to be in agreement with the data for pyridine and the picolines. Here the ΔH values very roughly parallel the ΔG values, whilst ΔS remains almost constant. Now it is suggested that polar effects, arising from inductive and resonance influence of the methyl substituent, affect ΔH, but not ΔS, which would make ΔH and ΔG values run parallel. In this series, then, it appears that polar or inductive effects predominate, and are not modified by either steric or solvent effects, both of which would alter ΔS. This is to be expected where the functional group (the nitrogen atom) is embedded in the ring.

2. Cresols

Where the functional group is not so embedded in the ring, as in the case of phenol and the cresols, we might anticipate that other effects would complicate a simple variation of ΔH due to polar causes.

In the *m*- and *p*-cresols both ΔH and ΔS are *lowered*, as compared with phenol. A methyl group in the *meta* position lowers ΔH by 0·70 kcal and one in the *para* position by 1·37 kcal/mole (in contrast to the pyridine case where the ΔH values become more positive). These effects presumably result from the intensification of the negative charges on the oxygen atom and on the *ortho* and *para* carbon atoms, due to the inductive effect of the methyl group. This intensification will result in an increased electrorestriction of water molecules, and a corresponding reduction in the enthalpy of the ion.

Now the ΔG values do not show this effect, in fact the trend is to slightly increased ΔG values of 0·13 and 0·37 kcal/mole for *m*- and *p*-cresol, as compared with phenol. It is concluded that the lowering of ΔS, (corresponding to a more positive value for $-T\Delta S$) resulting from the increased binding of water molecules to the ion,

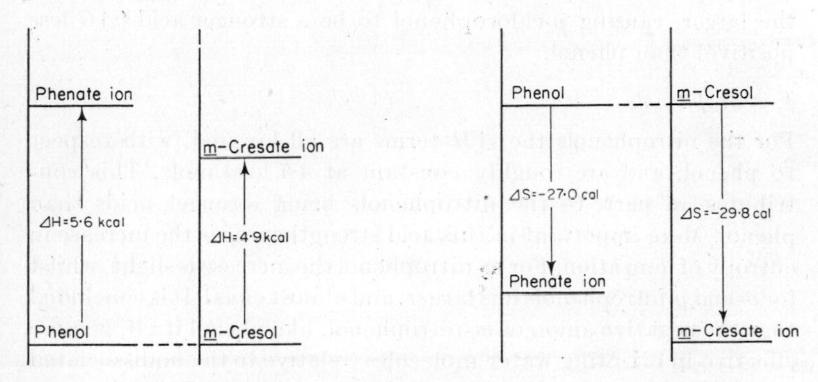

FIG. 1. Energy diagram of the heats and entropies of ionization of phenol and *m*-cresol

almost exactly compensates for the reduction in the enthalpy of the ion. This compensation effect is shown diagrammatically, in terms of ΔH and ΔS in Fig. 1 for *m*-cresol.

The *o*-cresol behaves differently, since here there is an *increase* in ΔH of 1·53 kcal/mole, and this is associated with an *increase* in entropy of 3·8 cal/mole deg. Since both the $-$OH and $-O^-$ groups are small, it is unlikely that there will be much steric interference between these groups and the methyl group in the *ortho* position. However, the presence of a methyl group in the *ortho* position will tend to decrease the extent of binding of water molecules, especially to the O^- ion, where operation of the inductive effect is favoured, and therefore increase the enthalpy and entropy of the ion, and hence the ΔH and ΔS ionization. For the cresols, then, it is the solvent effects which predominate.

3. Chlorophenols

In contrast to *m*- and *p*-cresols, where both ΔH and ΔS are *lowered* as compared with phenol, for *p*-chlorophenol ΔH and ΔS are *raised*, when compared with the parent phenol. The electron-attracting chlorine atom presumably reduces the negative charges on the oxygen atom attached to the *para* carbon atoms, (an effect more marked in the ion than on the neutral molecule) leading to decrease in electrorestriction of water molecules, and resulting in an increase in both the enthalpy and entropy of the ion. The entropy effect is the larger, causing *p*-chlorophenol to be a stronger acid (ΔG less positive) than phenol.

4. Nitrophenols

For the nitrophenols the ΔH terms are all lowered, with respect to phenol, and are roughly constant at 4·7 kcal/mole. This contributes, in part, to the nitrophenols being stronger acids than phenol. More important in this acid strengthening is the increase in entropy of ionization. For *m*-nitrophenol the increase is slight, whilst for *o*- and *p*-nitrophenols it is larger, and almost equal. It is concluded that the negative anion of *m*-nitrophenol, like phenol itself, is more effective in orienting water molecules (relative to the undissociated compounds) than are the anions of *o*-nitrophenols. Thus the *meta* substituted nitro group has little effect on the negative charge of the phenolic group, whilst the *ortho* and *para* substitute nitro groups tend to reduce this negative charge. In all these cases the major effects are due to solute-solvent interactions.

5. Toluidines

As with the phenols, but in contrast to the pyridines, for the methyl-substituted anilines there is a relationship between ΔH and ΔS. This is shown in Fig. 2, a plot of $T\Delta S$ against ΔH. It is seen that there is some compensation of ΔH by $T\Delta S$. This effect Laidler[(248)] ascribes mainly to solvent and steric factors.

The introduction of a methyl group into the *para* position of aniline causes a *decrease* in both ΔH and ΔS. A possible explanation of this is in terms of solvent effect. The $-CH_3$ group will tend to reduce the positive charge on the $-NH_3^+$ group; and there will, therefore, be less electrorestriction of water and a consequent increase in enthalpy and entropy of the cationic form, BH^+. For the *para* substituted compound the groups are too widely separated for steric factors to be operative.

In contrast, for *m*-toluidine, there is an *increase* in both ΔH and ΔS (the opposite of the effect observed for *m*-cresol) as compared with the values for aniline. Now it is likely that there is some steric interference between the $—NH_3^+$ and m-CH_3 groups and this will cause a lowering of the entropy of the cationic form, BH^+. In the neutral form this will not occur and there will be a consequent

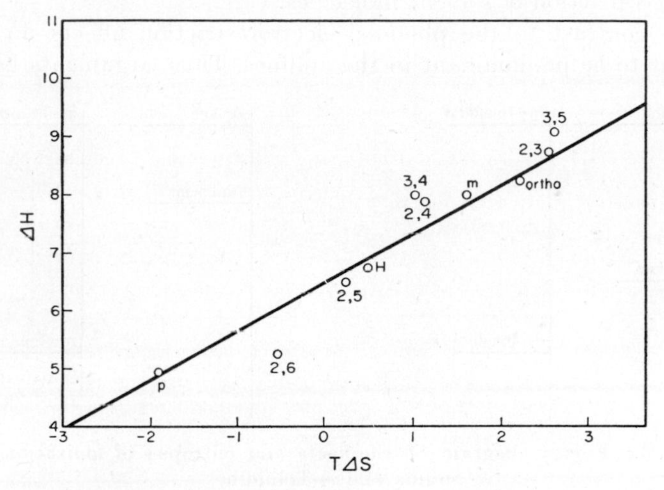

FIG. 2. Plot of ΔH against $T\Delta S$ for the ionization of the anilines (taken from Zawidski, Papée, Canady and Laidler, ref. 294).

increase in ΔS. The increase in ΔH can be attributed to the inductive effect (as in the pyridine) which will tend to lower the enthalpy of the cationic form BH^+, more than it will lower the enthalpy of the neutral molecule, and so lead to an increased ΔH. These effects are shown diagrammatically in Fig. 3. Again, these two effects of increased ΔH and increased ΔS compensate, so that the effect on ΔG is very small.

With a methyl group in the *ortho*-position the effect of an increased entropy of the cationic form, BH^+, will be much more marked, because of the much greater steric interference between $—NH_3^+$ and $—CH_3$ groups. The extent of this ΔS effect is now so great as to cause a decrease in ΔG as compared with aniline, and the protons can leave more readily. The steric effect is, therefore, more important than the inductive effect, which operates in the reverse sense, as far as ΔG is concerned.

It is significant that, in agreement with these ideas, these effects are not found in the pyridines, where steric effects are not to be expected. For the pyridines, the ΔS values are practically constant for the monomethyl derivatives, since the inductive effect leaves ΔS unaffected, except in so far as it causes alteration in electrorestriction of solvent molecules.

In contrast to the phenols, electrorestriction effects do not appear to be predominant in the anilines. Thus, arguments based

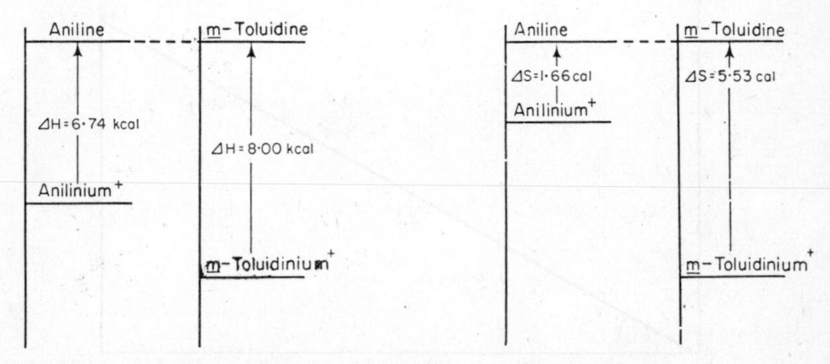

FIG. 3. Energy diagram of the heats and entropies of ionization of aniline and *m*-Toluidine.

on electrorestriction of water would suggest that the *o*-toluidine cation would have an abnormally high entropy, owing to the exclusion of water molecules, so that ΔS would be abnormally low, and this is not the case. This is no doubt due to the relatively large size of the $—NH_3^+$ group, so that an adjacent $—CH_3$ group has little effect in excluding water molecules, whereas the $—O^-$ group, being so much smaller is masked by a methyl group in the *ortho*-position.

6. *Methyl-Benzoic Acids*

The introduction of a methyl group into either the *meta* or *para* positions of benzoic acid is seen to increase ΔG very slightly. This is attributed to the inductive effect of the methyl group. It is seen that the alteration in ΔS is very small, which supports the idea that only polar effects are operative, since Laidler[291] has suggested that such effects influence ΔH and not ΔS.

The fact that steric and solvent effects are apparently not involved, in contrast to the situation with the phenols and anilines requires some explanation. The large size of the —COO⁻ group, and the fact that the charge is smeared by resonance over the two oxygen atoms, is probably responsible for there being little electrorestriction of water molecules by this group. Furthermore, structures involving resonance, such as those shown in Fig. 4 are unlikely, in view of the fact that two negative charges are brought close together. As a result, in contrast to the situation with, say, *m*- and *p*-cresol, there is not much electrorestriction at the benzene ring itself. Likewise steric effects due to a $—CH_3$ group, in the

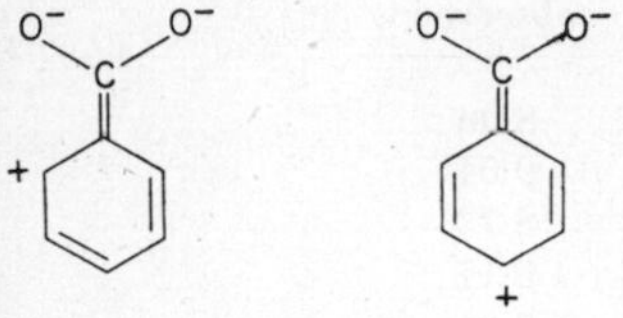

FIG. 4.

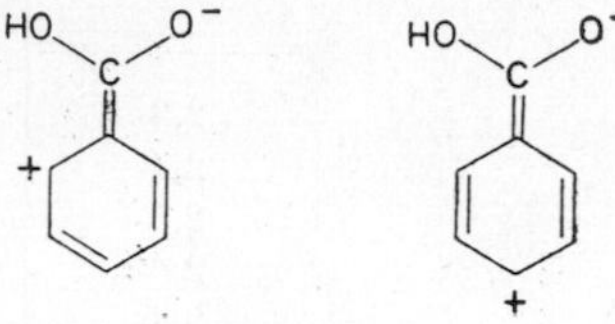

FIG. 5.

meta position will be less than suggested for *m*-toluidine, and will not be important in the present case. The situation is similar to the pyridines, in that only inductive effects appear to be involved.

When the substituents are in the *ortho* position, however, direct steric interference becomes important. The lower ΔG value for *o*-toluic acid may be explained [306] in terms of the inhibition of resonance involving the structures shown in Fig. 5.

Resonance of this type will be much more important in the undissociated molecules than in the anions, B^-, (as noted above), and will, therefore, constitute an acid strengthening effect. In these structures the $(—COOH)^-$ group lies in the plane of the benzene ring and an *ortho* substituent, by forcing the group out of the plane, will reduce the resonance, decrease the rigidity of the molecule, and will, therefore, raise the free energy of the undissociated form, relative to that of the anion.

This effect is also expected to give rise to an increased enthalpy of the undissociated form, and therefore, to a decrease in the ΔH of ionization. This is found to be the case.

The heat and entropy results for the *ortho* substituted compound therefore provide support for the concept that these groups interfere with the resonance in the undissociated molecule.

7. Lutidines and Xylenols

We turn now to the methyl disubstituted pyridines (lutidines), phenols (xylenols) and anilines, for which the ΔG, ΔH and ΔS values for the ionization process are available.

TABLE 3

Estimated and observed free energies of ionization for the lutidines (dimethylpyridines)

Lutidine	ΔG (kcal/mole)	
	estimated	observed
2,3-	8·69	8·96
2,4-	9·16	9·04
2,5-	9·69	8·73
2,6-	9·14	9·17
3,4-	8·71	8·81
3,5-	8·24	8·39

Despite the fact that ΔG is not a simple quantity, but a function of ΔH and ΔS, its variation with change of structural parameters obeys a simple relationship, as may be seen from the "additivity" of ΔG values. This term is used here in the sense that the thermodynamic quantities for disubstituted compounds may be predicted from the changes produced when single substituents are introduced separately. The free energies of ionization of some methyl disubstituted pyridines, anilines and phenols are shown in Table 4 (to which we shall refer in detail later). From ΔG values for the parent and mono-substituted compounds it is possible to estimate ΔG values for disubstituted compounds. Thus, from the ΔG values for pyridine and the picolines, the following increments are calculated:[292] 2-methyl 1·01, 3-methyl 0·56, 4-methyl 1·03.

The use of these values leads to the estimated ΔG values shown in Table 3, and these are in satisfactory agreement with the observed values. Similar correlations are found for the phenols and anilines.

In Table 4 there are shown the ΔG, ΔH and ΔS values for the ionization process of some methyl disubstituted pyridines, anilines and phenols. As might be expected, they are not as easily interpreted as the data for the methyl mono-substituted derivatives.

TABLE 4

Free energies, heats and entropies of ionization, methyl disubstituted compounds

Ionization process: $BH^+ + H_2O \rightarrow B + H_3O^+$

	ΔG (kcal/mole)	ΔH (kcal/mole)	ΔS (cal/mole deg)
Pyridine	7·12	5·70	− 4·76
2,3-Lutidine	8·96		
2,4-	9·04		
2,5-	8·73		
2,6-	9·17	6·15	− 10·11
3,4-	8·81		
3,5-	8·39		

Ionization process: $BH + H_2O \rightarrow B^- + H_3O^+$

	ΔG (kcal/mole)	ΔH (kcal/mole)	ΔS (cal/mole deg)
Phenol	13·63	5·60	− 27·0
2,3-Xylenol	14·14	6·61	− 25·3
2,4-	14·29	7·68	− 22·1
2,5-	13·90	6·22	− 25·7
2,6-	14·45	4·95	− 31·9
3,4-	13·86	8·24	− 18·9
3,5-	13·67	7·51	− 20·7

Whereas the ΔS values for pyridine and the picolines were virtually constant at about −4·0 cal/mole deg, the value for 2,6-lutidine is −10·11 cal/mole deg. In addition, the ΔH value of 6·15 kcal/mole is an increase of only 0·45 kcal as compared with the value for pyridine, in contrast to an increase of some 1·3 kcal/mole for the picolines. A plausible explanation of this, in terms of solvent effects, is that in the conjugate acid BH^+, electrorestriction of water molecules is considerably hindered by the presence of two methyl groups in the ortho positions. This would give an abnormally high enthalpy and entropy to the BH^+ ion. This effect is not revealed in the ΔG value; the effect therefore produces exactly compensating changes in ΔH and $T\Delta S$.

For the methyl mono-substituted phenols, the cresols, it has been suggested that solvent effects are predominant. The same seems likely in the xylenols.

The ΔS values for 2,4-, 3,4- and 3,5-compounds are especially high. A possible explanation of this is that the electrorestriction of water molecules to the aromatic ring plays a more important role

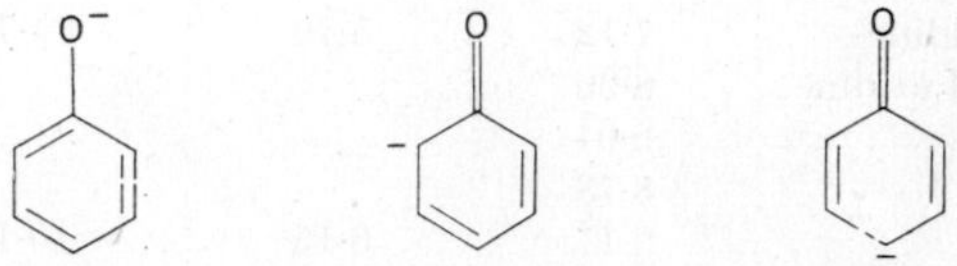

I II III

FIG. 6.

than has hitherto been supposed. In the anions of these compounds there are important contributions from the resonance structures shown in Fig. 6. There is, therefore, an appreciable amount of binding of water in the *ortho* and *para* positions. Groups attached to these positions, or even at neighbouring positions, may bring about an appreciable reduction of such electrorestriction and a consequent increase in energy and entropy of the ionized form, B^-. Such interference will be particularly important in the disubstituted compounds, and abnormally high ΔS and ΔH values for the 2,4-, 3,4- and 3,5-compounds may be related to this effect.

With the 2,6-compound a special explanation seems necessary, since here the ΔS value is considerably lower, at $-31{\cdot}9$ cal/mole deg, than the remainder. The introduction of a single methyl group into the *ortho* position tends to favour structures II and III owing to the inductive effect, as already mentioned in considering *o*-cresol. The introduction of a second methyl group into the *ortho* position, however, tends to counteract structure II, and hence lead to a reduction in entropy.

8. Summary of Data for Methyl-substituted Compounds

To summarize the thermodynamic findings of these ionization processes, Laidler[291] has made the following points.

Firstly: the fact that free energies for these processes in solution are quite strictly additive, whereas ΔH and $T\Delta S$ values are not, implies that ΔG is a simpler function than are ΔH and $T\Delta S$. Secondly: the existence of these linear free energy relationships in cases where there are no such relationships for ΔH and $T\Delta S$ requires that the latter functions are affected by factors that leave ΔG unchanged. Since ΔG is the difference between ΔH and $T\Delta S$ this can only be so if certain factors influence ΔH and $T\Delta S$ in a compensating manner so that there is little effect on ΔG. It is suggested that these factors are those associated with *steric* and *solvent-solute* interactions.

Variations in ΔH and ΔS have been accounted for by the following three effects:

(*a*) *Polar* effects, arising from inductive and resonance influences of substituents, are considered to affect ΔH but not ΔS. Examples of this are the picolines and toluic acids.

(*b*) *Steric* effects, such as those arising from the interference between an *ortho* substituent and the functional ionizing group, are considered to affect ΔH and ΔS. Under certain circumstances there is an approximate compensation between ΔH and $T\Delta S$, and ΔG retains an additivity relationship. This is the case with the anilines.

(*c*) *Solvent* effects, arising from solvent-solute interactions, are also considered to affect ΔH and ΔS. As with the steric effects, there may be a compensation between ΔH and $T\Delta S$, and an additivity of ΔG remains, although no such additivity relationships are found for ΔH and ΔS. This effect is found to predominate with the phenols.

Halogen-Substituted Acetic Acids

Using a method of enthalpy dependent "thermometric titrations", Jordan and Dumbaugh[298, 308] have measured the heats of ionization, at 25 °C, of a number of acids. The heats and derived entropies of ionization of the halo-acetic acids are shown in Table 5.

In all cases substitution of an α-hydrogen atom by a halogen increases the acid strength, (ΔG becomes less positive) and successive substitution further increases acid strength. However, this decrease in ΔG is much less a result of a more negative enthalpy change, ΔH, than it is due to the entropy factor. Thus, except for monofluoroacetic acid ($\Delta H = -1{\cdot}0$ kcal/mole) and monochloro-

TABLE 5

Free energies, heats and entropies of ionization, of the halo-acetic acids

	ΔG	ΔH	ΔS
	(kcal/mole)		(cal/mole deg)
Acetic	6·6	0·0 ± 0·3	− 22 ± 1
Monofluoroacetic	3·5	− 1·0 ± 0·1	− 15 ± 1
Difluoroacetic	1·8	0·0 ± 0·8	− 6 ± 3
Trifluoroacetic	0·3	0·0 ± 0·9	− 1 ± 3
Acetic	6·6	0·0 ± 0·3	− 22 ± 1
Monochloroacetic	4·1	− 1·3 ± 0·1	− 18 ± 1
Dichloroacetic	1·7	− 0·1 ± 0·5	− 6 ± 2
Trichloroacetic	2·1	+ 1·5 ± 1·5	+ 2 ± 5
Acetic	6·6	0·0 ± 0·3	− 22 ± 1
Monobromoacetic	4·0	− 0·5 ± 0·3	− 15 ± 1
Dibromoacetic	1·9	− 0·5 ± 0·9	− 8 ± 3
Tribromoacetic	− 0·2	− 0·8 ± 0·3	− 2 ± 1
Acetic	6·6	0·0 ± 0·3	− 22 ± 1
Monoiodoacetic	4·3	− 0·8 ± 0·1	− 17 ± 1

acetic acid ($\Delta H = -1{\cdot}3$ kcal/mole), as compared with acetic acid itself ($\Delta H = 0{\cdot}0$ kcal/mole), the change in the ΔH term in passing from acetic acid to the halo-acetic acids is less than 1·0 kcal/mole.

The explanation of the increase in acid strength on substitution is often expressed as follows:[307] that chlorine, for example, is strongly electron-attracting and produces a displacement of the type Cl ← C(O) ← O ← H. From this, it is usually implied that the result is a weakening of the O—H bond, leading to a more negative enthalpy of ionization. Such a simple explanation is not justified from the experimentally measured ΔH values.

The entropies of ionization do show a monotonous increase with halogen substitution. It may be that the inductive effect of the halogen atom is greater on the anion, $CH_{3-n}X_nCOO^-$, than on the acid from which it is derived, $CH_{3-n}X_nCOOH$, and this tends to delocalize the negative charge over the whole ion. This will cause less electrorestriction of water molecules, and a rise in the entropy of the ion, a situation just the opposite to that found in the series formic, acetic, and propionic acids.

Dibasic Organic Acids

Jordan and Dumbaugh have also measured [308] the heats of ionization of the series of dibasic acids from oxalic to azelaic acid (except suberic acid) and the results are shown in Table 6. Along this series

TABLE 6
Free energies, heats and entropies of ionization of some organic dibasic acids

	ΔG	ΔH	ΔS
	(kcal/mole)		(cal/mole deg)
Oxalic	8·9	− 0·7 ± 0·7	− 32 ± 2
Malonic	10·8	− 0·9 ± 0·7	− 39 ± 2
Succinic	9·9	1·5 ± 0·6	− 38 ± 2
Glutaric	13·1	− 1·3 ± 0·2	− 48 ± 1
Adipic	13·3	− 1·7 ± 0·4	− 50 ± 1
Pimelic	13·4	− 1·6 + 0·3	− 50 ± 1
Suberic	—	—	—
Azelaic	13·5	− 1·5 ± 0·3	− 50 ± 1

the ΔS term becomes increasingly negative, although it appears to level out to a value of − 50 cal/mole deg after adipic acid. Apart from the anomalous value of + 1·5 kcal/mole for the heat of ionization of succinic acid, the ΔH term steadily becomes more negative along the series, by about 1·0 kcal/mole.

The decrease in acid strength from oxalic acid to azelaic (except for succinic acid) is thus mainly an entropy effect once more. Presumably with the lower acids oxalic and malonic there is some steric restriction, due to the closeness of the negative charges, which reduces the extent of electrorestriction of water molecules. With increasing separation of the charges, as the series is ascended, the entropy losses on ionization will be increased.

Conclusion

The approach which has been used to interpret the varying strengths of the substituted acids and bases, considered so far, might be summed up in the words of Fernandez and Helper.[296] These authors stress that any attempt to calculate or correlate heats and entropies of ionization of a series of acids (or bases) must take account of the energy changes that occur *within* the acid as a result of losing (or gaining) a proton and acquiring a negative (or positive) charge. This problem is usually approached from the point of view of resonance, induction, etc., effects on the enthalpy and entropy difference between the acid and its anion (or the base and its cation). Equally important is the consideration of energy effects arising *outside* the molecule and ion, due to the differences between molecule-solvent and ion-solvent interaction. Since Pitzer[302] has shown that for a series of acids the "internal" entropies of the anions are less than those of the corresponding acids by an amount that is nearly constant, then in many cases entropies of ionization for acids are due mainly to differences in solvent-solute interactions. Moreover, the varying strengths of acids can in many cases be shown to depend on entropy rather than enthalpy factors.

CHAPTER 10

BOND STRENGTHS IN SILICON, PHOSPHORUS AND SULPHUR COMPOUNDS

Introduction

Two main causes have been suggested to account for bond strength-ening in covalent molecules. The first is that electronegativity differences between the atoms A and B, in a bond A—B, reflect a certain amount of polar character of the bond. This means that there is a charge distribution, say of the type $\overset{\delta+}{A}$—$\overset{\delta-}{B}$, and that the bond may be represented by both the covalent form A—B, and the ionic form $\overset{+}{A}\overset{-}{B}$. This "ionic-covalent" resonance causes a lowering of the energy of the molecule, and a strengthening of the bonds.

The other cause of bond strengthening has been attributed to some additional π-bonding. In the case of a chain of carbon atoms with conjugated double bonding, —C=C—C=C—, there may be a —p_π—p_π—p_π— bond. Now whereas bonding between elements of the first period of the Periodic Table involves only $2s$- and $2p$-orbitals, because of the relatively high energy of $3d$-orbitals, the second period elements can use $3d$-orbitals for bonding, since the energy difference between the $3d$- and the $3s$- and $3p$-orbitals is considerably less. The same situation obtains for the third and subsequent periods, and it has already been suggested that π-bonding involving d-orbitals is important in some molecular addition compounds, such as $Me_3P \cdot GaMe_3$, and in the metal carbonyl and cyclopentadienyl compounds.

π-Bonding involving d-orbitals is also likely to be found in compounds of sulphur and phosphorus and also in silicon compounds, for example in phosphoryl compounds, sulphoxides, siloxanes, silazanes, etc. In these compounds a second-period element is bonded to a first-period element, so that the π-bonding may be of the type d_π—p_π, involving the overlap of a d_π-with a p_π-orbital. This d_π—p_π-bonding is not confined to simple molecules and d_π-orbitals can also take part in delocalized π-bonding in compounds such as the cyclic phosphazenes (*I*) and the thiazyl compounds (*II*), Fig. 1. We shall review some of the thermochemical data which

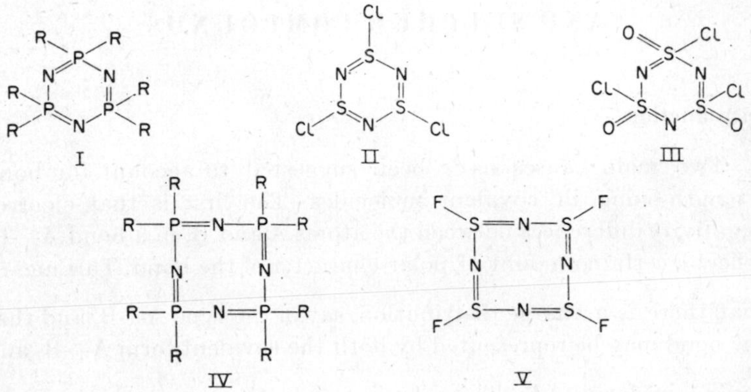

Fig. 1.

are available for silicon, phosphorus and sulphur compounds, to see if this type of bonding makes an important contribution to the overall energy content of the molecule.

d_π—p_π-Bonding in Simple Molecules

1. Silicon

Thermochemical data are available for some alkyl-substituted siloxanes and silazanes, and these are shown in Table 1. The bond energies E(Si—O) and E(Si—N) have been calculated from the heats of formation from the atoms, ΔH_f^a, in the usual way. The contributions to these ΔH_f^a values, due to the other bonds in the molecule are shown at the foot of the table. The most important of these is the sum of the bond energies in the group CH_3Si, i.e. E[SiMe]. This is calculated from the value $\Delta H_f^0[(Me_3Si)_2CH_2, g] = -85{\cdot}3$ kcal/mole.[309]

For the straight-chain polysiloxanes (*a*, *b*, and *c*, Table 1) the value of E(Si—O) increases as the chain length increases. This may be a real strengthening of these bonds due to greater electron delocalization, or conjugation, involving a continuous —d_π—p_π-bond. There is considerable evidence that d_π—p_π-bonding occurs in the siloxanes, for example the short observed bond length of *ca.* 1·64 Å,[312, 313] to be compared with a calculated length of 1·76 Å;[272] and the Si—O—Si bond angle of 155° found in the polysil-

TABLE 1
Bond energies in siloxanes and silazanes

Compound	$-\Delta H_f^0$ (l)[a]	$-\Delta H_f^0$(g)	$-\Delta H_f^a$ [b]	Bond energy[c]
				E(Si—O)
(*a*) $Me_3SiOSiMe_3$	194·1 ± 1·3[309]	185·2	2427·7	112·0 ± 0·7
(*b*) $Me_3SiOSi(Me_2)OSiMe_3$	341·4 ± 3·0[310]	332·5	3398·9	115·1 ± 0·7
(*c*) $Me_3SiO[Si(Me_2)O]_3SiMe_3$	650·3 ± 4·0[310]	637·6	5351·8	118·0 ± 0·5
(*d*) $[Me_2SiO]_4$	518·6 ± 1·2[309]	505·0	3800·5	107·8 ± 0·2
				E(Si—N)
(*e*) Me_3SiNEt_2	69·0 ± 1·5[329]	60·0	2468·9	73·9 ± 1·0
(*f*) $(Me_3Si)_2NH$	113·2 ± 1·7[309]	103·3	2451·4	77·1 ± 0·9
(*g*) $[Me_2SiNH]_4$	270·1 ± 2·5(c)[309]	251·1	3968·7	82·1 ± 0·3

[a] Based on $\Delta H_f^0(SiO_2$, amorph) = − 208·36 kcal/mole.
[b] ΔH_f^0(g) taken as follows: C, 170·9; H, 52·09; N, 112·9; O, 59·54[4]; Si, 110·0[309] kcal/g atom.
[c] Based on E[SiMe] = 367·3; $E[NEt_2]$ = 1293·1[311]; E(N—H) = 93·4 kcal/mole.[4]

oxanes,[314] which is much larger than that expected in terms of simple oxygen $2p$- or $2sp^3$-bonding. In view of this, the increase in bond energy of the silicon-oxygen bond might be attributed to conjugation, or increased electron delocalization along the chain. This is by no means the only explanation which can be offered, and reduction in steric strain, or changes in bonding power due to small changes in hybridization of the silicon orbitals might increase the silicon-oxygen bond strength. Such d_π—p_π-bonding would not, as might at first appear, affect the freedom of rotation about the silicon-oxygen bonds, because there are five orthogonal d-orbitals available on each silicon atom, and these make it possible for a π-bond to be formed to oxygen whatever the orientation of any one Si—O bond to any other in the chain; hence there is complete freedom of rotation in the chain as far as this effect is concerned.

However, for the eight-membered ring system, octamethylcyclotetrasiloxane (*d*), the value E(Si—O) = 107·8 kcal/mole is about 10 kcal/mole less than for the corresponding straight-chain polysiloxane. This is probably due to considerable strain in the cyclic molecule, caused by interaction between non-bonded methyl groups. This will be similar to the interaction in the corresponding cycloalkane, cyclo-octane, where there is a small strain energy due to repulsion between non-bonded hydrogen atoms. In the cyclic siloxane the strain is likely to be much greater.

Values for the silicon-nitrogen bond energy are known in three compounds, the "primary" N-diethyltrimethylsilazane (*e*), the "secondary" hexamethyldisilazane (*f*), and the cyclic octamethylcyclotetrasilazane. There is a slight increase of 3 kcal/mole in passing from the primary to the secondary silazane, which again might be attributed to increased delocalization in the Si—N—Si system. The steric requirements of two Me_3Si groups, in the secondary compound, are probably about the same as those of one Me_3Si group and two Et groups, so that it is unlikely that variation in E(Si—N) is due to steric factors.

Striking support for the idea of d_π—p_π-bonding comes from the non-basicity[315] of trisilylamine, $(SiH_3)_3N$, indicating extensive use of the nitrogen lone pair for π-bonding. In addition, the molecule is planar, and the Si—N bond length, 1·74 ± 0·02 Å, lies between that calculated for the single bond, 1·80 Å, and that for the double bond, 1·62 Å.[316, 317, 318] Unfortunately the heat of formation of this compound is unknown, so that it is not possible to calculate the silicon-nitrogen bond energy.

A surprising comparison between the silicon-nitrogen bond energies which are known is that for the eight-membered cyclic silazane (*g*), E(Si—N) = 82·1 kcal/mole is 5 kcal *greater* than E(Si—N) = 77·1 kcal/mole in the disilazane. This is in contrast to the corresponding comparison in the siloxane series where the silicon-oxygen bond energy in the cyclic siloxane is much *less* than in the disiloxane. It must be that strain in the cyclic silazane is more than balanced by increased stability due to electron delocalization.

In the cyclic siloxane the increased stability, compared with the disiloxane, due to electron delocalization round the ring, is much less and does not offset the strain energy. This is in keeping with the generally observed fact that nitrogen is a better electron donor than oxygen, so that where conditions allow, d_π—p_π-bonding will be more important in silicon-nitrogen bonds than in silicon-oxygen bonds.

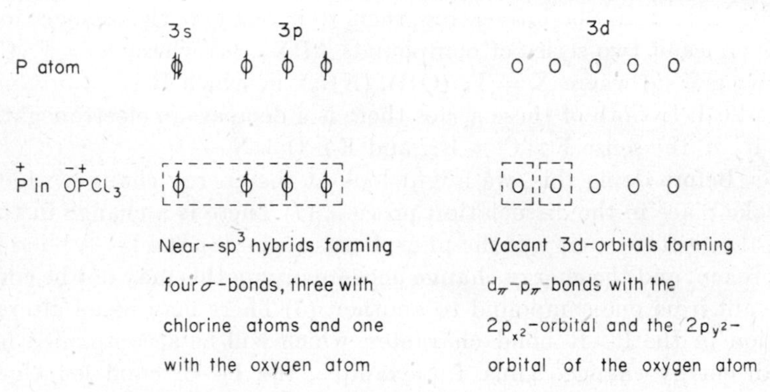

FIG. 2. Electronic structure of the molecule $OPCl_3$.

2. *Phosphorus*

For phosphorus compounds there are more thermochemical data available and the effects of d_π—p_π-bonding are much more apparent. A particularly interesting study is the variation in gas-phase dissociation energies of the general type $APX_3 \rightarrow A + PX_3$, where A = O (phosphoryl compounds), S (thiophosphoryl compounds), NR (phosphinimines), etc., and where X might be a halogen atom, or the groups OR, NR_2, CR_3, etc.

It has been suggested [319, 320] that the OPX_3 molecule should be regarded as a tetrahedral structure, involving sp^3 hybridization, $\overset{-}{O}$—$\overset{+}{P}X_3$, modified by back co-ordination from the $2p_{x^2}$- and $2p_{y^2}$-orbitals of $\overset{-}{O}$ to the vacant $3d_\pi$ orbitals of $\overset{+}{P}$, thus giving O—P triple bond character, with the further possibility of d_π—p_π-bonding by back co-ordination to P from the X atoms or groups, if these have donor electrons. This is shown diagrammatically in Fig. 2 for the molecule $OPCl_3$.

The amount of this additional π-bonding will depend on the electro-negativity of the ligands X and on their capacity to act as electron donors. Thus, the greater the electronegativity of X, the greater will be the positive charge on the P atom and the greater will be the strengthening both of the P—X and the P—O bonds. However, increased electronegativity is accompanied by reduced donating tendency, so that these factors will tend to work in opposition. It would be interesting, then, to investigate the dissociation energies of two series of compounds APX_3, (*a*) where X = F, Cl, Br; and (*b*) where X = F, (OR), (NR_2), in which R is an organic radical. In both of these series there is a decrease in electronegativity in the sense F > Cl > Br, and F > O > N.

Before doing this, we might look at the energy changes which take place in the dissociation process. (*1*) There is a change in the valence-state energy of the phosphorus atom. (*2*) The P—A bond is broken, and the energy change accompanying this may not be constant from one compound to another. (*3*) There may be an alteration in the P—R bond character, which will be accompanied by an energy change. Thus, for example, the P—Cl bond length is 1·99 Å[321] in phosphorus oxychloride, but 2·04 Å[322] in phosphorus trichloride, which suggests a weaker P—Cl bond strength in the trivalent compound. All these energy changes are included in $D(P{=}O)$, the dissociation energy of the process $OPX_3(g) \rightarrow O(g) + PX_3(g)$. The dissociation energy is given by the thermochemical equation

$$D(P{=}O) = \Delta H_f^0(PX_3, g) - \Delta H_f^0(OPX_3, g) + \Delta H_f^0(O, g).$$

Some bond dissociation energies corresponding to the dissociation of phosphoryl, thiophosphoryl, and N-alkyl (phosphinimine) compounds are shown in Table 2. In this last case dissociation gives rise to the trivalent PX_3 compound and the radical NR. Some of these values have been calculated from the difference between the heats of formation of APX_3 and PX_3 compounds, whilst others are derived from direct measurements of heats of oxidation.

In the phosphoryl halides, [series (*a*)], for the fluoride, chloride and bromide, $D(P{=}O)$ decreases from ~130 through 127·5 to ~125 kcal/mole, which runs parallel to a decrease in electronegativity from 3·9 (F), through 3·0 (Cl), to 2·8 (Br). The d_π—p_π-bonding in the molecule appears to be sensitive to electronegativity changes in X, though only slightly so.

TABLE 2
Gas-phase dissociation energies of phosphorus compounds (in kcal/mole)

$APR_3 \rightarrow A + PR_3$

Basis of estimate	$D(P{=}O)$
(*a*) $\Delta H_{oxidn.}$ PF_3 to OPF_3 [323]	129·8
ΔH_f^0 PCl_3 and $OPCl_3$ [25]	127·5
ΔH_f^0 PBr_3 and $OPBr_3$ [324]	124·9
(*b*) $\Delta H_{oxidn.}$ PF_3 to OPF_3	129·8
ΔH_f^0 $P(OEt)_3$ and $OP(OEt)_3$ [325, 326, 340, 114]	150·7
ΔH_f^0 $P(NEt_2)_3$ and $OP(NEt_2)_3$ [311]	160·0
$\Delta H_{oxidn.}$ PMe_3 to $OPMe_3$ [327]	139·3
ΔH_f^0 PPh_3 and $OPPh_3$ [114]	128·4
	$D(P{=}S)$
(*c*) $\Delta H_{oxidn.}$ $P(OEt)_3$ to $SP(OEt)_3$ [328]	90·6
$\Delta H_{oxidn.}$ PPr_3 to $SPPr_3$	91·6
	$D(P{=}N)$
(*d*) ΔH_f^0 PMe_3 and $EtN{=}PMe_3$ [327]	99
ΔH_f^0 PPh_3 and $EtN{-}PPh_3$	125

Along the series (*b*) OPF_3, $OP(OEt)_3$, $OP(NEt_2)_3$, there is an increase in $D(P{=}O)$ from ~130 through ~150 to ~160 kcal/mole, despite a decrease in electronegativity from 3·9 (F), through 3·5 (O), to 3·0 (N).[264] Here the overriding factor seems to be the relative electron donating power of the fluorine, oxygen and nitrogen atoms and the increase in $D(P{=}O)$ probably reflects a greater strengthening of the P—X bonds in the pentavalent compounds as compared with the trivalent compounds, since in the pentavalent compounds d_π—p_π-bonding is encouraged by the positive charge on the phosphorus atom. Since carbon atoms are much less powerful donors than either nitrogen or oxygen atoms, there should be less additional d_π—p_π-bonding associated with the phosphorus-carbon bonds in $OPMe_3$ and $OPPh_3$ than in say $OP(NEt_2)_3$. Consequently $D(P{=}O)$ values are expected to be less in $OPMe_3$ and $OPPh_3$ than in $OP(NEt)_3$ and $OP(OEt)_3$. The observed values are in keeping with these ideas.

In the thiophosphoryl compounds (*c*), $D(P{=}S)$ is almost independent of the particular X group. This is probably because the electronegativity difference between phosphorus (2·1) and sulphur (2·5) is very much smaller than between phosphorus and oxygen (3·5), leading to very little $\overset{-}{S}—\overset{+}{P}$ dipole, and a lesser tendency to back co-ordination to the phosphorus from the X atom.

Although in the phosphoryl compounds we have $D(Me_3P{=}O)$ = 139 kcal/mole, some 11 kcal *greater* than $D(Ph_3P{=}O)$ = 128 kcal/mole, in the phosphinimine series (*d*) the trend is reversed and $D(Me_3P{=}NEt)$ = 99 kcal/mole is about 26 kcal *less* than $D(Ph_3P{=}NEt)$ = 125 kcal/mole. An explanation of this different trend may be that whereas in the phosphoryl compounds the more electronegative phenyl group (electronegativity 2·4) tends to reduce back co-ordination between the phenyl group and the phosphorus atom, with no great strengthening of the P=O bond, the less electronegative methyl group (2·1) allows for a bond strengthening between the methyl group and phosphorus atom, which more than compensates for any loss in the P=O bond strength. In the phosphinimines the P=N bond is strengthened by the electronegative phenyl group to a greater extent than any loss in phenyl-phosphorus bond strength.

It may be, however, that some of the thermochemical data are incorrect and that the correct values would reverse one of these trends; however, support for the trend in the phosphinimines is found in the cyclic phosphazenes discussed later.

3. *Sulphur*

The thermochemistry of sulphur is complicated by the element showing oxidation numbers of +2, +4 and +6. Whilst there is a fair amount of information about compounds containing the sulphur-carbon bond of the type RSR, and RS–SR, where R is an organic radical, there are very few thermochemical data for the other oxidation states of +4 and +6. The heats of some gas-phase dissociation processes are shown in Table 3. The values of $D(S{=}O)$ refer to the reactions $SO_2R_2 \rightarrow O + SOR_2$. There are fewer data available than for the phosphorus compounds, and it is not possible to show trends in these dissociation energies. However, the point which does emerge clearly is that when nitrogen atoms are bonded to sulphur the heats of oxidation are considerably greater than when either chlorine or carbon atoms are involved.

This same effect has been noted with phosphoryl compounds. The explanation of the greater dissociation energies $D(R_3P=O)$ and $D(R_2S=O)$, where $R=NEt_2$, can probably be traced to a greater degree of d_π-p_π-bonding in the compounds where phosphorus or sulphur is showing its highest oxidation state. This conclusion is supported by measurements[330a] of the strength of the N→B bond in the complex compounds $(Me_2N)_2SO \cdot BF_3$ and $(Me_2N)_2SO_2 \cdot BF_3$. The N→B bond is much stronger in the former than in the latter. Burg and Woodrow[330a] attribute the weaker bonding in

TABLE 3

Gas-phase dissociation energies of sulphur compounds, in kcal/mole

$SO_2R_2 \rightarrow O + SOR_2$	
Basis of estimate	$D(S=O)$
ΔH_f^0 $SOCl_2$ and SO_2Cl_2[25]	94·2
$\Delta H_{oxidn.}$ Me_2SO to Me_2SO_2[330]	115·1
ΔH_f^0 $SO(NEt_2)_2$ and $SO_2(NEt_2)_2$[329]	130·0

$(Me_2N)_2SO_2 \cdot BF_3$ to the effect of the sulphur atom becoming more electronegative when two oxygen atoms are bonded to it. This makes for increased d_π-p_π-bonding between the nitrogen and sulphur atoms, which consequently decreases the external donor power of the nitrogen atom.

d_π—p_π-Bonding in Cyclic Systems

1. Cyclic Phosphazenes

(*a*) *Theoretical.* Electron delocalization in organic compounds is associated with the overlapping of p_π-orbitals on neighbouring atoms. For the ring systems $(AB)_n$ of first-period atoms A and second-period atoms B, the formulation of the π-electron system of such molecules, which appears most likely, uses p_π-orbitals of the A atom (say nitrogen) and d_π-orbitals of the B atom (say phosphorus or sulphur). Two quite distinct and different approaches have been made to the electronic structure of the cyclic phosphazenes, (Fig. 1, *I*, *IV*). On the one hand Craig and Paddock [331, 332, 333] suggest that these are aromatic compounds, in which there is a continuous π-bond round the ring in a manner analogous to the benzene molecule. On the other hand Dewar [334] has put forward the idea that the π-bonding in the six-membered phosphazene ring consists of the separate, three-centre π-bonds embracing two phosphorus atoms and a central nitrogen atom. Dewar suggests that there is little interaction between these π-bonds, although for reasons which will be pointed out later, the molecule will have a large resonance energy, nevertheless. We shall look at the two approaches in more detail.

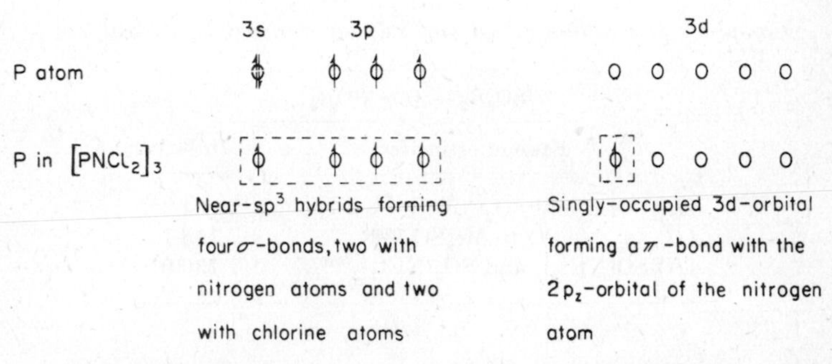

FIG. 3. Electronic structure of the molecule $[PNCl_2]_3$.

The σ-bonds in the cyclic phosphazenes, such as the hexachloro compound $[PNCl_2]_3$, are undoubtedly formed by sp^3- or near-sp^3-hybrid orbitals of phosphorus, since the phosphorus atoms are four-co-ordinated and X-ray analysis indicates that they are probably tetrahedral. Wilson and Carrol [335] suggest that the ring system is planar, whereas Liquori *et al.* [336] conclude that the ring is puckered, having a chair conformation. The larger ring systems are most certainly puckered. The electronic situation is shown diagrammatically in Fig. 3. The orbitals available for π-bonding are the nitrogen p_z- and the phosphorus d_{xz}- and d_{yz}-orbitals. It is in the interpretation of the nature of this π-bonding that Craig's and Dewar's approaches now diverge.

In Craig's explanation an analogy is drawn with the benzene molecule. In benzene, of the four valency electrons belonging to each carbon atom, three form σ-bonds with neighbours, two carbon atoms and one hydrogen atom. One unpaired electron remains on each carbon atom, occupying a p-orbital perpendicular to the plane of the ring. These can overlap, forming a molecular orbital of π-symmetry. By forming linear combinations of the p-orbitals six independent molecular orbitals can be constructed. The orbital of lowest energy has circular symmetry and with its two electrons this shell is complete. The next higher energy state is degenerate. There are two molecular orbitals corresponding to it, each with a plane of symmetry perpendicular to the ring, and also to each other. Each of these two filled orbitals, of identical energy, can

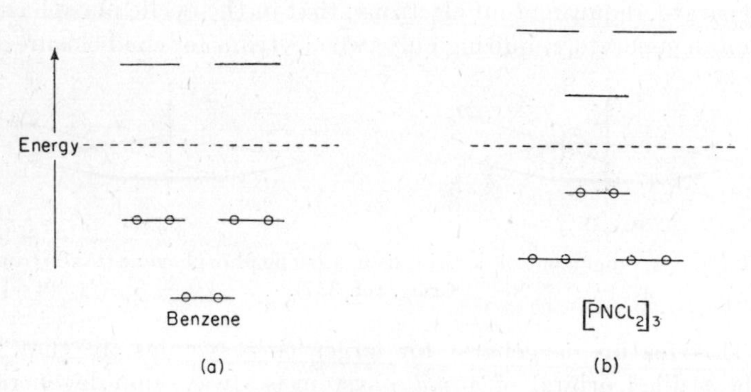

FIG. 4. Molecular-orbital energy levels, benzene, and hexachlorocyclotriphosphazatriene (taken from Craig, ref. 333).

accommodate two electrons. The two filled orbitals together have full circular symmetry, thus completing the second shell. The first two shells are then complete with six electrons, just the number provided by the benzene molecule. This energy sequence of molecular orbitals for the benzene molecule is shown in Fig. 4 (a). The special stability arises from two causes: (i) the delocalization of electrons, which lowers their energy and (ii) the fact that the molecular shell is complete in its number of electrons.

In the case of the phosphazene molecule, we assume first that the six-membered ring system is planar, and that any deviations from planarity will modify slightly the resultant picture. Of the two d_π-orbitals of the phosphorus atom d_{xz} is tangential to the plane of the ring and d_{yz} is radially disposed. These are shown in Fig. 5. Of these two, the d_{xz}-orbital will give greatest overlap with the nitrogen p_z-orbital. Craig concludes that interaction between the nitrogen p-orbital and phosphorus $3d$-orbitals gives rise to a continuous d_π-p_π π-bonding round the ring, and that this confers aromatic character. Molecular orbital theory can be applied to this alternating system of —p_π-d_π-p_π— orbitals. The linear combination of three d_π- and three p_π-orbitals gives rise to six molecular orbitals. However, as a result of the different symmetry, as compared with the p_π-p_π situation, the energy levels of the six-membered phosphazene rings are reversed with respect to those of benzene, as is shown in Fig. 4(*b*). The highest filled orbital of benzene is degenerate, requiring four electrons; that in the cyclic phosphazene is non-degenerate, requiring only two electrons for shell closure.

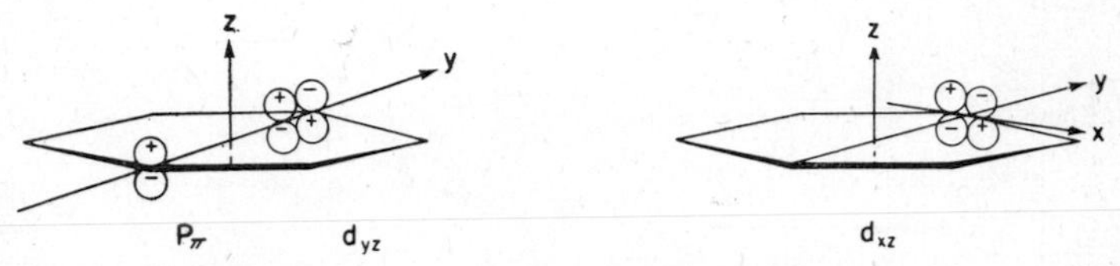

FIG. 5. Arrangement of d_π-orbitals in a cyclic phosphazene (taken from Craig, ref. 337).

This feature is general for larger ring systems, in that the highest filled orbital of a p-d π-system is always non-degenerate, so that an even number of electrons completes a shell. This is in contrast to a p_π-p_π system which forms closed shells for $4n + 2$ electrons. We have already seen that for the hypothetical, *planar* molecules, carbon ring systems of six, ten, or fourteen π-electrons have large resonance energies, whereas systems of eight or twelve π-electrons are stabilized very little. On the other hand the cyclic phosphazenes should not show this alternation of stabilization energy with ring size, and all should have a delocalization energy of similar magnitude.

Figure 6, taken from a paper by Craig[337], shows this graphically, in a plot of delocalization energy against the number of π-electrons. The full line refers to p_π-p_π-bonding, and the dotted line to d_π-p_π bonding. In the upper diagram the atoms have electronegativities differing by β, in the lower diagram the atoms have equal electronegativities. For reasons of symmetry of the d_π-orbitals the delocalization energy of —d_π-p_π-d_π— systems gradually increases for an increase in ring size, up to a limiting value.

This ideal picture is altered by the fact that rings may not be planar and this reduces the delocalization energy of p_π-p_π systems more than p_π-d_π systems. A $2p_z$-orbital of a first-period element has its orientation fixed relative to the σ-bond, and this leads to a very rapid loss of overlapping power with the $2p_z$-orbital of its

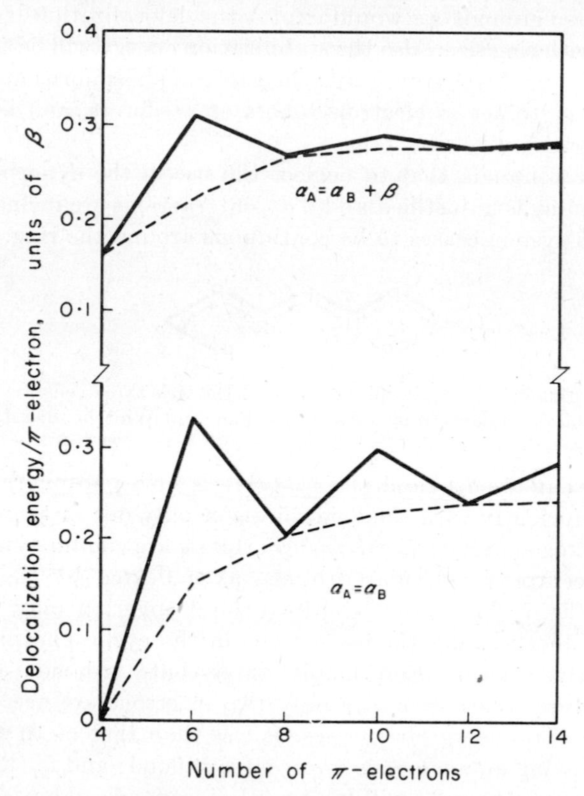

FIG. 6. Plot of delocalization energy against ring size. Cyclic phosphazenes. Upper diagram: electronegativites differing by β. Lower diagram: equal electronegativites (taken from Craig, ref. 337).

neighbours as the ring becomes puckered. (In the actual configuration of cyclo-octatetraene each π-orbital overlaps effectively with only one of its neighbours). A d_π-orbital of phosphorus does not have its axis of quantization so rigidly fixed, but may accommodate itself to give the best compromise bonding with its neighbours. In cruder terms we might say that it is more diffuse than the p_π-orbital, even when the d_π-orbital is contracted by the attachment of electronegative groups to the phosphorus atom. Generally this means that p_π-d_π bonding is less sensitive to non-planarity than is p_π-p_π bonding.

On these grounds we would expect the delocalization energy to increase with ring size. Also the stabilization energy will be affected by the nature of the groups attached to the phosphorus atom, by their ability to act as electron-donors or acceptors, and by their electronegativity.

Dewar contends that to neglect the use of the d_{yz}-orbitals in the π-bonding is unjustified and if d_{yz}-interactions are included the π-electron system ceases to be continuous around the ring. Dewar

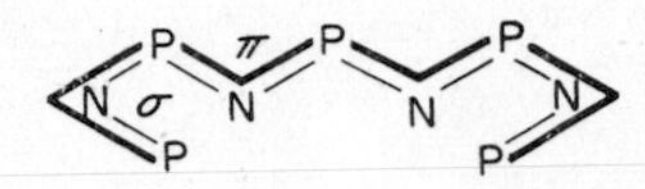

FIG. 7. Bonding in cyclic phosphazenes. Dewar's three-centre-π molecular orbitals (taken from Dewar, Lucken and Whitehead, ref. 334).

suggests that the d_{xz}- and the d_{yz}-orbitals of a phosphorus atom overlap efficiently with the $2p$-orbitals of only one of the two adjacent nitrogen atoms. The d- and p-orbitals are combined into sets of three-centre π-molecular orbitals, as indicated by the heavy lines in Fig. 7. These three-centre orbitals overlap only weakly with one another, and the π-electrons in the cyclic phosphazenes are effectively localized in definite three-centre π-bonds. In each of these three-centre π-bonds only two electrons are accommodated. The total energy from these is less than that of an electron pair occupying an analogous two-centre π-bond; and in this sense the cyclic phosphazenes will be strongly resonance stabilized, even though they are not aromatic. Dewar predicts that the resonance stabilization should be directly proportional to the number of three-centre bonds, i.e. the heat of formation per PNR_2 unit should be independent of ring size. The resonance energy of the compound $[PNCl_2]_3$ is calculated as $2{\cdot}5\,\beta$, as compared with $2{\cdot}0\,\beta$ for benzene. This approach also leads to the conclusion that no significant conjugation should occur between the phosphorus atom and the groups R attached to it.

The thermochemical evidence, which we shall now review, suggests that some of these points are confirmed and others not. Thus, for example, the heats of formation of $[PNCl_2]_3$ and $[PNCl_2]_4$ are virtually the same per $PNCl_2$ unit. The resonance energy of $[PNMe_2]_3$ of $\sim$65 kcal/mole is considerably greater than the value of 36 kcal/mole for benzene. However, the overall strength of the bonds in these molecules varies almost as much as in the phosphoryl compounds, OPR_3. This suggests that the R groups do influence the strength of the π-bonding in the ring, in keeping with Craig's views.

(*b*) *Experimental.* From heats of combustion, the heats of formation of a number of cyclic phosphazenes have been determined, including the six-membered ring systems $[PNCl_2]_3$, $[PNMe_2]_3$, $[PN(N(CH_3)_2)_2]_3$ and $[PN(OC_6H_{11})_2]_3$, where OC_6H_{11} is the cyclohexoxy group. For eight-membered rings two heats of formation are available, for $[PNCl_2]_4$ and $[PNPh_2]_4$. Values are shown in Table 4. The derived heats of formation from the atoms, $\Delta H_f^a[PNR_2]_n$, may be equated to the sum of the bond energies in the molecule, i.e.

$$\Delta H_f^a[PNR_2]_n = 2n\,E(P{-}N) + 2n\,E(P{-}R) + 2n\,E(R),$$

where E(P—N) is the bond energy of the phosphorus-nitrogen bonds in the ring, and E(R) is the group bond energy, the sum of the energies of the bonds in the group R. For example, $\Delta H_f^a[PN(CH_3)_2]_3$ is equal to the sum $6\,E(P{-}N) + 6\,E(P{-}C) + 6\,E(CH_3)$. In this case we have $E(CH_3) = 3\,E(C{-}H)$. The third column of Table 4 shows values for the sum E(P—N) + E(P—R) in the molecules $[PNR_2]_n$.

TABLE 4
Bond energies in cyclic phosphazenes (in kcal/mole)

Compound	ΔH_f^0 (g)	E(P—N) + E(P—R) in $[PNR_2]_n$	E(P—R) in PR_3	E(P—N) in $[PNR_2]_n$
$[PN(CH_3)_2]_3$	− 107·1[339]	140·7	61·6	79·1
$[PN(N(CH_3)_2)_2]_3$	− 124·1[345]	149·5	66·8	82·7
$[PN(OC_6H_{11})_2]_3$	− 564·0[339]	175·0	92·0	83·0
$[PNCl_2]_3$	− 175·9[338]	152·4	76·2	76·2
$[PNCl_2]_4$	− 236·1[338]	152·6	76·2	76·4
$[PN(C_6H_5)_2]_4$	+ 58·7[339]	153·1	67·5	85·6

The problem arises how to divide this sum into the two components, E(P—N) and E(P—R). One approach is to assume that the energy of the P—R bonds is the same as in the molecules PR_3, and so derive values for E(P—N). These are shown in Table 4. For the series of six-membered ring systems, where R = OC_5H_{11}, $N(CH_3)_2$, CH_3, the values of E(P—N) decrease. This change in E(P—N) is paralleled by the change in stretching frequency of the P—N bond in the ring system. These frequencies are shown in Table 5. This supports the idea that the strength of the phosphorus-nitrogen bonding in the ring is dependent on the nature of the attached R groups, as predicted by Craig.

TABLE 5

Stretching frequencies of P—N *ring bond in cyclic phosphazenes*

Compound	P—N Frequency (cm^{-1})	Compound	P—N Frequency (cm^{-1})
$[PNF_2]_3$	1297[343]	$[PNF_2]_3$	1297[343]
$[PN(OCH_3)_2]_3$	1242[343]	$[PNCl_2]_3$	1218
$[PN(N(CH_3)_2)_2]_3$	1195[344]	$[PNBr_2]_3$	1175
$[PN(CH_3)_2]_3$	1180[343]	$[PNCl_2]_4$	1305

The bond energies E(P—N) = 76·2 and 76·4 kcal/mole for the phosphorus-nitrogen bonds in the compounds $[PNCl_2]_3$ and $[PNCl_2]_4$ are very similar, a point in support of Dewar's approach to the structural interpretation of these molecules. These values are greater than E(P—N) = 66·8 kcal/mole in the trivalent phosphorus compound $P(N(C_2H_5)_2)_3$. This is in keeping with the shorter phosphorus-nitrogen bond length in the cyclic phosphazenes than the value for a normal single bond. The structure of the trimeric chloride has been investigated by Brockway and Bright,[341] using electron diffraction, and also by Wilson,[335] using X-rays. From electron diffraction the bond lengths are P—N, 1·65 ± 0·03 Å, and P—Cl, 1·97 ± 0·03 Å; from X-ray measurements the bond lengths are P—N, 1·57 ± 0·04 Å and P—Cl, 1·99 ± 0·04 Å. Although there is a difference between the P—N bond length, as determined by the two methods, the P—N bond length is considerably shorter than the value of 1·78 Å found for the P—N single bond in sodium phosphoramidate.[342]

It is possible to obtain a resonance energy of the compound $[PN(C_6H_5)_2]_4$ in the following way. We compare our derived value for E(P—N) in $[PNR_2]_n$ with a *mean* value of E(P=N) and E(P—N), as found in the phosphinimine $(C_6H_5)_3P{=}NC_2H_5$, and the aminophosphine $P(N(C_2H_5)_2)_3$. The heat of formation of gaseous N-ethyltriphenylphosphinimine has been given[327] as $-21{\cdot}9 \pm 2{\cdot}6$ kcal/mole, and if we assume that the bond energy of the $(C_6H_5)_3P$ and NC_2H_5 groups are the same as in trimethylphosphine and ethylamine, we calculate the bond energy $E(P{=}N) = 98{\cdot}4$ kcal/mole. The mean of this and the value $E(P{-}N) = 66{\cdot}8$ kcal/mole, in the aminophosphine, is 82·6 kcal/mole. This is 3·0 kcal/mole less than the value of 85·6 kcal/mole found in the cyclic phosphazene. This ring system, with eight phosphorus-nitrogen bonds, therefore has a resonance energy of 24 kcal/mole. Here, as in the calculation of all resonance energies, the value depends on the choice of the standard, non-resonating compound with which the resonance structure is compared. In this case it is the phosphinimine which is taken as a reference compound, despite the fact that there is probably considerable electron delocalization involving the phosphorus $3d$-electrons and the π-electrons of the phenyl groups. However, it is especially difficult to find a non-resonating structure as a standard.

2. Sulphanuric and Thiazyl Compounds.

Very little thermochemical work has been carried out on the corresponding cyclic sulphur compounds, with a six- or eight-membered ring system of alternate sulphur and nitrogen atoms. Examples of these compounds are shown in Fig. 1. In the thiazyl chloride, $[SClN]_3$ (*II*), and in the fluorine-substituted compound $[SFN]_{4\,(V)}$, with an eight-membered ring, the sulphur is in the oxidation state $+4$. In sulphanuric chloride, $[SOClN]_{3\,(III)}$, the sulphur is in the oxidation state $+6$.

The electronic structures of these compounds are given in Fig. 8. This shows that sp^3-hybrid orbitals of the sulphur atom are used for the σ-bonds. This leaves one singly-occupied $3d$-orbital in the case of thiazyl chloride, $[SClN]_3$, so that the situation is completely analogous to the phosphazene $[PNCl_2]_3$, as far as the π-bonding is concerned. From either Craig's or Dewar's approach a large resonance energy is to be expected for thiazyl chloride. In the case of sulphanuric chloride, $[SOClN]_3$, both the d_{xz}- and the d_{yz}-orbitals are singly occupied, and since one of the orbitals must be involved in a π-bond between the sulphur and oxygen atoms, the formation of three-centre π-bonds is less likely. On Craig's hypothesis, however, a continuous π-bond round the ring may be formed. As yet, however, there are no thermochemical data for these compounds.

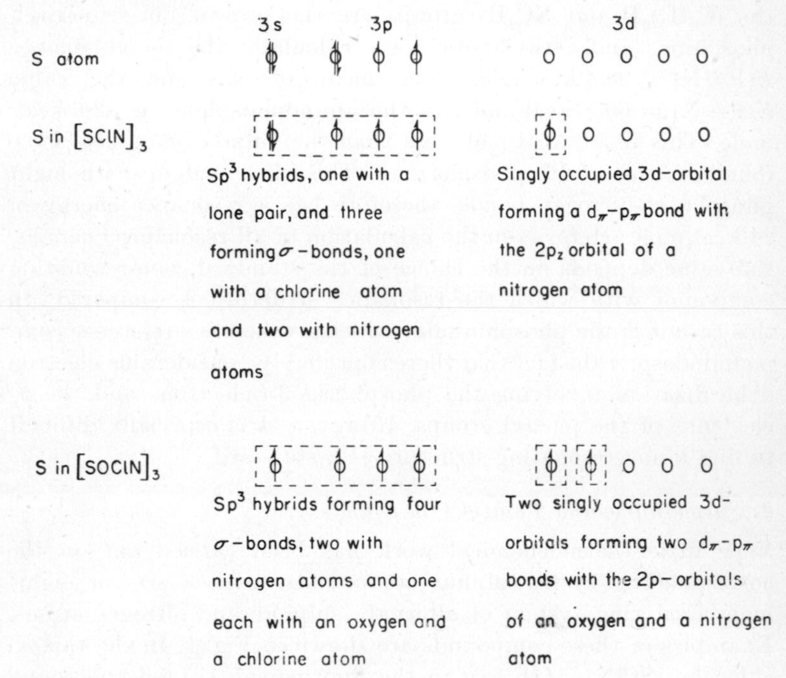

FIG. 8. Electronic structures of the molecules thiazyl chloride $(SClN)_3$ and sulphanuric chloride $(SOClN)_3$.

These few examples of "inorganic aromatic" compounds show how much more difficult it is to calculate bond energies and resonance energies in these compounds than in the equivalent carbon compounds. In carbon chemistry it is possible to "transfer" bond energies from one compound to another, because these quantities are constant, to within a few kcal, from one molecule to another. Thus, $E(C{=}C)$ in the molecule $CH_2{=}CH_2$ is not very different from the value in the molecule $CH_2{=}CCl_2$. In contrast, we find that in phosphorus and sulphur compounds much larger errors are introduced if bond energies derived from one compound are used in another. For example, the value for $E(P{=}N)$ varies considerably with the nature of the substituents attached to the phosphorus atom. Also, the existence of more than one oxidation state complicates the issue, since bond energies found for compounds in one state are not necessarily applicable to another oxidation state. Much work has yet to be done on the thermochemistry of these second-period elements before the bond strengths can be systematized in the quantitative way which has largely been achieved for carbon compounds.

REFERENCES

1. See for example, M. BERTHELOT, *Ann. Chim. (Phys.)*, (1884–1904).
2. See for example, J. THOMSEN, *Thermochemische Untersuchungen*, Barth, Leipzig, (1882–1886).
3. L. PAULING and D.M. YOST, *Proc. nat. Acad. Sci., Wash.*, **18**, 414 (1932).
4. T.L. COTTRELL, *The Strengths of Chemical Bonds*, 2nd ed. Butterworths, London, (1958).
5. K. FAJANS, *Ber. dtsch. chem. Ges.*, **53**, 64 (1920); and **55**, 2826 (1922).
6. *Amer. Petroleum Inst. Res. Project* **44**, Carnegie Press, Pitt., Penn., (1953).
7. M.J.S. DEWAR, *Conference on Hyperconjugation*, Indiana University, Bloomington, June, 1958. Pergamon Press, London, (1959).
8. L.H. LONG and J.F. SACKMANN, *Trans. Faraday Soc.*, **51**, 1797 (1958).
9. F.A. COTTON, A.K. FISCHER and G. WILKINSON, *J. Amer. chem. Soc.*, **81**, 800 (1959).
10. M.A. DOLLIVER, T.L. GRESHAM and G.B. KISTIAKOWSKY, *J. Amer. chem. Soc.*, **59**, 831 (1937).
11. G.B. KISTIAKOWSKY, J.R. RUHOFF, H.A. SMITH and W.E. VAUGHAN, *J. Amer. chem. Soc.*, **58**, 137 (1936).
12. J.R. LACHER, J.J. MCKINLEY, C. WALDEN, K. LEA and J.D. PARK, *J. Amer. chem. Soc*, **71**, 1334 (1949).
13. J.R. LACHER, A. KIANPOUR and J.D. PARK, *J. phys. Chem.*, **61**, 584 (1957).
14. H.A. SKINNER, *Royal Inst. Chem. Monograph No.* **3**, London, (1958).
15. F.D. ROSSINI (Editor), *Experimental Thermochemistry*, Interscience Publishers, New York, (1956).
16. F.D. ROSSINI *J. Res. Nat. Bur. Stand.*, **4**, 313 (1930).
17. W.D. GOOD, D. FAIRBROTHER and G. WADDINGTON, *J. phys. Chem.*, **62**, 853 (1958).
18. W.D. GOOD, D.W. SCOTT and G. WADDINGTON, *J. phys. Chem.*, **60**, 1080 (1956).
19. G.B. KISTIAKOWSKY, H. ROMEYN, J.R. RUHOFF, H.A. SMITH and W.E. VAUGHAN, *J. Amer. chem. Soc.*, **57**, 65 (1935).
20. J.R. LACHER, A. KIANPOUR, H. MONTGOMERY, H. KNEDLER and J.D. PARK, *J. phys. Chem.*, **61**, 1125, (1957).
21. R.B. TURNER, *Theoretical Organic Chemistry*, Butterworths, London, (1959).
22. H.A. SKINNER and A. SNELSON, *Trans. Faraday Soc.*, **55**, 404 (1959).
23. T. FLITCROFT, H.A. SKINNER and M.C. WHITING, *Trans. Faraday Soc.*, **53**, 784 (1957).

24. J.R. LACHER, A. KIANPOUR, F. OETTING and J.D. PARK, *Trans. Faraday Soc.*, **52,** 1500 (1956).
25. E. NEALE and L.T.J. WILLIAMS, *J. chem. Soc.*, 2156 (1954) and 4535 (1952).
26. J.B. PEDLEY, H.A. SKINNER and C.L. CHERNICK, *Trans. Faraday Soc.*, **53,** 1612 (1957).
27. P.A. FOWELL and C.T. MORTIMER, unpublished results.
28. E. CALVET, *Experimental Thermochemistry*, Chap. 12, Interscience, New York, (1956).
29. F.S. DAINTON, J. DIAPER, K.J. IVIN and D.R. SHEARD, *Trans. Faraday Soc.*, **53,** 1269 (1957).
30. *Amer. Petroleum Inst. Project 44*, Carnegie Press, Pitt., Penn., (1955).
31. R. SPITZER and H.M. HUFFMAN, *J. Amer. chem. Soc.*, **69,** 211 (1947).
32. J. COOPS and H. VAN KAMP, *Bull. chem. Thermodynamics, I.U.P.A.C.*, No. 2, (1959).
33. R.B. TURNER, *J. Amer. chem. Soc.*, **74,** 2118 (1952).
34. W.G. DAUBEN and K.S. PITZER, *Steric Effects in Organic Chemistry*, (Edit. by Newman), Wiley, New York, (1956).
35. W.S. JOHNSON, J.L. MARGRAVE, V.J. BAUER, M.A. FRISCH, L.H. DREGER and W.N. HUBBARD, *J. Amer. chem. Soc.*, **82,** 1256 (1960).
36. R.C. CASS, S.E. FLETCHER, C.T. MORTIMER, H.D. SPRINGALL and T.R. WHITE, *J. chem. Soc.*, 1406 (1958).
37. J.P. McCULLOUGH, H.L. FINKE, W.N. HUBBARD, W.D. GOOD, R.E. PENNINGTON, J.F. MESSERLY and G. WADDINGTON, *J. Amer. chem. Soc.*, **76,** 2661 (1954).
38. W.N. HUBBARD, C. KATZ and G. WADDINGTON, *J. phys. Chem.* **58,** 142 (1954).
39. M. DELÉPINE, *C.R. Acad. Sci., Paris,* **126,** 964 (1898).
40. D.L. HILDEBRAND, G.C. SINKE, R.A. McDONALD, W.R. KRAMER and D.R. STULL, *J. chem. Phys.*, **31,** 650 (1959).
41. D.H.R. BARTON, *J. chem. Soc.*, **34,** (1948).
42. G.F. DAVIES and E.C. GILBERT, *J. Amer. chem. Soc.*, **63,** 1585 (1941).
43. F.D. ROSSINI, quoted by T. MIYAZAWA and K.S. PITZER, *J. Amer. chem. Soc.*, **80,** 60 (1958).
44. D.M. SPEROS and F.D. ROSSINI, paper in preparation, referred to by W.G. DAUBEN, O. ROHR, A. LABBAUF and F.D. ROSSINI, *J. phys. Chem.* **64,** 283 (1960).
45. W.S. JOHNSON, *J. Amer. chem. Soc.*, **75,** 1498 (1953).
46. H.D. ORLOFF, *Chem. Rev.*, **54,** 431 (1954).
47. C.W. BECKETT, K.S. PITZER and R. SPITZER, *J. chem. Soc.*, **69,** 977 and 2488 (1947).
48. K.S. PITZER, *Chem. Rev.*, **27,** 39 (1940).
49. J.N. HARESNAPE, *Chem. & Ind.*, 1091 (1953).
50. C.C. BROWNE and F.D. ROSSINI, *J. phys. Chem.*, **64,** 927 (1960).
51. R.B. TURNER and W.R. MEADOR, *J. Amer. chem. Soc.*, **79,** 4133 (1957).
52. J.B. CONN, G.B. KISTIAKOWSKY and E.A. SMITH, *J. Amer. chem. Soc.*, **61,** 1868 (1939).

53. H. Leroux, *C.R.Acad. Sci., Paris*, **151,** 384 (1910).
54. R.B. Turner, D.E. Nettleton and M. Perelman, *J. Amer. chem. Soc.*, **80,** 1430 (1958).
55. T. Flitcroft and H.A. Skinner, *Trans. Faraday Soc.*, **54,** 47 (1958).
56. H.M. Huffman and S.W. Fox, *J. Amer. chem. Soc.*, **60,** 1400 (1938).
57. J.R. Lacher, T.J. Billings, D.E. Campion, K.R. Lea and J.D. Park *J. Amer. chem. Soc.*, **74,** 5291 (1952).
58. R.B. Turner, W.R. Meador and R.E. Winkler, *J. Amer. chem. Soc.*, **79,** 4116 (1957).
59. R. B. Turner and R. H. Garner, *J. Amer. chem. Soc.*, **80,** 1424 (1958).
60. A.F. Bedford, J.G. Carey, P.B. Edmondson, I.T. Millar, C.T. Mortimer and H.D. Springall, *J. chem. Soc.*, In press.
61. S.M. Skuratov, M. L. Kozina, S.M. Shteher and R.M. Varushyenko, *Thermochemical Bull. I.U.P.A.C.*, No. **3,** 3 (1957).
62. W.N. Hubbard, F.R. Frow, and G. Waddington, *J. phys. Chem.*, **62,** 821 (1958).
63. J.B. Conant and G.B. Kistiakowsky, *Chem. Rev.*, **20,** 181 (1937).
64. D. Cook, *J. chem. Phys.*, **28,** 1001 (1958).
65. M.J.S. Dewar and A.N. Schmeising, *Tetrahedron*, **5,** 166 (1959).
66. B. Stoicheff, Symposium on Molecular Structure and Spectroscopy, Ohio State University, Ohio, June, (1958).
67. L.E. Sutton, *Tetrahedron*, **5,** 118 (1959).
68. G.B. Kistiakowsky, J.R. Ruhoff, H.A. Smith and W.E. Vaughan, *J. Amer. chem. Soc.*, **58,** 146 (1936).
69. J.B. Conn, G.B. Kistiakowsky, E.A. Smith, and W.E. Vaughan, *J. Amer. chem. Soc.*, **60,** 440 (1938).
70. G.W. Wheland, *Resonance in Organic Chemistry*, Chapman & Hall, London, (1955).
71. G.B. Kistiakowsky, J.R. Ruhoff, H.A. Smith and W.E. Vaughan, *J. Amer. chem. Soc.*, **57,** 876 (1935).
72. R.S. Mulliken, C. Rieke and W.G. Brown, *J. Amer. chem. Soc.*, **63,** 41 (1941).
73. J.S. Roberts and H.A. Skinner, *Trans. Faraday Soc.*, **45,** 339 (1949).
74. C.A. Coulson and V.A. Crawford, *J. chem. Soc.*, 2052 (1953).
75. E.J. Prosen, F.W. Maron, and F.D. Rossini, *J. Res. Nat. Bur. Stand.*, **46,** 106 (1951).
76. J.D. Dunitz and J.M. Robertson, *J. chem. Soc.*, 48 (1947).
77. J.R. Lacher, L. Casali and J.D. Park, *J. phys. Chem.*, **60,** 608 (1956).
78. J.B. Conn, G.B. Kistiakowsky and E.A. Smith, *J. Amer. chem. Soc.*, **60,** 2764 (1938).
79. J.R. Lacher, J.J. McKinley, C.M. Snow, L. Michael, G. Nelson and J.D. Park, *J. Amer. chem. Soc.*, **71,** 1330 (1949).
80. C.A. Coulson, *Victor Henri Memorial Volume; Contribution à l'Etude de la Structure Moléculaire*, p. 15, Desoer, Liège, (1948); *Proc. roy. Soc.*, **A 207**, 91 (1951).
81. J.E. Bloor and S. Gartside, *Nature, Lond.*, **184,** 1313 (1959).

82. R.S. Mulliken, C.A. Rieke, D. Orloff and H. Orloff, *J. chem. Phys.*, **17,** 510 (1949).
83. C.A. Coulson, *Chem. Soc. Special Publ.* No. 12, p. 90, London, (1958).
84. R.S. Berry, *J. chem. Phys.*, **30,** 936 (1959).
85. H.C. Longuet–Higgins, *Theoretical Organic Chemistry,* p. 10, Butterworths, London (1959).
86. E. Hückel, *Z. Phys.*, **70,** 204, (1931).
87. C.A. Coulson, ref. 83, p. 92.
88. F. Sondheimer and R. Wolovsky, *Tetrahedron Letters,* No. 3, 3 (1959).
89. C. A. Coulson and S. L. Altman, *Trans. Faraday Soc.*, **48,** 293 (1952).
90. H.L. Finke, D.W. Scott, M.E. Gross, J.F. Messerly and G. Waddington, *J. Amer. chem. Soc.*, **78,** 5469 (1956).
91. J. Thiec and J. Wiemann, *Bull. Soc. chim. Fr.*, 177 (1956).
92. J.H. Day and C. Oestreich, *J. org. Chem.*, **23,** 214 (1957).
93. R.B. Turner, W.R. Meador, W. von E. Doering, J.R. Mayer and D.W. Wiley, *J. Amer. chem. Soc.*, **79,** 4127 (1957).
94. H.D. Springall, T.R. White and R.C. Cass, *Trans. Faraday Soc.*, **50,** 815 (1954); E.J. Prosen, W.H. Johnson and F.D. Rossini, *J. Amer. chem. Soc.*, **69,** 2068 (1947); *J. Amer. chem. Soc.*, **72,** 626 (1950).
95. W.C. Lothrop, *J. Amer. chem. Soc.*, **63,** 1187 (1941).
96. R.C. Cass, H.D. Springall and P.G. Quincey, *J. chem. Soc.*, 1188 (1955).
97. G.S. Parks and L.M. Vaughan, *J. Amer. chem. Soc.*, **73,** 2380 (1951).
98. E. Kováts, Hs.H. Günthard and Pl.A. Plattner, *Helv. chim. acta,* **38,** 1912 (1955).
99. J.W. Richardson and G.S. Parks, *J, Amer. chem. Soc.*, **61,** 3544 (1939).
100. P.B. Edmondson and C.T. Mortimer, unpublished results.
101. F. Klages, *Chem. Ber.*, **82,** 358 (1949).
102. N.F.H. Bright, *J. chem. Soc.*, 624 (1951).
103. A. Magnus, H. Hartman and F. Becker, *Z. physik. Chem.*, **197,** 75 (1951).
104. C.A. Coulson, *Theoretical Organic Chemistry,* p. 49, Butterworths, London, (1959).
105. F.J. Adrian, *J. chem. Phys.*, **28,** 608 (1958).
106. A. Albert, *Heterocyclic Chemistry.* Athlone Press, London, (1959).
107. M. Berthelot and G. André, *Ann. chim. (Phys.),* **17,** 433 (1899).
108. S. Sunner, *Acta chem. scand.*, **9,** 847 (1955).
109. G.E. Coates and L.E. Sutton, *J. chem. Soc.*, 1187 (1948).
110. T.M. Donavan, C. H. Shomate and W.R. McBride, *J. phys. Chem.*, **64,** 281 (1960); M.M. Williams, W.S. McEwan and R.A. Henry, *J. phys. Chem.*, **61,** 261 (1957).
111. P.B. Edmondson and C.T. Mortimer, unpublished results.
112. G.S. Parks and J.R. Morley, *J. Amer. chem. Soc.*, **22,** 1850 (1950); G.S. Parks and L.M. Vaughan, *J. chem. Soc.*, 624 (1951).
113. C.M. Anderson and E.C. Gilbert, *J. Amer. chem. Soc.*, **64,** 2369 (1942).
114. A.F. Bedford and C.T. Mortimer, *J. chem. Soc.*, 1622 (1960).

115. R. Roth, unpublished work, quoted in *Landolt–Börnstein Tabellen*, 1923.
116. P. B. Edmondson, unpublished results.
117. A. F. Bedford, D. M. Heinekey, I. T. Millar and C. T. Mortimer, unpublished results.
118. S. Sunner, *Acta chem. scand.*, **7**, 1112 (1953).
119. F. S. Dainton and K. J. Ivin, *Quart. Revs., chem. Soc., Lond.* **22**, 61 (1958).
120. F. S. Dainton and K. J. Ivin, *Trans. Faraday. Soc.*, **46**, 331 (1950).
121. D. E. Roberts, W. W. Walton and R. E. Jessup, *J. Polym. Sci.*, **2**, 420 (1947).
122. F. S. Dainton, J. K. Ivin and D. A. G. Walmsley, *Bull. chem. Thermodynamics, I.U.P.A.C.*, No. 3, p. 18, (1960).
123. L. K. J. Tong and W. O. Kenyon, *J. Amer. chem. Soc.*, **69**, 1402 (1927)
124. D. E. Roberts and R. S. Jessup, *J. Res. Nat. Bur. Stand.*, **46**, 11 (1951).
125. L. K. J. Tong and W. O. Kenyon, *J. Amer. chem. Soc.*, **69**, 2245 (1947).
126. L. K. J. Tong and W. O. Kenyon, *J. Amer. chem. Soc.*, **67**, 1278 (1945).
127. S. Ekegren, O. Öhrn, K. Granath and P. Kinell, *Acta chem. scand.*, **4**, 126 (1950).
128. G. C. Sinke and D. R. Stull, *J. phys. Chem.*, **62**, 397 (1958).
129. H. C. Duus, *Industr. Engng Chem. (Industr. edn.)* **47**, 1445 (1955).
130. F. W. Kirkbride and F. G. Davidson, *Nature, Lond.*, **174**, 79 (1954).
131. H. von Warterberg and J. Schiefer, *Z. anorg. Chem.*, **278**, 326 (1955)
132. D. W. Scott, W. D. Good and G. Waddington, *J. Amer. chem. Soc.*, **77**, 245 (1955).
133. F. S. Dainton, T. R. E. Devlin and P. A. Small, *Trans. Faraday Soc.*, **51**, 1710 (1955).
134. R. H. Boundry and R. F. Boyer, *Styrene*, p. 67, Reinhold, New York, (1952).
135. G. T. Furukawa and M. L. Reilly, *J. Res. Nat. Bur. Stand.*, **56**, 285 (1956).
136. S. Bywater, *Trans. Faraday Soc.*, **51**, 1267 (1955).
137. K. J. Ivin, *Trans. Faraday Soc.*, **51**, 1273 (1955).
138. G. T. Furukawa, R. E. McCoskey and M. L. Reilly, *J. Res. Nat. Bur. Stand.*, **51**, 69 (1953).
139. G. T. Furukawa, R. E. McCoskey and G. J. King, *J. Res. Nat. Bur. Stand.*, **49**, 273 (1952).
140. R. E. Cook, F. S. Dainton and K. J. Ivin, *J. Polym. Sci.*, **26**, 351 (1957).
141. K. J. Ivin, W. A. Keith and H. Mackle, *Trans. Faraday Soc.*, **55**, 262 (1959).
142. L. K. J. Tong and W. O. Kenyon, *J. Amer. chem. Soc.*, **71**, 1925 (1949).
143. F. S. Dainton and K. J. Ivin, *Trans. Faraday Soc.*, **53**, 1269 (1957).
144. M. W. Lister, *J. Amer. chem. Soc.*, **63**, 143 (1941).
145. R. B. Williams, *J. Amer. chem. Soc.*, **64**, 1395 (1942).
146. F. D. Rossini, *The Chemical Background for Engine Research* Chap. 2, Interscience Publishers, New York, (1943).
147. W. B. Person and G. C. Pimentel, *J. Amer. chem. Soc.*, **75**, 532 (1953).

148. P.A. Small, *Trans. Faraday Soc.*, **51,** 1717 (1955).
149. D.E. Roberts, *J. Res. Nat. Bur. Stand.*, **44,** 221 (1950).
150. J.B. Rose, *J. chem. Soc.*, 546 (1956).
151. S.M. Skuratov, M.L. Kozina, S.M. Shtekher, and R.M. Varushyenko, *C.R. Acad. Sci. U.S.S.R.*, **117,** 452 (1957).
152. F.S. Dainton and K.J. Ivin, unpublished observations.
153. F.S. Dainton. J.A. Davies, P.P. Manning and S.A. Zahir, *Trans. Faraday Soc.*, **53,** 813 (1957).
154. Yu.A. Strepikheev, *C.R. Acad. Sci. U.S.S.R.*, **102,** 105 (1955).
155. W.A. Piccoli, G.C. Haberland and R.L. Merker, *J. Amer. chem. Soc.*, **82,** 1883 (1960).
156. R.S. Mulliken, *J. Amer. chem. Soc.*, **74,** 811 (1952).
157. H.C. Brown, *J. chem. Soc.*, 1248 (1956).
158. G.E. Coates, *J. chem. Soc.*, 2003 (1951).
159. N.N. Greenwood and P.G. Perkins, *J. Inorg. Nuc. Chem.*, **4,** 291 (1957).
160. A.B. Burg and H.C. Schlesinger, *J. Amer. chem. Soc.*, **59,** 785 (1937).
161. H.C. Brown and R.M. Adams, *J. Amer. chem. Soc.*, **65,** 2557 (1943).
162. A.W. Laubengayer and G.R. Finlay, *J. Amer. chem. Soc.*, **65,** 884 (1943).
163. R.E. McCoy and S.H. Bauer, *J. Amer. chem. Soc.*, **78,** 2061 (1956).
164. H.C. Brown and R.B. Johanneson, *J. Amer. chem. Soc.*, **75,** 16 (1953).
165. F.A. Cotton and J.R. Leto *J. chem. Phys.*, **30,** 993 (1959).
166. F.G.A. Stone, *Chem. Rev.*, **58,** 101 (1958).
167. H.C. Brown and R.R. Holmes, *J. Amer. chem. Soc.*, **78,** 2173 (1956).
168. N.N. Greenwood, *Bull. chem. Thermodynamics, I.U.P.A.C.*, No. 1, 1958 and No. 2, 1959.
169. D.D. Eley and H. Watts, *J. chem. Soc.*, 1319 (1954); D.J.A. Dear and D.D. Eley, *J. chem. Soc.*, 4684 (1954).
170. *Nat. Bur. Stand. Circular 500*, Washington, D.C., 1952.
171. H.A. Skinner and N.B. Smith, *Trans. Faraday Soc.*, **49,** 601 (1953).
172. C.D. Meyers, M.S. thesis, Purdue University, 1953; quoted by D.R. Stull and G.C. Sinke, *Thermodynamic Properties of the Elements*, A.C.S., Washington, D.C., 1956.
173. H.O. Pritchard and H.A. Skinner, *Chem. Rev.*, **55,** 782 (1955).
174. W. Fischer and O. Kahlfs, *Z. anorg. Chem.*, **205,** 1 (1952).
175. J.P. Coughlin, *J. phys. Chem.*, **62,** 419 (1958).
176. G. Herzberg, *Molecular Spectra and Molecular Structure, II, Infrared and Raman Spectra of Polyatomic Molecules*, p. 178, van Nostrand, Princeton, N.Y. (1951).
177. J.L. Hoard, S. Geller and T.B. Owen, *Acta cryst.*, **4,** 405 (1951).
178. S. Sujishi and S. Witz, *J. Amer. chem. Soc.*, **76,** 4631 (1954).
179. G.E. Coates and R.A. Whitcombe, *J. chem. Soc.*, 3351 (1956).
180. N.N. Greenwood, P.G. Perkins and K. Wade, *J. chem. Soc.*, 4345 (1957).
181. N.N. Greenwood and K. Wade, *J. chem. Soc.*, 1527 (1956).
182. A. Kabesh and R.S. Nyholm, *J. chem. Soc.*, 3245 (1951).

183. A.W. Laubengayer and W.F. Gilliam, *J. Amer. chem. Soc.*, **63,** 477 (1941).
184. T.W. Coyle, H.D. Kaesz and F.G.A. Stone, *J. Amer. chem. Soc.*, **81,** 2989 (1959).
185. W.A.G. Graham and F.G.A. Stone. *J. Inorg. Nuc. Chem.*, **3,** 164 (1956).
186. C.A. Coulson, *Quart. Rev. chem. Soc., Lond.*, **1,** 144 (1949).
187. R.W. Parry and T.C. Bissot, *J. Amer. chem. Soc.*, **78,** 1524 (1956).
188. F.A. Cotton, R.D. Barnes and E. Bannister, *J. chem. Soc.*, 2199 (1960).
189. A.G. Gaydon, *Bond Dissociation Energies*, Chapman & Hall, London (1953).
190. M. Szwarc, *Chem. Rev.*, **47,** 75 (1950); *Quart. Rev. chem. Soc., Lond.*, **5,** 22 (1951).
191. J.A. Hipple and D.P. Stevenson, *Phys. Rev.*, **63,** 121 (1943).
192. D.P. Stevenson, *J. chem. Phys.*, **10,** 291 (1942).
193. D.P. Stevenson, *Trans. Faraday Soc.*, **49,** 867 (1953).
194. A.G. Harrison and F.P. Lossing, *J. Amer. chem. Soc.*, **82,** 519 (1960).
195. M. Szwarc, *J. chem. Phys.*, **16,** 128 (1948).
196. D.O. Schissler and D.P. Stevenson, *J. chem. Phys.*, **22,** 151 (1954).
197. J.B. Farmer, F.P. Lossing, D.G.H. Marsden and C.A. McDowell, *J. chem. Phys.*, **24,** 52 (1956).
198. S. Meyerson and P.N. Rylander, *J. chem. Phys.*, **27,** 901 (1957).
199. A.H. Sehon, M. Szwarc and B.N. Ghosh, *J. chem. Phys.*, **18,** 1142 (1950).
200. O. Gellner and H.A. Skinner, *J. chem. Soc.*, 1145 (1949).
201. R.J. Kandel, *J. chem. Phys.*, **22,** 1496 (1954).
202. M. Szwarc, *Proc. roy. Soc.*, **A198,** 267 (1949).
203. V.H. Dibeler, J.L. Franklin and R.M. Reese, *J. Amer. chem. Soc.*, **81,** 68 (1959).
204. R.C. Cass, S.E. Fletcher, C.T. Mortimer, P.G. Quincey and H.D. Springall, *J. chem. Soc.*, 958 (1958).
205. E.J. Prosen, personal communication, 1958.
206. J.R. Lacher, E. Emery, E. Bohmfalk and J.D. Park, *J. phys. Chem.*, **60,** 492 (1956).
207. J.R. Lacher, A. Kianpour and J.D. Park, *J. phys. Chem.*, **61,** 1125 (1957).
208. C.H. Leigh, M. Szwarc and J. Bigeleisen, *J. Amer. chem. Soc.*, **77,** 2193 (1953).
209. F.P. Lossing, K.U. Ingold and I.H.S. Henderson, *J. chem. Phys.*, **22,** 1489 (1954).
210. A.P. Irsa, *J. chem. Phys.*, **26,** 18 (1957).
211. C.A. McDowell and B.G. Cox, *J. chem. Phys.*, **20,** 1496 (1952).
212. H.C. Allen, E.K. Plyer and L.R. Blame, *J. Amer. chem. Soc.*, **78,** 4843 (1956).
213. M. Ladacki and M. Szwarc, *Proc. roy. Soc.*, **A 219,** 341 (1953).
214. T.L. Cottrell, T.E. Graham and T.J. Reid, *Trans. Faraday Soc.*, **47,** 584 (1951).

215. J. Collin, *Bull. Soc. Sci. Liège,* **20,** 707 (1951).
216. L.H. Long, *Proc. roy. Soc.,* **A192,** 143 (1949).
217. C.A. McDowell and J.W. Warren, *Trans. Faraday Soc.,* **48,** 1084 (1952).
218. L. Brewer, L.K. Templeton and F.A. Jenkins, *J. Amer. chem. Soc.,* **73,** 5308, (1951).
219. J.W. Knowlton and E.J. Prosen, *J. Res. Nat. Bur. Stand.,* **46,** 489 (1951).
220. F.W. Evans and H.A. Skinner, *Trans. Faraday Soc.,* **55,** 255 (1959).
221. J.B. Farmer, I.H.S. Henderson, F.P. Lossing and D.G.H. Marsden, *J. chem. Phys.,* **24,** 348 (1956).
222. M. Szwarc and A.H. Sehon, *J. chem. Phys.,* **19,** 656 (1951).
223. V. Braunwarth and H.J. Schumaker, *Kolloidzschr.,* **89,** 184 (1939).
223a. V.H. Dibeler and R.M. Reese, *J. Res. Nat. Eur. Stand.,* **54,** 127 (1955).
224. J.H. Sullivan and N. Davidson, *J. chem. Phys.,* **19,** 143 (1951).
225. L. Pauling, *The Nature of the Chemical Bond* 2nd. ed. p. 235 Oxford University Press, London (1940).
226. P. Gray, *Trans. Faraday Soc.,* **52,** 344 (1956).
227. A. Terenin and H. Neujmin, *J. chem. Phys.,* **3,** 436 (1935).
228. J.L. Franklin and H.E. Lumpkin, *J. Amer. chem. Soc.,* **74,** 1023 (1952).
229. D.P. Stevenson and J.A. Hipple, *J. Amer. chem. Soc.,* **64,** 1588 and 2766 (1942).
230. J.P. McCullough, W.N. Hubbard, F.R. Frow, I.A. Hossenlop and G. Waddington, *J. Amer. chem. Soc.,* **79,** 561 (1957).
230a. T. Allen, *J. chem. Phys.,* **31,** 1039, (1959).
231. W.N. Hubbard and G. Waddington, *Rec. Trav. chim. Pays-Bas,* **73,** 910 (1954).
232. W.N. Hubbard, W.D. Good and G. Waddington, *J. phys. Chem.,* **62,** 614 (1958).
233. A.H. Sehon and B. de B. Darwent, *J. Amer. chem. Soc.,* **76,** 4806 (1954).
234. D.W. Scott, J.P. McCullough, W.N. Hubbard, J.F. Messerly, I.A. Hossenlopp, F.R. Frow and G. Waddington, *J. Amer. chem. Soc.,* **78,** 5463 (1956).
235. D.W. Scott, H.L. Finke, J.P. McCullough, J.F. Messerly, R.E. Pennington, I.A. Hossenlopp and G. Waddington, *J. Amer. chem. Soc.,* **79,** 1062 (1957).
236. W.N. Hubbard, D.R. Douslin, J. P. McCullough, D.W. Scott, S.S. Todd, J.F. Messerly, A.G. Hossenlopp and G. Waddington, *J. Amer. chem. Soc.,* **80,** 3547 (1958).
237. R.C. Harshmann, *Jet Propulsion,* **27,** 398 (1957).
238. T.M. Donovan, C.H. Shomate and W.R. McBride, *J. phys. Chem.,* **64,** 281 (1960).
239. J.G. Aston, E.J. Rock and S. Isserow, *J. Amer. chem. Soc.,* **74,** 2484 (1952).
240. J.D. Ray and R.A. Ogg, *J. phys. Chem.,* **60,** 1460 (1956).

241. A. Rembaum and M. Szwarc, *J. Amer. chem. Soc.*, **76,** 5975 (1954).
242. A. Rembaum and M. Szwarc, *J. chem. Phys.*, **23,** 909 (1955).
243. L. Jaffe, E.J. Prosen and M. Szwarc, *J. chem. Phys.*, **27,** 416 (1957).
244. F.W. Evans, and H.A. Skinner, *Trans. Faraday Soc.*, **55,** 260 (1959).
245. M. Davies, P. Jones, D. Patnaik and E.M. Moelwyn-Hughes, *J. chem. Soc.*, 1249 (1951).
246. W.J. Canady, H.M. Papée and K.J. Laidler, *Trans. Faraday Soc.*, **54,** 502 (1958).
247. H.F. Halliwell and S.C. Nyburg, *J. chem. Soc.*, 4603 (1960).
248. R.F. Barrow and A.R. Downie, *Proc. Phys. Soc.*, **A 69,** 179 (1956).
249. P. Gray, *Trans. Faraday Soc.*, **55,** 408 (1959).
250. P.A. Giguère, B.G. Morisette, A.W. Olmos and O. Knop, *Canad. J. Chem.*, **33,** 804 (1955).
251. P.A. Giguère, I.D. Liu, J.S. Dugadle and J.A. Morrison, *Canad. J. Chem.*, **32,** 117 (1954).
252. B.G. Gowenlock, personal communication, 1959.
253. J.A. Leermakers, *J. Amer. chem. Soc.*, **55,** 2719 (1933).
254. P. Gray, *Proc. roy. Soc.*, **A 235,** 481 (1956); B.L. Evans, A.D. Yoffe and P. Gray, *Chem. Rev.*, **59,** 515 (1959).
255. J.D. Waldron, *Trans. Faraday Soc.*, **50,** 102 (1954).
256. A. Langer, J.A. Hipple and D.P. Stevenson, *J. chem. Phys.*, **22,** 1836 (1954).
257. P.A. Fowell and C.T. Mortimer, *J. chem. Soc.* 3793 (1961).
258. L.H. Long and R.C.W. Norrish, *Phil. Trans.*, **A 241,** 587 (1949).
259. A.S. Carson, K. Hartley and H.A. Skinner, *Trans. Faraday Soc.*, **45,** 1159 (1949).
260. C.T. Mortimer, H.O. Pritchard and H.A. Skinner, *Trans. Faraday Soc.*, **48,** 220 (1952).
261. P.A. Fowell and C.T. Mortimer, *J. chem. Soc.*, 3734 (1958).
262. S. Tannenbaum, *J. Amer, chem. Soc.*, **76,** 1027 (1954).
263. W.D. Good, D.W. Scott, J.L. Lacina and J.P. McCullough, *J. phys. Chem.*, **63,** 1139 (1959).
264. H.O. Pritchard and H.A. Skinner, *Chem. Rev.*, **55,** 745 (1955).
265. H.H. Jaffé, Abstracts 122nd Meeting, *Amer. Chem. Soc.* (1952).
266. H.H. Jaffé and G.O. Doak, *J. chem. Phys.*, **21,** 196 (1953).
267. W.D. Good, D. Fairbrother and G. Waddington, *J. phys. Chem.*, **62,** 853 (1958).
268. F.A. Cotton and K.R. Mouchamp, *J. chem. Soc.*, 533 (1960).
269. T. Moeller, *Inorganic Chemistry*, p. 135, Wiley, New York (1954).
270. J.W. Cable and R.K. Sheline, *Chem. Rev.*, **56,** 1 (1956).
271. G.E. Coates, *Organo-Metallic Compounds*, Methuen, London (1956).
272. D.P. Craig, A. Maccoll, R.S. Nyholm, L.E. Orgel and L.E. Sutton *J. chem. Soc.*, 332, (1954).
273. F.A. Cotton and G. Wilkinson, *J. Amer. chem. Soc.*, **74,** 5764 (1952).
274. L. Kaplan, W.L. Kester and J.J. Katz, *J. Amer. chem. Soc.*, **74,** 5531 (1952).

275. G. Wilkinson, P. A. Pauson and F. A. Cotton, *J. Amer. chem. Soc.*, **76**, 1970 (1954).
276. E. O. Fischer, F. A. Cotton, and G. Wilkinson, *J. phys. Chem.*, **63**, 154 (1959).
277. E. R. Lippincott and R. D. Nelson, *J. chem. Phys.*, **21**, 1307 (1953).
278. K. Wieland, *Helv. chim. acta*, **24**, 1285 (1941).
279. H. V. Carter, E. I. Chapell and E. Warhurst, *J. chem. Soc.*, 106 (1956).
280. S. J. W. Price and A. F. Trotmann–Dickenson, *Trans. Faraday Soc.*, **53**, 1208 (1957).
281. H. A. Skinner, *Trans. Faraday Soc.*, **45**, 20 (1949).
282. C. T. Mortimer, *J. chem. Educ.*, **35**, 381 (1958).
283. H. A. Skinner, personal communication 1960.
284. M. S. Kharasch, *J. Amer. chem. Soc.*, **54**, 674 (1954).
285. J. Sheridan and W. Gordy, *J. chem. Phys.*, **22**, 92 (1954).
286. H. A. Skinner, *Rec. Trav. chim. Pays-Bas*, **73**, 991 (1954).
287. P. B. Asycough and H. J. Emeléus, *J. chem. Soc.*, 3381 (1954).
288. G. Pilcher and H. A. Skinner, *J. Inorg. Nuc. Chem.*, **7**, 8 (1958).
289. D. H. Everett and W. F. K. Wynne–Jones, *Trans. Faraday Soc.*, **35**, 1380 (1939).
290. H. S. Harned and B. B. Owen, *Chem. Rev.*, **25**, 31 (1939).
291. K. J. Laidler, *Trans. Faraday Soc.*, **55**, 1725 (1959).
292. C. T. Mortimer and K. J. Laidler, *Trans. Faraday Soc.*, **55**, 1731 (1959).
293. H. M. Papée, W. J. Canady, T. W. Zawidzki and K. J. Laidler, *Trans. Faraday Soc.*, **55**, 1734 (1959).
294. T. W. Zawidzki, H. M. Papée, W. J. Canady and K. J. Laidler, *Trans. Faraday Soc.*, **55**, 1738 (1959).
295. T. W. Zawidzki, H. M. Papée and K. J. Laidler, *Trans. Faraday Soc.*, **55**, 1743 (1959).
296. L. P. Fernandez and L. G. Helper, *J. Amer. chem. Soc.*, **81**, 1783 (1959).
297. T. L. Cottrell, G. W. Drake, D. L. Levi, K. L. Tully and J. H. Wolfenden, *J. chem. Soc.*, 1016 (1948).
298. W. H. Dumbaugh, Jr., *Dissertation Abstr.*, **20**, 1559 (1959).
299. T. W. Richards and A. W. Rowe, *J. Amer. chem. Soc.*, **44**, 684 (1922).
300. T. W. Richards and L. P. Hall, *J. Amer. chem. Soc.*, **51**, 731 (1929).
301. F. D. Rossini, *J. Res. Nat. Bur. Stand.*, **6**, 847 (1931).
302. K. S. Pitzer, *J. Amer. chem. Soc.*, **59**, 2365 (1937).
303. P. Bender and W. J. Bierman, *J. Amer. chem. Soc.*, **74**, 322 (1952).
304. W. J. Bierman and N. Weber, *J. Amer. chem. Soc.*, **76**, 4289 (1954)
305. H. M. Papée, W. J. Canady and K. J. Laidler, *Canad. J. Chem.*, **34**, 1682 (1956).
306. H. C. Brown, D. H. McDaniel and O. Häfliger, *Determination of Organic Structures by Physical Methods*, (Edited by Braude and Nachod), Chap. 14, Academic Press, New York (1955).
307. L. F. Fiesor and M. Fiesor, *Introduction to Organic Chemistry*, Heath, p. 130, Boston (1957).

308. J. Jordan and W.H. Dumbaugh, *Bull. Chem. Thermodynamics*, I.U.P.A.C. No. 2 (1959).
309. W. Dupree, G. C. Sinke and D. R. Stull, personal communication 1960.
310. R. Thompson, *J. chem. Soc.*, 1908 (1953).
311. P.A. Fowell and C.T. Mortimer, *J. chem. Soc.*, 2913 (1959).
312. E.W. Aggarwall and S.H. Bauer, *J. chem. Phys.*, **40,** 18 (1950).
313. A. Kotera, Y. Uedea, K. Yamasaki and M. Yokoi, *J. chem. Phys.*, **18,** 1414 (1950).
314. R.F. Carl and K.S. Pitzer, *J. Amer. chem. Soc.*, **80,** 2371 (1958).
315. H.J. Emeléus, A.G. MacDiamid and A.G. Maddock, *J. Inorg. Nuc. Chem.*, **1,** 194 (1955).
316. K. Hedberg, *J. Amer. chem. Soc.*, **77,** 6491 (1955).
317. V. Schomaker and D.P. Stevenson, *J. Amer. chem. Soc.*, **63,** 37 (1941).
318. W. Gordy, *J. chem. Phys.*, **15,** 81 (1947).
319. H.H. Jaffé, *J. Inorg. Nuc. Chem.*, **4,** 372 (1957).
320. C.L. Chernick and H.A. Skinner, *J. chem. Soc.*, 1401 (1956).
321. P. Kisluik and C.H. Townes, *J. chem. Phys.*, **18,** 1109 (1950).
322. J.Q. Williams, W. Gordy and J. Sheridan, *J. chem. Phys.*, **20,** 164 (1952).
323. Fr. Ebel and E. Bretscher, *Helv. chim. acta*, **12,** 450 (1929).
324. T. Charnley and H.A. Skinner, *J. chem. Soc.*, 450 (1953).
325. C.L. Chernick, H.A. Skinner and C.T. Mortimer, *J. chem. Soc.*, 3936 (1955).
326. C.L. Chernick and H.A. Skinner, *J. chem. Soc.*, 1401, (1956).
327. Ann P. Claydon, P.A. Fowell and C.T. Mortimer, *J. chem. Soc.*, 1622 (1960).
328. C.L. Chernick, J.B. Pedley and H.A. Skinner, *J. chem. Soc.*, 1851 (1957).
329. Ann P. Claydon and C.T. Mortimer. unpublished results.
330. T.B. Douglas, *J. Amer. chem. Soc.*, **68,** 1072 (1946).
330a. A.B. Burg and H.W. Woodrow, *J. Amer. chem. Soc.*, **76,** 219 (1946).
331. D.P. Craig, *Chem. & Ind.*, 3 (1958).
332. D.P. Craig and N.L. Paddock, *Nature, Lond.*, **181,** 1052 (1958).
333. D.P. Craig, *Theoretical Chemistry; Looking Before and After*, Lewis, London (1957).
334. M.J.S. Dewar, E.A.C. Lucken and M.A. Whitehead, *J. chem. Soc.*, 2423 (1960).
335. A. Wilson and D.F. Carrol, *J. chem. Soc.*, 2548 (1960).
336. A.M. Liquori, F. Pompa, and A. Ripamonti, XVIIth Internat. Congr. Pure & Appl. Chem., Munich, (1959).
337. D.P. Craig, *Theoretical Organic Chemistry*, Butterworths, London (1959).
338. S.B. Hartley, N.L. Paddock and H.T. Searle, *J. chem. Soc.*, 430 1961.
339. A.F. Bedford and C.T. Mortimer, *J. chem. Soc.*, 4649 (1960).

340. E. NEALE and L. T. D. WILLIAMS, *J. chem. Soc.*, 2485 (1955).
341. L. O. BROCKWAY and W. M. BRIGHT, *J. Amer. chem. Soc.*, **65**, 1551 (1943).
342. E. HOBBS, D. E. C. CORBRIDGE and B. RAISTRICK, *Acta cryst.*, **6**, 621 (1953).
343. N. L. PADDOCK and H. T. SEARLE, personal communication (1960).
344. R. A. SHAW, *Chem. & Ind.*, 54 (1959).
345. A. F. BEDFORD and C. T. MORTIMER, unpublished result.

AUTHOR INDEX

SUBJECT INDEX

b.d.e., bond dissociation energy; *b.e.*, bond energy